D1498247

ANIMAL AGGRESSION: SELECTED READINGS

Wild elephants grazing peacefully across the Dhikala flats of the Ramganga River in northern India. Female elephants have strong loyalty to their social groups and normally live in peaceful association within the group. Occasionally some individuals become solitary and ill-tempered. See page 11 in Chapter 1 (Photograph by C. H. Southwick).

ANIMAL AGGRESSION: SELECTED READINGS

CHARLES H. SOUTHWICK

The Johns Hopkins University

1970

VAN NOSTRAND REINHOLD COMPANY

New York

Cover Photograph Indian black buck (*Antilope cervicapra*) in a ritualized sparring duel. Such contests are brief and relatively mild in natural populations. Injury is rare, and the match serves to establish a dominance-subordinance relationship without wounding or great expenditure of energy. (Photograph by Ylla, with permission of La Guilde lu Livre, Lausanne, Copyright © 1958.)

Van Nostrand Reinhold Company Regional Offices:
Cincinnati, New York, Chicago, Millbrae, Dallas

Van Nostrand Reinhold Company Foreign Offices:
London, Toronto, Melbourne

Published by Van Nostrand Reinhold Company
450 West 33rd Street, New York, N.Y. 10001

Published simultaneously in Canada by
Van Nostrand Reinhold Company (Canada), Ltd.

10 9 8 7 6 5 4 3 2 1

PREFACE

Since the comparative method in all areas of biology, psychology and sociology first requires some knowledge of the animal world, this book begins the study of aggression by focusing on this aspect of behavior in animals. This approach is based on the premise that the comparative study of animal aggression is necessary if we are to understand the biological and evolutionary backgrounds of aggressive behavior, including that of humans. At the same time, it recognizes that human aggression takes a wide variety of forms, and that much of it is vastly more complex and more socially organized than that occurring in animals. Thus, the comparisons *per se* between man and animals are not developed at length in this book. This is not a tacit admission that the points of relevance between animal studies and human problems are not worthy of consideration; it is rather an admission that this relevance is hard to define at the present state of our knowledge.

Two persistent problems in the study of aggressive behavior have been: (1) the extent to which animal aggression is intrinsically or extrinsically induced—that is, whether it arises in response to an internal drive or always comes from some external provocation; and (2) the extent to which extrapolations from animals to man are valid—that is, whether we can, in fact, learn something about human behavior by studying animals.

On the first problem, one leading school of psychologists, championed particularly by J. P. Scott and K. E. Moyer, believes that aggression is inevitably the product of external stimulation. They feel that "There is no evidence for the existence of a physiological mechanism that could produce spontaneous internal stimulation to fight." (Scott, Chap. 7). On the other hand, an outstanding group of zoologists and ethologists, exemplified by Konrad Lorenz and I. Eibl-Eibesfeldt, believes that many animals have an innate drive for aggressive behavior; that there is, in fact, an instinct for aggression. The controversy is at least 30 years old, and shows no signs of

diminishing. It is not necessarily the most important question in the study of aggressive behavior, but it is one which requires some type of resolution. It still occupies center stage in scientific discussions on aggressive behavior, and often blocks effective communication on other vital issues.

Despite this controversy on the causation of aggressive behavior, both ethologists and psychologists would agree that aggression, like all behavior, has a developmental history within an individual, and the real task of behavioral research is to unravel the key events in this developmental history. When these events are fully documented for any given animal group, they should help us understand both species–specific characteristics (as, for example, why rhesus monkeys are more aggressive than squirrel monkeys), as well as individual deviations from the species norm (as, for example, why there are individual killers and rogues among normally passive species).

On the second problem, the extent to which extrapolations from animals to man are valid, a similar controversy prevails. The question was answered in the affirmative many years ago in the fields of anatomy, physiology, biochemistry, and related biomedical sciences where well-recognized similarities and homologies are evident, but in the area of behavior, where similarities cannot be subjected to the same material analysis, a good deal more confusion and refractory opinion prevails. Not long ago I gave a talk to a group of University students in Baltimore on the biology of aggressive behavior, and I spoke enthusiastically about comparative studies. I emphasized the insights which animal research could give to our understanding of human behavior. Shortly thereafter, a friend of mine who is a social anthropologist gave a related talk on human aggression to the same group of students. He began by stating his premise in quite different terms. "Let's get one point straight at the very beginning," he said. "We can learn absolutely nothing about human behavior from the study of animal behavior!"

He was being purposely provocative and perhaps even somewhat facetious, but there was little doubt that he was basically sincere to his own convictions. Although this viewpoint now represents a minority opinion in the behavioral sciences, it is an amazingly tenacious idea. Man is still placed on a pedestal frosted with what is often considered to be an impermeable layer of culture. There is, in such a viewpoint, little recognition of the biologic bases of human behavior on one hand, or the strength and importance of learned social tradition in animals on the other. With modern research, both of these phenomena are becoming more evident, and the value of the comparative method in behavioral study more secure.

The practical problem in editing a book of this type is one of selection. Out of the hundreds of books and thousands of papers written on the subject of animal aggressive behavior, how does one select less than 20 short chapters? This becomes a highly subjective matter—to choose what one considers the best and most representative. It is perhaps comparable to picking the best musician from all the orchestras of the world.

Still, despite the volume and extent of literature in this field, certain authors and scientists stand out. In presenting the 1944 article by Dr. N. E. Collias, for example, there is little doubt in my mind that this is one of the best reviews of aggressive behavior in vertebrates that has ever been written. It is remarkably accurate and thorough. Considering the modern popularity of this field, and the great abundance of writings on aggression within the last 5 years, it is impressive and humbling to see how much was known and well written more than 25 years ago by Professor Collias. This, I think, represents the great value of returning to earlier writings. It often becomes apparent that many ideas which seem strikingly new and glamorous aren't really so new after all. It brings into sharper focus the advancements and shortcomings of current scientific work.

After the important reviews of Collias, the next selection jumps almost 10 years into the early 1950's to document the emerging insights of European ethology. The chapters by Tinbergen and Lorenz summarize this approach and bring forth new viewpoints on the function and causation of aggressive behavior.

Subsequent selections were all drawn from the recent literature or from current research to represent various disciplines now concerned with animal aggression. Thus, zoology, psychology, physiology, genetics, neurology, endocrinology, biochemistry, ecology and ethology are all represented, and the theme threads back and forth across various controversial points of view. If we can fit the pieces of this multidisciplinary scientific puzzle together in the proper way, we may be able to understand some of the major questions about this fascinating topic. Why is aggression such an important component of animal behavior? How does it arise and develop within an individual and within a species? What factors influence its frequency and patterning? How may it be kept within normal limits without erupting into a destructive and malevolent force?

This collection of papers provides much of the essential information on which an intelligent discussion of these and related questions may be based.

Charles H. Southwick

BALTIMORE, MARYLAND
August 3, 1970

ACKNOWLEDGMENTS

I am indebted to John Emlen, Joseph Hickey, Robert McCabe, Robert Ellarson, and Nicholas Collias for first arousing my interests in aggressive behavior of animals during my graduate studies at the University of Wisconsin, and to Niko Tinbergen, H. N. Southern, Charles Elton, and Dennis Chitty for expanding this interest while I was a postdoctoral fellow at Oxford University. I am also indebted to my students and colleagues at Johns Hopkins University for many lively discussions on aggression and related topics in ecology and behavior. My wife, Heather, has maintained constant interest and enthusiasm in animal behavior, and has helped substantially with this compilation. Mrs. Barbara Hamilton has provided careful secretarial assistance.

The initial idea for this collection of readings arose during courses and seminars conducted at Johns Hopkins in a training program in the biological sciences related to behavior sponsored by the National Institutes of Mental Health. I am indebted to the Chief of the Biological Sciences Training Program in NIMH, Dr. Fred Elmadjian, for many stimulating discussions on these and related topics in the sciences of behavior.

I also extend my special appreciation to all the authors of these chapters who have consented to my editorial work on their material, and to Drs. J. L. Brown and B. L. Welch who have taken time from their busy schedules to write original chapters at my request.

CONTENTS

1

CONFLICT AND VIOLENCE IN ANIMAL SOCIETIES

CHARLES H. SOUTHWICK

Portions of this material and that in Chapter 15 were first presented by the Editor of this book in a Symposium on "Violence in Contemporary American Society," held in May, 1967, at the Center for Continuing Liberal Education of Pennsylvania State University under the leadership of Drs. Dale Harris and John Sample, and was published by Pennsylvania State University Press in 1969.

Conflict and aggression are frequent and widespread forms of behavior in animal societies. They may be observed in almost every species which has the capacity to fight. Violence, if defined as behavior which inflicts some form of injury, is much less common, except in predator-prey relations. The predator, such as the hawk, weasel, or tiger, inflicts fatal injury upon its prey, but since this is an aspect of natural feeding behavior, it is basically different from conflict and fighting among individuals of the same species. This book is devoted to the latter type of behavior and is not concerned with predatory activity. A special category of behavior bordering between aggression and predation, that of animal attacks on man, will be discussed later in this chapter.

Natural selection has placed a favorable premium on certain aspects of aggressive behavior for the individual. Animals often live in competitive situations where aggressive individuals may have greater success in obtaining food, shelter, and mating opportunities. It is more than coincidental that some of the world's most successful animals are characteristically aggressive and adaptable: that is, they may be described as both behaviorally and ecologically aggressive. Ecological aggressiveness enables them to invade and colonize new areas and exploit new habitats. Behavioral aggressiveness may enable them to survive in competitive situations. The rhesus monkey in India, the baboon in Africa, the starling and house sparrow in the United States, the Norway rat and house mouse throughout the world, and man himself, have all achieved numerical success in competitive situations through both their behavioral and ecological aggressiveness.

Although the aggressive individual or group may have priority to limited resources and may thus be favored in natural selection, there are selective advantages in nonaggressive behavior which permits co-operation, reproduction and parental care. It is apparent, therefore, that natural evolution in animal societies has achieved a balance between aggressive and cooperative behavior. Animals can thus maintain themselves in a competitive community, but with definite limits upon aggression so that fighting does not completely disrupt favorable social interactions.

Aggressive behavior is so widespread in the animal kingdom that it is virtually universal in some form or another in almost every animal which has the necessary motor apparatus to fight or inflict injury. It is absent or rare in only those invertebrates such as some worms and oysters which have no physical means of inflicting damage, whereas it is common in most arthropods and vertebrates which have appendages, claws, teeth, or other structures capable of damaging movements. Lobsters, crayfish, spiders, most insects, and most vertebrates are all capable of severe aggressive behavior, which can be seen in both natural and experimental conditions. Scott,[21] in a review of aggressive behavior, concludes that any animal which has the equipment for attack or defense is likely to exhibit aggressive behavior. Among vertebrates, Scott[21] summarized the extent of aggressive behavior as follows:

"Fighting occurs in all classes of vertebrates: fishes, amphibia, reptiles, birds, and mammals. The vicious combats of Siamese fighting fish can be observed by any aquarium owner. The males of many other varieties of fish, including the common sunfish, habitually defend their nests against others of their kind. The amphibia, with no teeth or claws, were once con-

sidered completely pacific, but Test has described a species of South American frog whose members maintain small territories on the bank of a stream. When a strange frog comes near, the owner jumps into the air and comes down heavily on the intruder's back. Reptiles are better armed and are likely to fight both between and within species. Some of the most spectacular combats occur between male alligators. Most birds show some kind of aggressive behavior, and the common barnyard fowl rates near the top level of combativeness. Finally, fighting occurs in all the important orders of mammals, whether they are herbivorous or carnivorous.

"The primates, which compose the group to which man belongs, show a considerable range in aggressiveness, from the gibbons, in which both sexes fight so vigorously that they can exist only in small family groups, to the howling monkeys, whose fighting almost never goes beyond vocalization in either sex. As for man, there is no doubt that he stands in the upper part of the scale of primate aggressiveness.

"Fighting occurs so widely in the animal kingdom that it cannot be dismissed as accidental or abnormal in occurrence. In reality, aggressive behavior is a common and apparently useful part of the daily lives of many animals, and only exceptionally does it become destructive or harmful."

Although aggressive behavior is very widespread among animals, it is remarkable how rarely it leads to serious injury or death. This is emphasized by Matthews[17] in a review of fighting in mammals:

"Indeed on examining intraspecific fighting more than superficially it is at once apparent that an important part of animal behavior, at least in the mammals, is directed towards avoiding intraspecific fighting. The weapons are potentially so dangerous that fighting is ritualized into display, threat, and submission or appeasement, so that fights are generally no more than trials of strength followed by disengagement and rapid withdrawal by the weaker. This does not mean that fights never end fatally, for a threat that is never carried out loses its meaning, but fighting to the death rarely happens in the normal environment.

"It is, indeed, very difficult to find any examples of true overt fighting resulting in the death of the loser among mammals under normal conditions in the wild. It occurs only when population numbers have overtaken the resources of the environment so that serious overcrowding is brought about. This produces a situation similar to that of animals in captivity where the environment is artificially restricted so that aggression is in-

creased and any chance of escape from the aggressor is denied. In both situations the animals are living in a biologically unsound environment which inevitably distorts the normal patterns of social behaviour."

Many of the writings of Konrad Lorenz[16, 16a] have made the same point: namely, that some animals best equipped to inflict fatal damage seem to have developed the most elaborate behavioral means of preventing this. Thus mammals with conspicuous aggressive weapons, such as carnivores and ungulates, usually have ritualized postures and movements which serve as threat displays so that direct fighting is often averted.

As pointed out by Matthews,[17] however, it would be a misconception to assume that violent fighting among members of the same species never occurs in nature. Attacks and fighting leading to serious injury or death have been observed in natural populations of animals as diverse as social insects,[27] lizards,[17] muskrats,[10] California ground squirrels,[15] elephants,[6] tigers,[20a] hippopotami,[26] musk oxen,[17] grizzly bears,[8] and langur monkeys.[25] Undoubtedly this list could be extended, not to emphasize that violent fighting is frequent in natural animal populations, but to point out that it does sometimes occur.

Lorenz and others have observed that damaging violence in animals is usually confined to: (1) unusual environmental circumstances, such as captivity, when animals are crowded, irritated, or suddenly disturbed; (2) intergroup conflicts when individuals from one social group invade the territory or home range of another social group; or (3) various forms of social disorganization.

The first principle can readily be seen among the primates. It was thought for many years that most primates are exceedingly pugnacious and aggressive animals because many of the early behavioral studies were done on captive animals. Thus, baboons, macaques, chimpanzees and gorillas were all thought to be dangerous and violent because they behaved this way in captivity and laboratory confinement. Recent field studies have shown, however, that in their natural environments all of these animals can lead peaceful and well-integrated social lives with relatively rare aggressive conflict. Only when they become disturbed, crowded, or confined does violent aggressive behavior break forth. For many years we have had a distorted picture of primate behavior by excessive concentration on animals in confinement. Field observations, of the type pioneered in the 1930's by Dr. C. R. Carpenter of Penn State University, did not become a widely used form of study until the mid and late 1950's. When the first major field study of mountain gorillas was undertaken by Schaller and Emlen about 10 years ago, this animal was found to be remarkably docile[20]—certainly not the ferocious beast of folklore. With other studies of this type on natural populations, aggressive behavior has now been seen in a more realistic light, with a more accurate appreciation of its natural occurrence and the ecologic variables affecting its frequency and intensity.

Overcrowding and confinement have also been observed as a cause of violent and sometimes fatal aggression in deer parks, where stags fight throughout the year and may often kill calves and females, an event which is rare in natural populations.[9] In crowded populations of tree shrews, mothers fail to rub their young with sternal gland secretions, and without this special protective odor, the young shrews are attacked and killed by other members of the group.[14] Other examples of increased aggression in crowded populations will be given in subsequent portions of this book.

Although crowding has been shown to increase aggression in many animals, a reverse phenomenon can also be seen in some cases. If crowding exceeds certain levels, some animals may exhibit a reduced reactivity to normal psychosocial stimuli, and there may be an actual reduction of aggression. In other words, animals under extreme crowding may become passive and nonreactive. This is sometimes true of laboratory mice in cages, as pointed out in Chapter 12 by Welch, and it has also been observed in confined populations of Norway rats by Calhoun.[2] There is still much to be learned about behavioral responses to crowding in order to understand those circumstances in which crowding increases aggression, and those in which it decreases aggression.

The second principle, that of intergroup conflict, can be illustrated in studies of social insects, rodents, and primates.

In social insects, violent aggressive conflicts can occur between different colonies. If individuals from one colony of ants invade or are displaced into the midst of another colony, violent slaughter usually results. Several investigators have shown that the basis for colony insects is primarily odor. The ants of one colony may spontaneously attack any members of their species which have the odor of another colony. If ants from a foreign colony are chemically deodorized and then given the odor of another colony they are often accepted by that colony; conversely, if they have a foreign odor, they are usually attacked and killed by members of their own colony.

Rats and mice may display the same kind of extreme social intolerance for individuals of another social group, although the basis of group recognition is probably more complex than a single odor. If a stranger is released into an established social colony, he may be viciously attacked and killed. Lorenz[16a] describes the work of Steiniger who witnessed violent intergroup fights between different social clusters of Norway rats. In my own studies of *Peromyscus leucopus,* the whitefooted mouse, I have observed that social congeners can be very peaceful and seldom show aggressive behavior so long as they have all grown up together, but if a stranger is introduced to their midst, he is investigated, often for several hours, but eventually attacked and killed.[22b] House mice show similar patterns of behavior, but the attack may be much more immediate.

Many primates also exhibit intergroup intolerance. In rhesus monkeys, the most severe and damaging fights occur during sudden contacts between two different groups. Rhesus groups are not strictly territorial, but they do recognize group identity, and unexpected meetings between members of different groups often result in severe fights.[23, 23a]

These patterns of behavior have adaptive value in population limitation and in the spacing of animal groups throughout the available habitat. Thus intragroup compatibility insures that favorable social interactions such as reproduction and parental care will proceed, while incompatibility between groups prevents excessive crowding and limits the population to the level of its resources.

The third principle, social disorganization, can also be illustrated in studies of rodents and primates. Experimental mouse populations at the University of Wisconsin, reached states of highly injurious aggressive behavior as populations became crowded and social disintegration occurred. During these episodes of social disorganization, mice spent increasing amounts of time and energy in aggressive behavior (Figure 1), they became wounded, their health deteriorated, parasitic infections increased, and cannabalism of young became frequent.[22, 22a] Similar observations have been made by Calhoun in his well-known studies on wild Norway rat populations,[2] by Myers[19] on the European rabbit in Australia, and by Burns[1] and Stokes[24] on the Uinta ground squirrel in western United States.

In primate populations, two well-studied cases of aggressive behavior related to social disorganization were a population of baboons in the London zoo, studied by Zuckerman,[28] and a colony of rhesus macaques transplanted from India to Cayo Santiago, a small island off the coast of Puerto Rico, and studied by Carpenter.[5] Both popula-

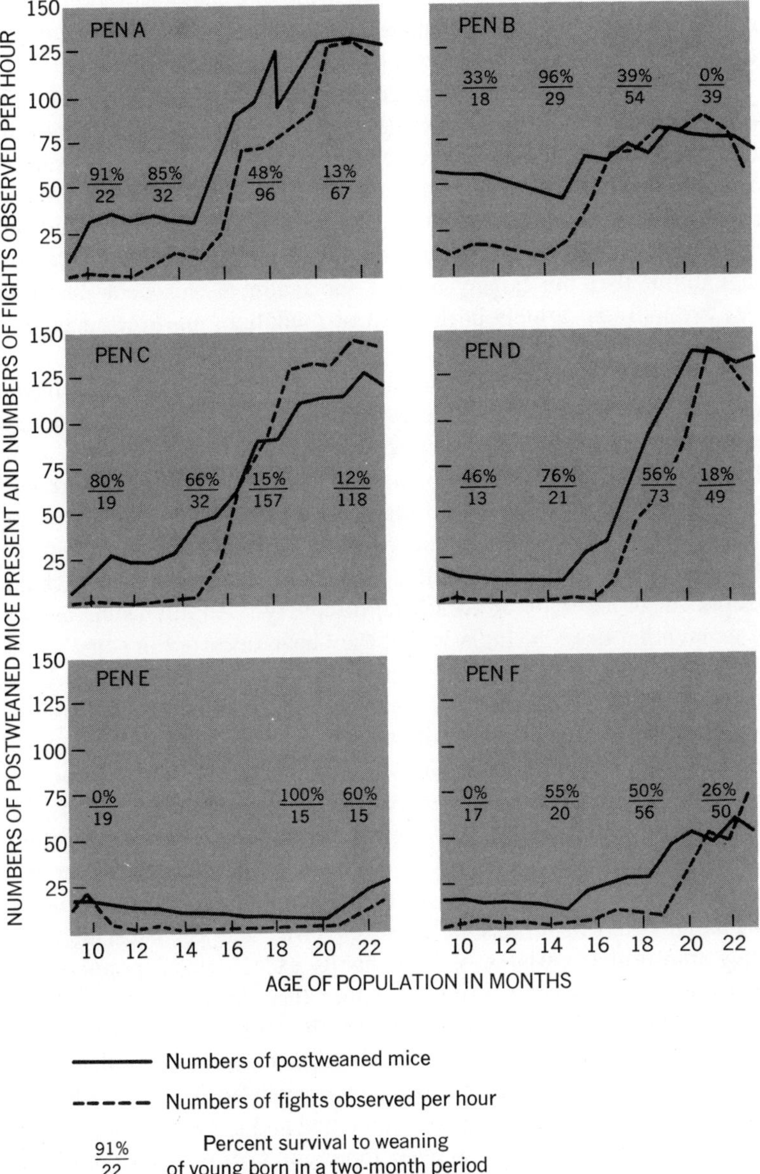

Figure 1 Relationships of population growth and aggressive behavior in semi-natural populations of house mice (*Mus musculus*).

tions went through periods of social instability and disruption after initial formation. During this time severe violence occurred, fatal injuries were common, and infant mortality was particularly high.

A special type of animal aggression, but one of particular interest to man, is that of animal attacks upon man. Some of the best-known and most dramatic examples come from the literature on man-eating tigers, man-eating sharks, rogue elephants and grizzly bears, though obviously the list could be extended beyond this to include many wild animals. Animal attacks upon man obviously involve aggressive behavior, but they are largely outside the realm of this book because they are more accurately in the area of predation, misdirected predation, or accidental occurrences.

Corbett[7] has emphasized, for example, that most man-eating tigers in India have been found to be wounded, crippled, or senile individuals who take to preying upon people because they no longer have the strength and capabilities to capture wild animals which represent their normal prey. He gives numerous examples of famous man-eaters in India who were found to have infirmities of teeth, limbs, muscles, or senses. He feels that they began the habit of attacking people out of necessity or accidental discovery. An interesting aspect of man-eating tigers in India is that they have occurred in some areas and not in others. For example, the Kumaon hills in northern U.P. contained several man-eaters throughout the early 20th century, as did also the Sundarbans, the delta area of the Ganges River in Bengal; where other parts of India, such as the Kanha area of central Madhya Pradesh, have traditionally been free of man-eaters. This raises the interesting question of whether these local patterns of the man-eating habit are the result of ecology (a shortage of natural food?) or the result of social traditions in food habits. We know from many studies of animal behavior, especially those on birds and primates, that socially transmitted patterns of food habits exist in local populations, since the young of some animals acquire their feeding patterns from their parents. One could hypothesize, therefore, that a man-eating tigress, who acquired the habit through necessity or accident due to an injury, could then transmit her behavior socially to her offspring. So far as I know, this has not been documented and is merely conjectural.

Shark attacks upon people also represent a dramatic example of aggression which again is probably a type of misdirected predation. Gilbert (quoted by Kenney[13]) pointed out, "A shark is an opportunist. It frequently hunts the weak, the old, the stupid and the crippled. Like any predator, it may improve the prey animals by taking misfits out of the breeding stock. In the shark's case, the prey animals are often weakened fishes. Thus a man in the sea should avoid appearing like a crippled fish." Predatory sharks find unarmed man in the sea an easy and helpless prey. Man's movements while swimming generate low-frequency sound or pressure waves which apparently attract sharks, arouse their curiosity, and may stimulate attack and feeding behavior. Although more than 10 species of sharks have been known to attack man, including the mako, bull, lemon, tiger, dusky, blue, whitetip, and hammerhead sharks, shark attacks are relatively rare. There are probably only 200 to 300 shark attacks on man per year throughout the entire world, and considerably more people than this are struck by lightning each year. This, however, is not meant to imply that sharks are not highly aggressive and predatory animals. They definitely are. In fact, one of the most dramatic examples of intraspecific aggression may also be found in sharks—in the sand tiger shark, the young pups begin aggressive behavior *in utero,* and the first young shark to hatch from the egg actually cannabalizes its weaker brothers and sisters *in utero* as they emerge from eggs before birth.[13] One could argue that this is also natural feeding behavior and not aggression—it becomes a moot point.

Rogue elephants and grizzly bears are two others animals known for their violent attacks upon man. The actual frequency of attacks is very low in both species, but when they occur they are spectacular and receive widespread publicity. In India, for example, some rogue elephants became famous throughout the country, and their episodes were repeated by storytellers and writers for decades. The stories of the famous rogue elephant of Kankankote, a village 50 miles from Mysore in South India, who lived in the 1870's are still told, as are those of the Mandla rogue, who also lived in the 1870's.[6]

Rogue elephants are usually solitary and ill-tempered bulls. They are extremely dangerous animals and may violently attack people, houses, or even villages. The famous rogue of Kankankote dominated a road leading to the village and viciously attacked people on the road, stomping them to death and dismembering them with its trunk and legs. There has been no thorough study of why or how rogues develop or even why individual elephants become solitary. Carrington[6] states, "It seems that the typical rogue is either mad, like a homicidal maniac in our own species, or is berserk." Carrington believes that various factors which might drive an elephant into a solitary state and aberrant behavior would include decay of the molar teeth, overstrained tusks, painful injuries or diseases, such as gunshot

Figure 2 A wild tusker trumpeting in the jungles of Mysore, south India. Approaching a camp of working elephants, he will at times engage a tame tusker in a fierce fight that often does not end until one of the animals has lost a tusk in the fighting. (Photograph and description by Ylla, with permission of La Guilde du Livre, Lausanne, Copyright © 1958.)

wounds or arthritic conditions. He points out, "Rendered bold by pain or madness, rogue elephants soon acquire contempt for mankind. They lose their natural timidity and caution, and make daring raids onto cultivated land. They knock down fences, and even houses, with malicious abandon, and immediately attack any human being who crosses their path." Fortunately, rogue elephants are rare and apparently most of them have had a history of accidental or extenuating experiences.

In their own intraspecific behavior elephants do not have a high frequency of aggression as do some sharks, though occasionally serious fights occur between males. As described by Carrington, "They fight head to head, either attempting to push one another backwards with their foreheads, or intertwining their trunks and engaging in a titanic tug of war, so that one animal is drawn into the other's tusks. The struggle may continue until one of the contestants is killed. This usually happens through the weaker elephant breaking away, thereby exposing his unprotected flank to the tusks of his opponent. When thus caught at a disadvantage an elephant can be disembowelled with a quick lunge of the head. The bodies of elephants are sometimes found with their heads battered in, their abdomens ripped open, and great holes torn out of their sides, bearing witness to the ferocity of the struggle."

Grizzly bear attacks have received widespread publicity in the United States in recent years because of five dramatic killings in western United States, and some biologists have gone so far as to propose that grizzly bears be eliminated from some national parks.[18] The fact remains, however, that there have been only five human deaths from grizzly bear attacks recorded in the U.S. National Parks in the last 97 years, all of them occurring in the last five years as our National Parks have become crowded with people at the rate of 37,000,000 visitors per year.[3] In comparison with these five deaths from grizzly bear attacks, during the same time there have been 627 human deaths from automobile accidents and drowning in our National Parks.

In 1968, a total of 38 people were injured by bear attacks in U.S. National Parks, but only one of these attacks was by a grizzly. All of the others were injuries by black bears, usually upon people trying to feed or photograph them in inadvisable circumstances. Even the grizzly bear attacks over the last five years have generally been due to a startled response when the animal has been suddenly surprised while feeding or sleeping. This is not to deny the possibility of unprovoked attacks, for the grizzly bear is an unpredictably aggressive animal.

Violent battles have been observed between male grizzly bears, especially during the mating season of June and early July, and females are known to be very aggressive when they have young cubs.[8]

The major aspects of aggression to be explored more fully in the subsequent chapters are focused around four major topics: (1) the extent of intraspecific aggression and violence in animals; (2) various adaptations which have arisen in animal societies to meet problems of aggressive and violent behavior; (3) physiological and neurological aspects of aggressive behavior; and (4) the interaction of genetic and environmental variables affecting the expression of aggressive behavior.

Although these topics are not necessarily presented in this sequence, these themes interweave throughout most of the subsequent papers. All of these papers represent major contributions of the last 25 years to our understanding of the psychology and biology of aggressive behavior in animals.

REFERENCES

1. Burns, R. D. 1968. The role of agonistic behavior in regulation of density in Uinta ground squirrels, *Citellus armatus*. M.S. thesis, Utah State University.
2. Calhoun, J. B. 1962. The ecology and sociology of the Norway rat. *U.S. Public Health Service Publication No. 1008*. 288 pp.
3. Caras, R. 1969. In defense of the grizzly. *Audubon,* **71**(3): 52–5.
4. Carpenter, C. R. 1934. A field study of the behavior and social relations of howling monkeys. *Comp. Psychol. Monog.,* **10**(2): 1–168.
5. ———. 1942. Societies of monkeys and apes. *Biol. Symposia,* **8**: 177–204.
6. Carrington, R. 1958. *Elephants. A Short Account of Their Natural History, Evolution and Influence on Mankind.* New York: Basic Books. 272 pp.
7. Corbett, J. 1957. *Man-eaters of India.* New York: Oxford University Press.
8. Craighead, F. and Craighead, J. 1966. Trailing Yellowstone's grizzlies by radio. *Nat. Geographic,* **130**(2): 252–67.
9. Darling, F. F. 1937. *A Herd of Red Deer.* Oxford: Oxford University Press. 215 pp.
10. Errington, P. 1963. *Muskrat Populations.* Ames, Iowa: Iowa State University Press. 665 pp.
11. Gilbert, P. W. 1968. The shark: barbarian and benefactor. *Bioscience,* **18**(10): 946–50.
12. Harris, D. B. and Sample, J. A. (Editors). 1969. *Violence in Contemporary American Society.* University Park, Pa.: The Pennsylvania State University Press. 261 pp.

13. Kenney, N. T. 1968. Sharks: wolves of the sea. *Nat. Geographic,* **133**(2): 222–57.
14. Kummer, H. 1970. Spacing mechanisms. *Smithsonian Third International Symposium, Man and Beast: Comparative Social Behavior.* Washington, D.C. May 16–19, 1969 (in press).
15. Linsdale, J. M. 1946. *The California Ground Squirrel.* Berkeley: University of California Press. 475 pp.
16. Lorenz, K. 1952. *King Solomon's Ring.* London: Methuen.
16a. ———. 1966. *On Aggression.* New York: Harcourt, Brace and World.
17. Matthews, L. H. 1964. Overt fighting in mammals. In *The Natural History of Aggression.* Edited by J. D. Carthy and F. J. Ebling. New York: Academic Press. 23–32 pp.
18. Moment, G. 1968. Bears: the need for a new sanity in wildlife conservation. *Bioscience,* **18**(12): 1105–8.
19. Myers, K. 1966. The effects of density on sociality and health in mammals. *Proc. Ecol. Soc. Australia,* **1**: 40–64.
20. Schaller, G. B. 1963. *The Mountain Gorilla: Ecology and Behavior.* Chicago: University of Chicago Press.
20a. ———. 1967. *The Deer and the Tiger. A Study of Wildlife in India.* Chicago: University of Chicago Press. 370 pp.
21. Scott, J. P. 1958. *Aggression.* Chicago: University of Chicago Press. 149 pp.
22. Southwick, C. H. 1955. The population dynamics of confined house mice supplied with unlimited food. *Ecology,* **36**(2): 212–25.
22a. ———. 1955. Regulatory mechanisms of house mouse populations: social behavior affecting litter survival. *Ecology,* **36**(4): 627–34.
22b. ———. 1964. *Peromyscus leucopus:* An interesting subject for studies of socially induced stress responses. *Science,* **143**: 55–6.
23. Southwick, C. H., Siddiqi, M. R. and Beg, M. A. 1965. Rhesus monkeys in north India. In *Primate Behavior: Field Studies of Monkeys and Apes.* Edited by Irven DeVore. New York: Holt, Rinehart and Winston. pp. 111–59.
23a. ———. 1969. Aggressive behavior of rhesus monkeys in natural and captive groups. In *Aggressive Behaviour.* Edited by S. Garattini and E. B. Sigg. Amsterdam: Excerpta Medica Foundation. pp. 32–43.
24. Stokes, A. W. 1969. *Aggressive Man and Aggressive Beast.* 39th Honor Faculty Lecture. Utah State University. 22 pp.
25. Sugiyama, Y. 1967. Social organization of Hanuman langurs. In *Social Communication among Primates.* Edited by S. A. Altmann. Chicago: University of Chicago Press. pp. 221–36.
26. Verheyen, R. 1954. *Monographie ethologique de l'hippopotame.* Bruxelles: Institut des Parcs Nationaux du Congo Belge. Exploration du Parc Nationaux Albert.
27. Wilson, E. O. 1970. Competitive behavior. *Smithsonian Third International Symposium, Man and Beast: Comparative Social Behavior.* Washington, D.C. May 13–16, 1969. Smithsonian Institution.
28. Zuckerman, S. 1932. *The Social Life of Monkeys and Apes.* London: Routledge and Kegan Paul, Ltd.

2

AGGRESSIVE BEHAVIOR AMONG VERTEBRATE ANIMALS*

NICHOLAS E. COLLIAS
University of California, Los Angeles

This article is reprinted from Physiological Zoology, *1944,* **XVII***(1): 83–123 (excerpted). Reprinted with permission of the University of Chicago Press.*

Individual aggressiveness, as shown by threatening or fighting, plays a central role in vertebrate societies and populations. It also occurs in a number of insects, but the matter has not been generally investigated in other groups of animals. It is possible that aggressiveness in a more subtle form may be expressed simply by independence of action, and its opposite, submissive behavior, merely by avoidance of another animal. Any general study of the matter in vertebrates

* The present paper is expanded from part of a Doctor's thesis entitled: "Aggressive Behavior among Vertebrate Animals: Some Implications and a Statistical Analysis." The statistical part has been published elsewhere. My studies in this field were made, in part, while occupying a Robert Ridgway Fellowship in Zoology at the University of Chicago. I wish to express great appreciation to my special adviser Professor W. C. Allee, for numerous critical and valuable comments and for his generous assistance with the preparation of this paper for publication and to Miss Elizabeth Beeman and Mrs. Miriam Posner Finkel for checking many references after my entrance into the United States Army in the summer of 1942. I am happy to acknowledge the aid received from the critical reading of an earlier version of the manuscript or parts of it by Professor Sewall Wright, Professor Calvin P. Stone, Professor C. R. Carpenter, and Mr. Bernard Greenberg. Responsibility for all statements and for the final form of the paper is, of course, my own.

must at present be largely limited to the more obvious expressions of aggressiveness.

The general purpose of this article is to attempt to place aggressive behavior in its proper perspective as an aspect of the biology of vertebrate animals and so to gain some idea of the generalizations possible and of the current problems concerning this trait. This purpose involves a survey of the role of aggressive behavior in the ecological pattern of living systems, of the associated psychological, physiological, and genetic mechanisms, and of the evolutionary changes in aggressive behavior patterns. It must be recognized at the outset that, as a result of the undeveloped nature of this field of study, any suggestions which are made are often to be regarded as a framework for continued research rather than as well established rules.

Living systems are organized into patterns in which integrated systems at one level of organization may themselves be units of a more inclusive grouping, as is illustrated by the following series: individual, social group, population, and animal community. The first problem is to clarify the role of aggressive behavior at each of these different levels of organization.

ROLE OF AGGRESSIVE BEHAVIOR

I. Welfare, Survival, and Reproduction of Individuals

Individual aggression in vertebrates is frequently expressed in two special forms, which are not necessarily mutually exclusive and which include (a) defense of a given area (territory) and (b) hierarchies of precedence within social groups. These hierarchies consist of the disposition of two or more animals, or animal groups, in ranks or orders, each subordinate to the one above it with respect to the aggressive-submissive dominance relations. Examples of the two different kinds of behavior are exhibited within each of the classes of vertebrates, with the possible exception of the Amphibia.

Good reviews of territorial relations have recently appeared for fish[54] and for birds.[52b] The present survey places more stress on social hierarchies under more or less natural conditions, strongly supplemented by observations on captive or domestic animals. This procedure may help to close the gap between field and laboratory studies of social organization of vertebrate animals by demonstrating that many similarities, as well as differences, exist in the way that animals behave in the field and in the laboratory. Social hierarchies have been described for most domestic animals and have often been observed among those in cages or in pens and among fish in aquaria. Most of the field studies have dealt with birds and mammals.

Aggressiveness may lead to the establishment of high social rank within a group; and high rank frequently gives precedence to food, to mates, and at times even to territory. However, in the last case the reverse is often true; and possession of a territory usually means social domination of that territory, so far as the given species is concerned, and tends to prevent formation of a rigid social hierarchy.

Social Hierarchies and the Individual. Social rank is often, perhaps generally, decided by fighting, bluffing, or passive submission at the initial encounter between any given pair of individuals or by an early series of such encounters. This holds almost diagrammatically with adults of the common domestic fowl[13, 66, 66a] (and citations); it has also been observed in captivity for diamond doves,* for mice,[30, 72] for macaques,[49b] for chimpanzees,[16] for the American chameleon,[26] and for the fish *Platypoecilus*.[6] It has been noted in the field for the birds called "blue tits";[14] during field studies on various infrahuman primates, Carpenter[9d] observed that fighting or the threat of fighting was important in helping to establish dominance status.

In general, when a number of strange chickens or fish[6] are grouped in the laboratory, a period of active fighting may precede the later period of greater social stability; this has been observed under natural or field conditions for valley quail.[21, 40] Among valley quail partially established members of a covey dominate aliens of subsequent introduction.[40] Strangers among the vertebrates appear almost invariably to be attacked when they try to enter small groups organized on a hierarchical basis.[5, 9c, 47, 60] If they are permitted to enter, they tend to be relegated to the bottom of the social order, and they may gradually fight their way up—for example, as in winter flocks of chickadees.[60]

Once social rank is established, it is maintained by the habit of subordination of those in lower positions, reinforced by threats or punishment dealt out by those of higher rank. The exact method of coercion varies with the special weapons of the species. "Tension" often appears to be greatest between closely ranked individuals and may be shown by mutual avoidance or tendencies toward revolt, as has been noted in chickens,[66a] or by the increased frequency of blows

* Results of experiments that are unsupported by citations and based on my own observations, hitherto unpublished.

dealt to immediate subordinates, as has been observed in fish[54a], jackdaws,[47] and chickens.*

Revolts and reversals in the social scale are not very common in stable groups and usually require active battle. Shoemaker[68] noted that canaries of low rank, when injected with testosterone propionate, were subjected to increased pecking by the given despot shortly before reversal of relative ranks took place. Under similar conditions, low-ranking hens revolt and reverse position most often with reference to the individual immediately above the rebel in the general social scale.[2]

There are a number of ways in which an animal of inferior caliber but especially favored by circumstances may gain more or less temporary ascendancy over another superior to it in most respects. These have been described for chickens by Schjelderup-Ebbe.[66a] Our observations agree with those of Murchison[51a] and of Sanctuary[65] that complex, triangular hierarchies, such as are common in all but very small flocks of chickens, as a rule tend to simplify and straighten out with time, presumably because each individual gravitates toward its appropriate place in the scale of relative aggressiveness. This important phenomenon deserves additional study.

In laboratory studies of primates, precedence to food is commonly used as an indicator of social dominance; and such precedence, according to social ranking based on aggressiveness, has been noted for certain other mammals,[41, 77] for fish,[54a] for turtles,[26a] and for many birds. Thus the struggle for food among nestlings of the black-crowned night heron leads to a hierarchy of dominance based on aggressive behavior.[57] Under somewhat more natural, free-ranging conditions, precedence to food according to social level has been observed in winter flocks of chickadees,[60] blue tits,[14] and other birds[52] and in various primates.[9d]

The degree of competitive action may be greatly increased by hunger—for example, in laboratory groups of monkeys,[49] chimpanzees,[59] rats,[7] and chickens. The frequency of pecking of subordinates can readily be increased several fold in flocks of hens by placing the birds on short rations.* In the field, muskrats may be crowded by drought into small waterholes without severe friction; but if there is also a food shortage, as is often the case, aggressive interaction may be severe and often lethal.[23]

Adverse previous experience may be an important factor in some cases. Chickens that have been strongly persecuted learn not to come

* *Ibid.*

to the food hopper until the dominant birds have finished eating. Starving birds frequently feed despite blows from their despots. Among chimpanzees extreme food deprivation by itself may not be sufficient cause for a subordinate to respond positively in food competition with a dominant animal unless there is high expectancy of success.[59] Apparently, the balance between fear of despots and degree of hunger is an important element in food competition, at least as seen in the laboratory.

Satisfactory studies on the possible survival value of high rank in relation to food shortage in nature do not seem to have been made. Winter starvation is an important decimating factor in populations of northern bobwhite quail, and it is also known that well-fed birds withstand adverse whether conditions much better than do poorly nourished individuals.[23a] Recent evidence gathered in this laboratory suggests that in flocks of hens on short rations birds of high rank usually get more to eat and maintain weight better than do birds of low rank. Whether this is true or not among quail and other birds in nature is a problem for investigation.

Individual survival value would favor the leaving of more descendants by such individuals, and the same end may be more directly attained by increased success in mating. The dominant male in caged groups of the lizard, *Anolis carolinensis* generally mates most frequently.[56] Laboratory studies on domestic cocks in relation to their place in the social hierarchy[34] have shown a decidedly greater frequency of mating by males high in the social hierarchy. This has been strikingly noted in field studies of sage grouse[67, 67a] and more precisely in rhesus monkeys.[9c] The males of many polygynous ungulates will herd together as many females as they can defend from other males.[5, 18] In the late winter flocks of the monogamous Gambel's quail a female will often pair off with the winner of a fight, even after pair formation with the loser had apparently recently taken place.* The female of the salmon, which is the sex that builds the nest, may be attended by a succession of males as the larger, cruising males drive off smaller rivals and usurp their position.[54]

Females may compete among themselves for mates, as in the case of the rhesus monkey.[9b] Females of the monogamous gibbon probably drive maturing daughters out of the family group, as the males

* "In a mating of long duration, however, this may not hold and both hen and cock frequently unite to drive away any intruder on their domestic tranquility."[32]

do their sons.[9a] Defense of the male mate against other females is common among birds, as in the willow wren and snow bunting;[70] and mild aggressive competition between females for the attentions of a male has been observed for the sage grouse, which is characterized by promiscuous polygyny.[67a] In the European three-spined stickleback the most sexually advanced female dominates and drives other females from the immediate vicinity of the nest in which she intends to lay.[54] Unmated jewel fish in breeding condition confine their attacks to members of the same sex; but, after pairs are formed and the members of a pair have learned to know each other as individuals, they drive off other jewel fish from their territory, regardless of sex.[55] Such mutual jealousy in the early stages of pairing probably helps to facilitate monogamy.

With many vertebrates it is known that fighting between males greatly increases in frequency and intensity in the presence of females. Food or territory as complicating factors can be clearly ruled out in some cases. Food may be largely ignored during the breeding season by male fur seals[5] and red deer stags,[18] especially during the period of intense competition for females. Many monogamous male birds are known to become much more aggressive toward other males after pair formation is definitely effected; and some birds, like the willet, may pair, and the male will then defend the female before establishing a territory.[44] The Sierra Nevada rosy finch is said to have no fixed territory, and defense reactions are displayed by a paired male only when another male approaches his mate.[71] Fighting between males in the presence of females is not inevitable, since, among rhesus monkeys, a subordinate male may consort first with a female if there is a plentiful supply of females, but, if there is only a single female available, she is always possessed first by the dominant male of the group.[9c] The same author[9] found no fighting over females in groups of howler monkeys.

Adverse previous experience with sex rivals may be important. Subordinate cocks of the domestic fowl, after continued persecution and suppression by the dominant cock of a flock, will tread much less frequently, even when tested in the absence of the dominant cock, or with different hens, resulting in what Guhl[34] has called "psychological castration." According to A. A. Allen,[4] ruffed grouse which have been strongly subjugated (under laboratory confinement) may die shortly thereafter, apparently from some obscure mental shock rather than from wounds or food deprivation; the dominant grouse survive.

TERRITORY AND THE INDIVIDUAL

Details of the operation of territorial mechanisms have been most thoroughly worked out for birds. A high place in the social order may at times give precedence to the occupation of open territories, but eviction of a bird from its territory by another member of its species does not seem to be very common in nature. In winter flocks of chickadees Odum[60] found that the three topranking males were the ones that remained on or near the winter feeding grounds to breed in the following spring. It is possible that here, as in blue tits, these birds were dominant in the winter flock because they had held near-by territories in the preceding spring rather than because of innate aggressiveness. There is always at hand a reservoir of young birds; these birds, usually low in the social order, are available to supply replacements for vacated and suitable territories within the area covered by the flock. It remains to be determined whether such occupancy may take place according to social precedence in the pre-existing hierarchy of the winter flock.

In the case of migratory and many lek birds in which breeding or mating territories are set up anew each year, a complete and clear-cut social hierarchy may not be established before territorial claims are laid. In such cases possession of a territory often depends on priority in staking out the claim. However, early territorial boundaries are very labile and subject to reduction in size as later arrivals carve out places for themselves, which they must do by physical or psychological combat unless population density is low.[43, 52a] A high degree of aggressiveness is evidently of advantage in securing a foothold. During early spring, among prairie chickens there apparently is general fighting over the whole booming grounds as each cock establishes his place; but, once boundaries are set, each cock tends to remain in his own territory, where he is dominant.[37] According to Chapman,[10] a socially subordinate male of Gould's manakin, a tropical lek bird, may not defend as large a mating territory as a more dominant and more sexually active bird.

Territorial defense reactions tend to increase in frequency and intensity with crowding, as in the case of terns[61] and house wrens.[43] As an opposite tendency, Kendeigh noted that the vigilance of territorial defense decreased as the birds learned each other's boundaries.

Possession of a territory gives precedence to food in that territory. This is important for birds which get their food within the territorial limits, especially for the nestlings.[52a] Compression of breeding territories in birds may be permitted to a considerable extent if the food supply is abundant, as in kestrels and white storks.[52b] Defense of territories is a phase of aggressive behavior which may lead indirectly to precedence in mating. In the song sparrow[52a, 52b] the male arrives before the female in the spring, and the females come to those males which have established territories.

II. Aggressive Behavior in Relation to Stability and Subdivision of Social Groups

The term "social" has been loosely used and variously defined with reference to animals.[1a] Basically, the term signifies group cooperation and, in a broad sense, may refer to interpersonal cooperation at any level of organization. This section, for purposes of convenience, refers mainly to social groups the members of which live together and which in many cases move about as coherent units over a common area, as do flocks or herds, and whose integration appears to be primarily and essentially dependent on interindividual, rather than on habitat, stimuli. This latter attribute conforms to Wheeler's[74] definition of animal societies. In many ways, perhaps, "society" would be the most satisfactory available term; however, it has been used with many different meanings, and, accordingly, the aggregations under consideration will somewhat arbitrarily be referred to merely as "social groups."

SPECIFIC TOLERANCES AND THE FORMATION OF AGGREGATIONS

Aggressive behavior can be regarded as asocial in so far as it acts to prevent, decrease, or disrupt the integration of vertebrate societies, and it can be regarded as social in so far as it furthers the integration and organization of such societies. Aggressive behavior is at one and the same time an active force in the subdivision of societies and in the integration of the smaller units so formed. Social life becomes possible when social tolerance is greater than asocial tendencies within the group.[1] Cooperation, as shown by the more widespread existence of social or subsocial aggregations of some sort, is more basic and widespread among vertebrate animals than is aggression. The individual aggressive tendencies which exist in a great many vertebrates and which might be strong enough to overbalance the generalized drive toward sociality are often counteracted by certain specific tolerances or attractions, with a resulting decrease in aggressive behavior. This, in turn, permits the formation of social systems of various sorts.

At the level of the species, tolerance for individuals or groups of the same species with increasing distance between them may result in organization of populations on a territorial basis. At the level of the animal community, tolerance for other species enables many individuals of diverse species to live together. Tolerance within each type of social unit may be greatly increased by decreasing the need for competition, i.e., under conditions of plentiful food supply, shelter, breeding sites, or mates. For example, male western fence lizards ordinarily hold separate territories; but, where food and shelter are abundant, several males may live in close association with one male dominant.[28] The controlling consideration is the balance between the degree of aggressive behavior of the members of a group and their mutual toleration, as shown objectively by their tendency to aggregate, whatever the mechanisms that are involved in either.

A CLASSIFICATION OF SOCIAL GROUPS AMONG AGGRESSIVE SPECIES OF VERTEBRATES

The following tentative classification of social groups according to the degree of integration and organization also affords a means of summarizing the more important literature which concerns social hierarchies of nondomestic vertebrate animals formed under free-ranging and natural or seminatural conditions.

A. Individual competition for food, mates, or territory dominates; group open, usually more temporary; fighting frequent.
   1. Toleration minimum; dispersed populations, and societies in the process of formation or disintegration. Nice[52b] has classified territories among birds according to their size and the number of functions (mating, nesting, feeding) subserved; size of territory generally increases with number of its functions. Territorial rodents may have a considerable extent of more or less neutral area about their territories, wherein a definite chasing order is present, as in the case of the golden-mantled ground squirrel and of certain chipmunks.[31] Groups of more or less free-ranging American chameleons[33] and of western fence lizards[28] may at times exhibit dominance hierarchies which seem to be based primarily on modified territorial relations. Among certain deer, antelope, gazelles, and buffaloes, the young males may unite to form bachelor packs in which

there are no leaders and in which there is continual quarreling, especially during the mating season.[5] Such disintegrating groups are frequently found when males compete directly for mates as in late winter flocks of Gambel's quail[32] and red-deer stag parties at the onset of the rutting season.[18] In this category also belong the feeding assemblages where precedence is marked, especially in heterospecific groups—for example, different species of birds at a winter feeding station.[14, 52]

2. Toleration greater and group consequently more evident and coherent. An incomplete social hierarchy may be formed within the group; i.e., dominance relations may not be settled between all individuals. Mating assemblages of sage grouse[67, 67a] and many feeding assemblages, where food is plentiful and individual competition is relatively low, are appropriate examples. Female *Anolis carolinensis* (confined under rather free-ranging conditions) may fight among themselves in a male's territory, and the resultant order may be a straight-line hierarchy.[33]

B. Social group dominates and moves as a more or less coherent unit over a common area; individual composition of group more consistent, and dominance relations between individuals generally stabilized in a social hierarchy.

1. Social hierarchy evident within group.
    a) Social order less stable; group temporary and semiclosed. Examples are winter flocks of chickadees[60, 60a] and blue tits.[14] Coveys of valley quail[22] may fight as a group at times, and they represent a transitional type to the next category.
    b) Social order more stable; group more permanent and more nearly closed and may act as a unit to drive invaders off of a common territory; some division of labor in the form of leaders or sentinels. Hordes of rhesus monkeys where the dominance of the group seemingly depends on the dominance of the supreme despot.[9b, 9c, 9d] Family groups of gibbons where the dominance of the group depends to a large extent on size and aggressiveness of the group and proximity of the territorial center of the group.[9a] Family groups of fullgrown blue geese where the defended area or sphere of influence moves with the group.[35, 42]

2. Exercise of aggressive relations within the group largely suspended; group closed, permanent, highly social, with division

of labor, and frequently acting as a unit to drive intruders off a group territory.

a) Exercise of aggressive dominance relations generally pronounced only between closely ranked individuals. This is a transitional type and is found among the colony-nesting jackdaws.[47, 47a, 47b]

b) Exercise of aggressive dominance relations within group not very evident, or suspended. Howler-monkey clans where the males may share the same female peacefully,[9] and possibly societies of the cuckoolike anis in which several birds may lay and incubate in the same nest.[19] The family in blue geese[42] until the young begin to mature. Permanent sex pairs, such as those of blue geese, which involve both physiological and morphological division of labor, with the preceding, represent the better-integrated types of social groupings among subhuman vertebrates.

The degree of aggressiveness and the strength of the territorial instincts determine to a large extent the nature of the dominance relations seen among many cages animals. Laboratory mice[72] and captive lions[15] both of which are very aggressive toward other members of their species, show a monarchistic type of social order in which the despot tends to inhibit aggressive relations between his subordinates. This is the case in caged American chameleons[26] which are strongly territorial in nature.

Aggressive dominance relationships may be suspended by some animals when in very small cages. Among captive lions its appears that serious fighting will not take place in close quarters. But, if two strangers are housed together, they will begin to fight as soon as they get into an outside inclosure.[15]

ASOCIAL ASPECTS OF AGGRESSIVE BEHAVIOR

Any changes in aggressiveness of individuals influence the degree of social integration. Both absolute and relative levels of aggressiveness within a group are important. Among chickens, flocks composed only of cocks have a less stable order than that which characterizes flocks of the less aggressive hens.[50] Markedly increasing the aggressiveness of low-ranking hens by injecting them with testosterone propionate caused them to rise in the social order of hens.[2] When the ovaries were removed from 6 birds selected from various social levels in a flock of 12 pullets, all of the operates fell below the intact birds, but they retained the same social rankings relative to each other.*

Both psychological conditioning and physical maturation influence the amount of intragroup aggression and are important factors in the establishment of a peck-order among chickens. In a flock of hens an initial period of fighting and social instability is followed by the establishment of a more rigid social order and, finally, in the absence of special disturbing factors, by an amelioration of dominance relations and increased tolerance of subordinates. However, baby chicks do not fight and have no dominance hierarchies based on aggressiveness.

Physiological changes induced by the environment may increase intragroup aggression and, correspondingly, decrease social integration. Winter flocks of birds may break up on a warm day into sex pairs, or males may occupy territories; with a succeeding cold spell the flock may re-form, the individual territories be released, and the sex pairs be disunited.[52a] At the same time the progressive recrudescence of the gonads steadily forces a trend toward disruption of the winter flock, toward individual territoriality, and toward sex-pair formation. Hunger, as has been pointed out, is a potent factor helping to determine the degree of intragroup aggression. It cannot be too strongly emphasized that a dynamic picture should be maintained with respect to the degree of integration of any given group. It might have been possible to remove the qualifying terms in the foregoing classification if the phenomena under consideration were more rigid and less subject to variation with the environmental situation.

Numbers present exert a general influence on the stability of a social group. With the addition of each new individual the number of specific intragroup paired relationships increases disproportionately, as noted by Carpenter[9a] in this connection, by use of the formula $N(N-1)/2$. For example, the number of such relationships rises rapidly from 10 in a group of 5 animals to 45 in a group of 10 animals. In large acquaintanceship groups there is probably more fighting, as in chickadees;[36] triangular dominance relationships are much more common; and it takes much longer for the social hierarchy to become stabilized. Our observations agree with those of Schjelderup Ebbe[66a] that straight-line dominance is rare in flocks of chickens with more than 10 birds. Murchison,[51a] studying five groups of

Ibid.

cockerels of 2–6 birds each, described a disproportionate relationship between the size of the group and the length of time it took for straightline dominance to become established. By extrapolation to larger groups he predicted that in a group of 10 birds it would take about 15 months—a prediction not supported by observation in this laboratory even though the general principle is sound. With groups larger than about 20 the number of possible relations becomes so great that precise study of group organization becomes impractical. It would appear that with more highly organized groups the integration of a small stable group tends to break down with increasing size of the group, possibly because recognition of individuals becomes more difficult.

SOME SOCIAL ASPECTS OF AGGRESSIVE BEHAVIOR

Aggressive behavior may be regarded as social in some respects; for example, it may help set up social barriers which limit the size of small groups down to the point where effective group organization is possible. This is the point of view stressed in this paragraph; but it is also true that, in so far as it tends to prevent federation of such groups, aggression could be regarded as asocial. The density and mobility of the species population as a whole is often important in determining the extent to which social groups remain open. As a group becomes larger and more loosely integrated, it sooner or later passes the threshold for individual recognition; tolerance for strangers apparently then increases. At low densities in laboratory populations of mice Crew and Mirskaia[17] and Retzlaff[63] observed that the entrance of any newcomer was at once noted and that the subsequent fighting commonly continued until it had been killed; in higher densities the immigrant had a better chance of surviving. The newcomer loses himself in the larger group. In low-density populations of valley quail, trespassers from other coveys are recognized and excluded.[21, 40] Where the quail are abundant and covey contacts more frequent, social barriers are less rigid.

The arrangement of social groups according to the degree of integration shows that, as egocentric intragroup aggression declines, cooperation in intergroup aggression increases and the amount of social service within groups increases. The gradual change from defense of individual pair territories to cooperative defense of communal territories—inversely related phenomena—is clearly seen in the various members of the Crotophaginae, a subfamily of cuckoos which includes the anis.[19] Since group territories tend to be larger than individual territories, each individual within a society can range freely over a wider area. In so far as cooperative aggressiveness favors group life, it facilitates the various other benefits to be derived from this habit, such as increased safety from predators.

Social service within the group is itself frequently closely related to aggressive behavior. The despot in some species may be leader, as in kangaroos,[5] or sentinel, as in families of blue geese.[35, 42] Jackdaws have a form of "police force" in which excessive despotism of any individual is blocked by cooperative attacks by the rest of the flock.[47, 47b] Defense of the young by the parents is common from fish to man. Something akin to discipline of the young is seen in howler monkeys.[9]

The "social service," so-called, may be rendered to a part of the group rather than to all the associated animals and may take the form of mutual aid in establishing social status. For example, in blue geese[35, 42] and monkeys[49] subordinates by a united attack may secure temporary dominance over a common despot. Among rhesus monkeys the male consort helps the oestrus female to rise in the hierarchy of females,[9b] while in flocks of geese and jackdaws the female assumes the social rank of the male to which she becomes mated.[47b]

Certain aspects of territorial defense can be considered as different forms of social service; these are more or less specifically related, in various species, to copulation, nest-building, egg-laying, and successful incubation and rearing of young. Recent laboratory studies, although somewhat limited in this respect, indicate that domination of a territory may be essential to prevent interference with reproduction in territorial species—at least under the conditions of observation, for example, in jewel fish,[55] in canaries,[68] and in robin redbreasts and chaffinches.[44a]

One form of social service of territory is that it helps prevent interference with normal functioning of a mated pair of individuals. Many male vertebrates attack or interfere with copulating males. If pigeons, which ordinarily hold small territories, are greatly crowded, the males continually interfere with each other's attempts at copulation, and percentage of fertility is greatly reduced.[29] Female pigeons may similarly attack a copulating female, pecking its head;[75] but such female intolerance among vertebrates seems, as a rule, to be less common or intense than in males.

Reiffer's hummingbird in Central America may show nesting

failures up to 50 per cent as a result of the stealing of nesting material from nests of other hummingbirds; this difficulty was apparently related to the lack of territorial defense reactions.[19]

In flocks of domestic hens which are not generally considered to be territorial birds, the low egg production of pullets at the bottom of the peck-order can be decidedly increased by removing them from the domination of their more aggressive flock-mates.[65] Individual territories would appear to help egg-laying, at least under certain conditions, in hens. Individual laying cages are often used in the egg-production industry.

Among fish, defense of the territory or nest may help prevent destruction of the eggs or young by other males or by fish of other species.[58] In nature, terns, which are unable to maintain their small territories under very crowded conditions, desert their eggs and nests.[61] In monogamous birds where the males share the duties of incubation or care of the young, it may be of added advantage for the female to drive other females from the territory or neighborhood of her mate. The near presence of a strange, sexually active female may more or less inhibit broody behavior and crop growth in the male of an incubating pair of pigeons.[62] Territorial defense by male birds may also be important in preventing the breakup of nesting by an intruding male.[52b]

The role of aggressive behavior in the integration of the sex pair deserves more detailed attention. Dominance relations between the sexes must often be established for harmony, but excessive aggressiveness toward the opposite sex is probably an obstacle to mating. Males generally dominate females, particularly during the breeding season; and female dominance over the male, while it may not be completely prohibitive, is said to hinder mating in caged monkeys[49a] and in chickens.[66a]

Courtship frequently serves to ameliorate the dominance relations and promote propinquity between the sexes. Many male birds, as well as some fish,[54a] practically cease to exercise aggressive dominance over the female during the breeding season. Male monkeys and apes grant the oestrus female greater feeding privileges.[9b] The domestic cock calls hens to food, and more or less formalized courtship-feeding occurs in many birds.

Courtship behavior, which is usually presumed to be sexually stimulating, grades off indistinguishably and in a complex way into aggressive-submissive behavior. Adoption of a submissive display by a male night heron helps keep the female in his territory, so that pair formation may take place. The male then gains the dominance in subsequent mutual ceremonies. If a male night heron adopts a subordinate head position, he may be permitted to remain in another male's territory, and the two individuals may form a pair.[57] According to Roberts,[64] the essential difference in the behavior of the sexes of the gentoo penguin, *Pygoscelis papua,* is that during the breeding season a male always tries to dominate weaker birds, while a female loses this dominating urge during the short period when fertilization must take place. Female terns inhibit attack from the male when pair formation takes place by adopting a submissive head posture, and the males inhibit male behavior in the females with an intimidation posture.[61] A rhesus monkey of either sex can often avoid attack from another individual by presenting as for copulation.[9b, 9c, 49a] This appears to be a sign of subordination, and in homosexual pairs of many vertebrates it is the dominant individual that generally mounts. Mounting by a subordinate monkey often stimulates the dominant to mount this subordinate, which then becomes more tractable.[49a] A number of female mammals when in oestrus exhibit mounting behavior; and oestrus-female mammals generally cease to fight, scratch, bite, or kick or persistently to avoid sexually driving males.[78]

AGGRESSIVE BEHAVIOR IN RELATION TO SUBDIVISION AND SPLITTING OF SOCIAL GROUPS

Aggressive behavior may play a role in the subdivision of large societies. The threshold for effective group organization varies with the capacity of the species, but most simple and relatively closed societies are small. Wing,[76] in an extensive numerical summary, has recently shown that winter flocks of birds in the majority of cases consist of two dozen birds or less. Probably even these, like larger groups, are often composed of subgroups. Fischel[27] observed that a flock of 500 white leghorn hens broke up readily each day into open subgroups.

Favorable conditions of habitat permit crowding, while previous acquaintanceship leads to the consistent association of particular individuals to form a semiclosed group which may gradually merge into, and later split out as, a unit from the larger compound group; for example, large winter flocks of chickadees readily break up into subgroups with usually less than about 8 individuals.[73] Similar subdivision is seen in coveys of valley quail,[40] in coveys of northern bobwhite quail,[25] and in herds of red deer which are composed of a varying number of family groups.[18] Addiction to special places within the area ranged over by the entire group also favors subdivision into subgroups—for example, as in red deer and chickadees.

Since different degrees of tolerance are likely to exist between the members of a large group, any general increase of aggressiveness, whether expressed actively or merely by independence of action, may be expected to subdivide the group into corresponding subgroups. When a group has increased beyond a certain size, subdivision into subgroups may be followed by competition between these subgroups. An interesting parallel can be drawn between the dominance hierarchy within winter flocks of blue tits at a food hopper, where rank is related to individual aggressiveness, size (possibly), and distance to the center of a given individual's territory, and the similar hierarchy at a higher level of organization between family groups of gibbons, where rank has been related to the same criteria but applied to the group as the competing unit.

III. Density and Spread of Species Populations

Formal schemes dealing with the economy of animals have uniformly used density of the animals as the unit of measurement, emphasized the problem of overpopulation in relation to the capacity of the habitat, and proceeded from the assumption that the requirement for living and reproducing were met by random search for the necessary objects.[53] While such a random element undoubtedly exists, especially in the case of young, inexperienced animals, these theories must be modified, to a considerable degree, in the vertebrates as a result of such manifestations of aggressive behavior as shown in territorial defense and in social hierarchies, and of tendencies toward the formation of aggregations. This later phase of the subject will not be discussed here.[1, 1a]

Random dispersal of the young, usually within limits of more or less suitable habitat types, has been described for many vertebrates. When the young are fairly well grown, they may wander off; active driving by the parents assists or stimulates this initial movement in some species.[5, 18] The degree of toleration varies with the species, but the nomadic young are not infrequently harried from place to place until they find an open niche, often in a suboptimal habitat, or otherwise perish.

Restrictions of habitat, from whatever cause, such as are common on the periphery of a species' range, result in increased competition; and those animals unfortunate enough to be evicted from their territories here or elsewhere become nomads and receive the same aggressive treatment as is usual for the young until they become established again. A succession of favorable years may build up a relatively large density in peripheral habitats; later, severe restrictions of living conditions may force emigration from the area and may result even in the irruptive type of emigration. Quail are most likely to undergo violent fluctuations on the borders of their range.[46] Carrying capacity of a given area itself may depend, in good part, on the degree of social tolerance of the particular individuals which compose the group of quail which occupies an area.[23b]

Defense of territories is an important factor making for population stability in the case of many vertebrates. Predators, such as the territorial horned owl, resident in areas with alternative and abundant species of prey, may at times be self-limited and maintain relatively stable numbers.[24] Territorial size is readily compressible in the ruffed grouse,[11] which undergoes cyclic fluctuatians in density. In birds the ease of compression of territories varies considerably with the species,[52b] as well as with population density;[43, 61] and such differences in tolerance may eventually help explain, to some extent, the nature of the population fluctuations which are exhibited. There is a possibility[52b] that intraspecies aggression, whether of a territorial nature or otherwise, by providing increasingly great resistance to crowding, helps cut down the incidence of disease and therefore the intensity of cyclic fluctuations which, in their more extreme form, appear to be a rather wasteful method of regulating numbers.

In addition to forcing diffusion of the excess population into suboptimal habitats, intraspecies aggression, which increases with crowding, may exert a regulatory action on population size by causing mortality directly. Field voles are territorial and, unlike Crew and Mirskaia's[17] mice, will often fight to the death when crowded. In describing the results of an investigation of cycles in voles, mice, and lemmings Elton[20] states that

This social antagonism among voles probably exists in nature and may be very important at different levels of population and may prove to explain some of the mortality at higher numbers . . . ; we can see that there are inherent properties of the population dynamics of voles that may eventually explain their cycle as a self-contained system that is not so much dependent on other animals like predators and parasites as we first supposed.

Cannibalism of the young by older, larger individuals is common in aggregations of young black bass[45] and has been described for various other vertebrates.[48] Under certain conditions, many male carnivorous mammals will kill and eat the young.[5] Mortality in nature due directly to social antagonism has been observed for tern colonies,[61] red deer,[18] and muskrats.[23] Summer muskrats have few wounds, in contrast with the chewed-up, wandering, and ill-situated muskrats of the late-fall and early-winter period of population readjustment.

Intraspecific strife may also stimulate the spread of a species into new geographic areas. Movement over suboptimal barriers into more favorable regions may be related to the territorial habit, as has been suggested by Burt[8] for certain rodents.

A frequent consequence of the increased mobility at higher densities appears to be some reshuffling of the membership of local groups; this may take place about a nucleus of older residents, as in the case of bobwhite quail[23b] and blue tits.[14] This reshuffling is characteristic of the period of population readjustment that follows the breeding season. It seems probable that a more rigid social organization exists within societies at lower densities of the species population above, and it may well be that this would facilitate survival in the species as a whole. Recent studies by Allee and Guhl[3] indicate that in organized flocks of hens, as compared with groups kept in a state of social disorganization by shifting membership, the average individual usually gets more to eat and gains more, or loses less, in body weight.

The existence of well-integrated societies requires a minimal number of individuals, and decrease in population density beyond a certain point may act to weaken social integration rather than to strengthen it. The importance of the problem of underpopulation in regulation of density has generally been underestimated.[1,1a] In a number of species this phenomenon is clearly related to aggressive behavior. Reproductive success is said to be relatively poor in small tern colonies because only a large colony can form an excited mob sufficient to frighten away the marauding gulls from the eggs of the terns.[18a, 69] When local numbers of American antelope fall below a critical level, the antelope fail to stand their ground or to bunch into a defensive formation which enables the bucks to fight off predators when the need arises—instead, they stampede and scatter, so that weak individuals fall an easy prey to their enemies.[46] A similar phenomenon has been noted for certain other ungulates.[5]

IV. Relation of Aggressive Behavior to Animal Communities

Animal communities, like human communities, consist of progressively subordinated units. The role of aggressive behavior at the level of the individual, social group, and species has been suggested. It remains to discuss the relationship of aggressive behavior to the balance of density ratios of different species, in the relationship commonly known as the "web of life." The term "aggressive behavior" as used in this paper should not be confused with the idea of ecological aggressiveness, which is sometimes a synonym for high ability of a species to spread into new areas or to maintain position in regions already occupied, and with which, like the various concepts of ecological dominance,[12] this article is not directly concerned.

Interspecies competition may take the form of a direct attack of one species upon another, as in the oft-cited case of the English sparrow versus the bluebird and purple martin. Another case is that of the lizards, *Lacerta agilis* and *L. vivapara,* of Germany.[38] The former eats the young of *vivipara,* which is able to maintain itself only in regions where *agilis* cannot live. When the discrepancy in size of two competing species is very great, the smaller may simply avoid the larger species, making no attempt at physical combat, as in the case of bobwhite quail versus the ring-necked pheasant.[23b]

There is evidence that aggressive competition may be more intense within species than between species, and between kindred species of the extent to which they compete for similar objects than between species which are not closely equivalent ecologically. Gibbons will feed contentedly in the same tree with macaques and langurs, but they will not tolerate the presence of another gibbon group of the same species.[9a] Howard[39] has summarized many cases of interspecific strife in birds. Some birds, like the moor hen, will attack almost any species of bird, not too large, which approaches their territories; but, in general, strife appears to be greatest between kindred forms and often involves competitors for nest sites or territory—for example, in birds of prey, in the tit family, and in woodpeckers. When not breeding, these birds sometimes travel in loose flocks made up of different species.

SUMMARY

Aggressive behavior plays a major role among vertebrate animals. Competition for food, mates, or territory is frequently based on direct conflict, the intensity of which varies with the shortage of these requirements. When individuals live together as a group and share a common territory, dominance relations tend to become stabilized by habit into a social order of precedence. Such hierarchies intergrate with territorial populations, where distance from the territorial center of individuals does much to determine the order of social dominance. Both types of hierarchies are common in the various classes of vertebrates from fish to man, with the possible exception of the amphibians.

Social rank in the hierarchy is decided by fighting, bluffing, or passive submission at the initial encounter between individuals or during an early series of encounters. Specific tolerances form much of the basis for integration of groups of various kinds of organization, such as the sex pair, family, acquaintanceship group, species, or animal community. Each of these types of group may be integrated to a different degree in different species, and within species the degree of integration varies with intragroup aggressiveness as influenced by the environmental situation, physiological state of individuals, numbers within the group, density and mobility of the species. Classification of vertebrate social groups according to the degree of integration reveals that increase in cooperative aggression by the group as the competing unit is paralleled by decrease in intragroup aggression.

Intraspecies conflict helps to regulate density to an important extent in overcrowded populations, especially by forcing diffusion of the surplus population into suboptimal habitats. For a number of social and infrasocial species, undercrowding is known to become dangerous where local numbers of individuals are too few to enable them to form into an effective group for purposes of defense.

REFERENCES

1. Allee, W. C. 1931. *Animal Aggregations: A Study in General Sociology.* Chicago: University of Chicago Press. 431 pp.

1a. ———. 1938. *The Social Life of Animals.* New York: Norton. 293 pp.

2. Allee, W. C., Collias, N. E., and Lutherman, C. Z. 1939. Modification of

the social order in flocks of hens by the injection of testosterone propionate. *Physiol. Zool.*, **12**: 412–40.

3. Allee, W. C., and Guhl, A. 1942. Concerning possible survival value of socially organized as compared with disorganized groups of hens. *Anat., Rec. Suppl.*, **84**: 497–98.
4. Allen, A. A. 1934. Sex rhythm in the ruffed grouse, *Bonasa umbellus Linn.* and other birds. *Auk*, **51**: 180–99.
5. Alverdes, F. 1935. The behavior of mammalian herds and packs. A chapter in Murchison's *Handbook of Social Psychology*. Worcester, Mass.: Clark University Press.
6. Braddock, J. C. 1942. Some aspects of the dominance-subordination relationship in *Platypoecilus maculatus*. Thesis on file in University of Chicago library.
7. Bruce, R. H. 1941. An experimental analysis of social factors affecting the performance of white rats. *Jour. Comp. Psychol.*, **31**: 395–412.
8. Burt, W. H. 1940. Territorial behavior and populations of some small mammals in southern Michigan. *Univ. Mich., Misc. Pub. Zool.*, **45**: 1–58.
9. Carpenter, C. R. 1934. A field study of the behavior and social relations of howling monkeys. *Comp. Psychol. Monog.*, **10**(2): 1–168.

9a. ———. 1940. A field study in Siam of the behavior and social relations of the gibbon, *Hylobates. lar. Ibid.*, **16**(5): 1–212.

9b. ———. 1942. Sexual behavior of free ranging rhesus monkeys, *Macaca mulatta*. I. Specimens, procedures and behavioral characteristics of estrus. *Jour. Comp. Psychol.*, **33**: 113–42.

9c. ———. 1942. Sexual behavior of free ranging rhesus monkeys *Macaca mulatta*. II. Periodicity of estrus, homosexual, autoerotic and nonconformist behavior. *Ibid.*, 143–62 pp.

9d. ———. 1942. Societies of monkeys and apes. A chapter in *Levels of Integration in Biological and Social Systems*. Edited by R. Redfield, Lancaster, Pa.: Jacques Cattell Press. 177–204 pp.

10. Chapman, F. M. 1935. The courtship of Gould's manakin, *Manacus vitellinus vitellinus* on Barro Colorado Island, Canal Zone. *Bull. Amer. Mus. Nat. Hist.*, **68**: 471–525.
11. Clarke, C. H. D. 1936. Fluctuations in numbers of ruffed grouse *Bonasa umbellus* (Linné), with special reference to Ontario. Univ. Toronto, *Biol. Ser.*, No. 41: 5–118.
12. Clements, F. E., and Shelford, V. E. 1939. *Bioecology*. New York: Wiley, 425 pp.
13. Collias, N. E. 1943. Statistical analysis of factors which make for success in initial encounters between hens. *Amer. Nat.*, **77**: 519–38.
14. Colquhoun, M. K. 1942. Notes on the social behavior of blue tits. *Brit. Birds*, **35**: 234–40.
15. Cooper, J. B. 1942. An exploratory study on African lions. *Comp. Psychol. Mono.*, **17**(7): 1–48.
16. Crawford, M. P. 1942. Dominance and the behavior of pairs of female chimpanzees when they meet after varying intervals of separation. *Jour. Comp. Psychol.*, **33**: 259–66.
17. Crew, F. A. E., and Mirskaia, L. 1931. Effect of density on adult mouse populations. *Biol. generalis*, **7**: 239–50.

18. Darling, F. F. 1937. *A Herd of Red Deer.* London: Oxford University Press. 215 pp.

18a. ———. 1938. Bird flocks and the breeding cycle. Cambridge, England: Cambridge University Press. 124 pp.

19. Davis, D. E. 1942. The phylogeny of social nesting habits in the Crotaphaginae. *Quart. Rev. Biol.,* **17**: 115–34.

20. Elton, C. 1942. Voles, mice and lemmings. Oxford: Clarendon Press. 496 pp.

21. Emlen, J. T. 1939. Seasonal movements of a low density valley quail population. *Jour. Wildlife Management,* **3**: 118–30.

22. Emlen, J. T., and Lorenz, F. W. 1942. Pairing responses of free-living valley quail to sex-hormone implants. *Auk,* **59**: 369–78.

23. Errington, P. L. 1939. Reaction of muskrats to drought. *Ecology,* **20**: 168–86.

23a. ———. 1939. The comparative ability of the bobwhite and the ring-necked pheasant to withstand cold and hunger. *Wilson Bull.,* **51**: 22–37.

23b. ———. 1941. An eight-winter study of central Iowa bobwhites. *Ibid.,* **53**: 91–102.

24. Errington, P. L., Hamerstrom, F., and Hamerstrom, F. N., Jr. 1940. The great horned owl and its prey in north-central United States. *Iowa Agric. Exper. Sta. Res. Bull.,* **277**: 760–850.

25. Errington, P. L., and Hamerstrom, F. N., Jr. 1936. The northern bob-white's winter territory. *Iowa Agric. Exper. Sta. Res. Bull.,* **201**: 301–443.

26. Evans, L. T. 1936. A study of a social hierarchy in the lizard, *Anolis carolinensis. Jour. Genet. Psychol.,* **48**: 88–111.

26a. ———. 1940. Effects of testosterone propionate upon social dominance in young turtles, *Chrysema picta. Biol. Bull.,* **79**: 371.

27. Fischel, W. 1927. Beitrage zur Soziologie des Haushuhns. *Biol. Zentralbl.,* **47**: 678–95.

28. Fitch, H. S. 1941. A field study of the growth and behavior of the fence lizard. *Univ. Calif. Publ. Zool.,* **44**: 151–72.

29. Fulton's book of pigeons with standards for judging. Edited by Lewis Wright. 1895. New edition revised, enlarged and supplemented by the Rev. W. F. Lumley. London, Paris, and Melbourne: Cassell.

30. Ginsberg, B., and Allee, W. C. 1942. Some effects of conditioning on social dominance and subordination in inbred strains of mice. *Physiol. Zool.,* **15**: 485–506.

31. Gordon, K. 1940. Territorial behavior and social dominance among Sciuridae. *Jour. Mammalogy,* **17**: 171–72.

32. Gorsuch, D. M. 1934. Life history of the Gambel quail in Arizona. *Univ. Ariz. Bull.,* **5**(4). *Biol. Sci. Bull.* (2): 5–89.

33. Greenberg, B. and Noble, G. K. 1942. Dominance, social order and territory in the lizard. *Anat. Rec.,* **84**: 58 (abstract).

34. Guhl, A. M. 1941. The frequency of mating in relation to social position in small flocks of white leghorns. *Anat. Rec. Suppl.,* **81**: 113.

35. Hale, B. 1941. Peck order and grouping of birds under seminatural conditions. Unpublished manuscript.

36. Hamerstrom, F. 1942. Dominance in winter flocks of chickadees. *Wilson Bull.,* **54**: 32–42.

37. Hamerstrom, F. N., Jr. 1939. A study of Wisconsin prairie chicken and sharp-tailed grouse. *Wilson Bull.*, **51**: 105–20.
38. Hesse, R.; Allee, W. C., and Schmidt, K. P. 1937. *Ecological Animal Geography*. New York: Wiley. 597 pp.
39. Howard, H. E. 1920. *Territory in Bird Life*. London: John Murray. 308 pp.
40. Howard, W. E. and Emlen, J. T. 1942. Intercovey social relationships of the valley quail. *Wilson Bull.*, **54**: 162–70.
41. James, W. T. 1939. Further experiments in social behavior among dogs. *Jour. Genet. Psych.*, **54**: 151–64.
42. Jenkins, D. 1944. Territory as a result of despotism and social organization as shown by geese. Accepted for publication in the *Auk*.
43. Kendeigh, S. C. 1941. Territorial and mating behavior of the house wren. *Ill. Biol. Mono.*, **18**(3): 1–120.
44. Lack, D. 1939. The behaviour of the robin. *Proc. Zool. Soc. London*, **A**(109): 169–219.
44a. ———. 1940. Observations on captive robins. *Brit. Birds*, **33**: 262–70.
45. Langlois. T. H. 1937. Sociological succession. *Ecology*, **18**: 458–61.
46. Leopold, A. 1933. *Game Management*. New York: Scribner's. 481 pp.
47. Lorenz, K. 1931. Beitrage zur Ethologie sozialer Corviden. *Jour. f. Ornith.*, **79**: 67–127.
47a. ———. 1934. A contribution to the comparative sociology of colonial-nesting birds. *Proc. Eighth Intl. Ornith. Cong.* Oxford. 207–18.
47b. ———. 1935. Der Kumpan in der Umwelt des Vogels. *Jour. f. Ornith.*, **83**: 137–213, 289–413.
48. McAtee, W. L. 1936. The Malthusian principle in nature. *Sci. Monthly*, **42**: 444–56.
49. Maslow, A. H. 1936. IV. The role of dominance in the social and sexual behavior of infra-human primates. The determination of hierarchy in pairs and in a group. *Jour. Genet. Psychol.*, **49**: 161–98.
49a. ———. 1936. The role of dominance in the social and sexual behavior of infra-human primates. III. A theory of sexual behavior of lower primates. *Ibid.*, 310–38.
49b. ———. 1940. Dominance quality and social behavior in infra-human primates. *Jour. Soc. Psychol.*, **11**: 313–24.
50. Masure, R., and Allee, W. C. 1934. The social order in flocks of the common chicken and the pigeon. *Auk*, **51**: 306–27.
51. Murchison, C. 1935. The experimental measurement of a social hierarchy in *Gallus domesticus*. IV. Loss of body weight under condition of mild starvation as a function of social dominance. *Jour. Genet. Psychol.*, **12**: 296–312.
51a. ———. 1936. The time function in the formation of social hierarchies of different sizes in *Gallus domesticus*. *Jour. Soc. Psychol.*, **7**: 3–18.
52. Nice, M. M. 1929. Adventures at a window shelf. *Oologist*, **46**: 161–3.
52a. ———. 1937. Studies in the life history of the song sparrow. I. A population study of the song sparrow. *Trans. Linaean Soc. New York*, **4**: 1–247.
52b. ———. 1941. The role of territory in bird life. *Amer. Midl. Nat.*, **26**: 441–87.

53. Nicholson, A. J. 1933. The balance of animal populations. *Jour. Animal Ecol.*, **2**: 132–78.
54. Noble, G. K. 1938. Sexual selection among fishes. *Biol. Rev.*, **13**: 133–58.
54a. ———. 1939. The experimental animal from the naturalist's point of view. *Amer. Nat.*, **73**: 113–26.
55. Noble, G. K., and Curtis, B. 1939. The social behavior of the jewel fish, *Hemichromis bimaculatus*. *Bull. Amer. Mus. Nat. Hist.*, **73**: 1–76.
56. Noble, G. K., and Greenberg, B. 1941. Induction of female behavior in male *Anolis carolinensis* with testosterone propionate. *Proc. Soc. Exper. Biol. and Med.*, **47**: 32–7.
57. Noble, G. K., Wurm, M., and Schmidt, A. 1938. Social behavior of the black-crowned night heron. *Auk*. **55**: 7–40.
58. Norman, J. R. 1931. *A History of Fishes.* London: Ernest Benn. 463 pp.
59. Nowlis, V. 1941. The relation of degree of hunger to competitive interaction of chimpanzees. *Jour. Comp. Psychol.*, **32**: 91–116.
60. Odum, E. P. 1941. Annual cycle of the black-capped chickadee. *I. Auk*, **58**: 314–33.
60a. ———. 1942. Annual cycle of the black-capped chickadee. *III. Ibid.*, **59**: 499–531.
61. Palmer, R. S. 1941. A behavior study of the common tern. *Proc. Boston Soc. Nat. Hist.*, **42**: 1–119.
62. Patel, M. D. 1936. The physiology of the formation of pigeon's milk. *Physiol. Zool.*, **9**: 129–52.
63. Retzlaff, E. 1938. Studies in population physiology with the albino mouse. *Biol. generalis*, **14**: 238–65.
64. Roberts, B. 1940. The breeding behavior of penguins with special reference to *Pygoscelis papua* (Forster). *Brit. Graham Lands Exped. 1934–7, Sci. Rept.*, **1**: 195–254.
65. Sanctuary, W. C. 1932. A study in avian behavior to determine the nature and persistency of the order of dominance in the domestic fowl and to relate these to certain physiological reactions. Thesis for M.S. degree, Massachusetts State College, Amherst. Unpublished.
66. Schjelderup-Ebbe, T. 1922. Beitrage zur Sozial-psycholgie des Haushuhns. *Zeitschr. f. Psychol.*, **88**: 225–52.
66a. ———. 1935. Social behavior of birds. Chap. xx in Murchison's *Handbook of Social Psychology*. Worcester, Mass.: Clark University Press. 947–73 pp.
67. Scott, J. W. 1941. Sexual selection in the sage grouse. Anat. Rec., *Suppl.*, **81**: 51.
67a. ———. 1942. Mating behavior of the sage grouse. *Auk*, **59**: 477–98.
68. Shoemaker, H. H. 1939. Social hierarchy in flocks of the canary. *Auk*, **56**: 381–406.
69. Stresemann, E. 1928. Vogel. Vol. 7 of *Handbuch der Zoologie*. Edited by Kukenthal. Berlin: Walter de Gruyter & Co. 897 pp.
70. Tinbergen, N. 1936. The function of sexual fighting in birds and the problems of the origin of territory. *Bird-banding*, **7**: 1–8.

71. Twining, H. 1938. The significance of combat in male rosy finches. *Condor,* **40**: 246–47.

72. Uhrich, J. 1938. The social hierarchy in albino mice. *Jour. Comp. Psychol.,* **25**: 373–413.

73. Wallace, G. J. 1941. Winter studies of color-banded chickadees. *Bird-banding,* **12**: 49–67.

74. Wheeler, W. M. 1930. Societal evolution. Chap. vi in *Human Biology and Racial Welfare.* Edited by E. V. Cowdry. New York: Paul B. Hoeber, Inc., pp. 139–55.

75. Whitman, C.O. 1919. The behavior of pigeons. Edited by H. A. Carr. *Carnegie Inst. Wash. Pub.,* **3**: 161 pp.

76. Wing, L. 1941. Size of bird flocks in winter. *Auk,* **58**: 188–94.

77. Winslow, C. N. 1938. Observations of dominance-subordination in cats. *Jour. Genet. Psychol.,* **52**: 425–28.

78. Young, W. C. 1941. Observations and experiments on mating behavior in female mammals. *Quart. Rev. Biol.,* **16**: 135–56, 311–35.

3

AGGRESSIVE BEHAVIOR AND EVOLUTION

NICHOLAS E. COLLIAS*
University of California, Los Angeles

This is the final section of the same review article from which Chapter 2 was taken. It was originally published in Physiological Zoology, *XVII(1): 106–123 (excerpted). Reprinted with permission of the University of Chicago Press.*

FACTORS OF EVOLUTIONARY CHANGE

Aggressive behavior is an important organizing force in social and community integration of many vertebrates, and selection has drawn on it to determine a specific set of adaptive reactions, just as selection has operated on cell reactions in relation to individual organization. Some idea of adjustments to environmental stress within the species limit may be drawn from a study of the basis of covey size in bobwhite quail. These birds are especially subject to winter starvation and losses from very cold weather in the northern parts of their range.[33] During severe winters the birds in whole counties may be wiped out. Quail huddle together under stress of cold, and in a laboratory analysis Gerstell[21] found that within limits the temperature of the group and the survival rate were directly proportional to the size of the group. Quail coveys keep down their own size by aggressive behavior[17] within the usual limits of 10–30 birds,

* See footnotes for Chapter 2, on pp. 14 and 16.

which appears to be the number that can roost together comfortably in the characteristic circle with heads facing out.[17a] Isolated birds may be excluded from the covey, and their greater mortality agrees well with Gerstell's findings. Interestingly enough, the average covey size of 1,100 flocks of bobwhite was found to be larger (12.5) in the north-central states and smaller (10.5) in the Gulf states.[54] It is apparently unknown whether this difference has any genetic basis; it clearly has survival value. It is possible[17] that this adjustment is not based on genetic differences and therefore does not represent true organic evolution, if by the latter is meant some shift in gene frequency of a natural population.[56] This phenomenon in quail is a social application of Bergmann's rule that among homoiothermal animals the same or related species attain a larger size in colder than in warmer regions.[25]

Relaxation of selection pressure results in the decline and loss of territorial defense reactions in the more parasitic species of cowbirds and in the decline and loss of secondary sex plumage in the various species of Galapagos finches.[51] The causes of degeneration are to be found in the random effects on organization (of a complex pattern of habit, color, etc.) of mutation pressure or of local inbreeding; it is also possible that selection for some other character might be exerting an indirect and deleterious influence on a given character freed from selection pressure.[56b]

Aggressive behavior is selected with reference to its influence on different levels of organization. It should be noted that Darwin (1859; 6th ed., Carlton House, N.Y., 1872, p. 52) used the term "struggle for existence" to include not only the life of the individual but success in leaving progeny. That there need be no ambiguity here becomes clear when we consider that two different levels of selection are involved—that of the individual and that of the group. Such considerations lead to the recognition of important relations between aggressive behavior and competition, on the one hand, and co-operation, on the other; and these relations have real evolutionary significance both for the evolving individual and for the evolving social unit.

Aggressive behavior may serve as an important social mechanism in many vertebrates; and integration at one level of organization is based, in good part, on integration at lower levels, just as the proper functioning of an individual animal depends on the proper working of its organs, tissues, and cells. It has not been sufficiently recognized that competition at one level of organization may be regarded as co-operation at another level. Competition between individuals for food would seem to be the most egocentric type of competition, but from the point of view of the family it means that the animals which become parents are likely to be those which are most efficient in securing food for their progeny. Close competition may lead to a considerable individual increase in food intake as compared to more isolated animals, as has been experimentally demonstrated in chickens[4] and other vertebrates; and presumably this might facilitate the development of social life apart from any necessary connection with the family. Competition between individuals for mates is co-operation in the sense that the formation of the most vigorous and synchronized sex pairs is favored. Competition between sex pairs or family groups, such as those of geese and gibbons, is co-operation from the viewpoint of subspecies or other major subdivisions of the species, in the sense that the more prolific the family groups the greater the local emigration from a particular subpopulation is likely to be. This leads to competition between the subgroups, with dispersal tending to equilibrate the population at the points of dispersal. The effective invaders interbreed with or replace the rest of the species and so tend to tone up the whole species.[56a] This process can be considered as co-operation from the viewpoint of the species. Competition between species and even the predator-prey and plant-herbivore relationship can be looked upon as co-operative processes in the exploitation of the energy resources of the inanimate environment by the community. The data of paleontology tell us that predator and prey pace each other in an evolution toward reciprocal adaptations, and this principle can be extended throughout the animal community wherever species are subject to opposed selection pressures. Since this results in a moving equilibrium, we are led to the principle of community evolution, with excessive emigration leading to the spread of the communities best fitted to the environment.

Increased competition at one level may therefore mean increased co-operation at a higher level of organization, which in turn means increased efficiency in intergroup competition at this higher level. Similarly, increased co-operation at the lowest levels may lead to increased efficiency in intergroup competition at higher levels, and the relationship just outlined is repeated. Competition and co-operation are each exerting such influences at every level of selection. Individuals are very often selected in terms of *social* values; and competition, provided it does not become excessive, is very often desirable from a social point of view. Groups seem to be the usual units of selection. This latter conclusion has been reached in somewhat different ways by Allee,[1, 1a, 1d] Wright, [56, 56a, 56b] Emerson,[16] and Thomas Park.[45]

Allee,[1a, 1b, 1c, 1e] Emerson,[16] and Gerard[20] have emphasized the co-operative relationships of animals in recent reviews. The many parallelisms and analogies which the latter two authors point out for insect and human societies, when compared with the organization of individual animals, including man, serve to bring out the point that selection has operated toward a similar end in both cases. The extensive convergence means that societies can be considered the biological servants of their component individuals, in the same sense that individuals could be looked upon as servants of their component cells.

Aggressive behavior is, of course, only part of a complex of many characters subject to selection at any particular level of organization. Aggressive behavior may be reduced, may be enhanced, or may assume special forms of expression according to the nature of associated organizing and integrating factors. For example, adjustment to cold weather by quail favors social tolerance over aggressiveness; the parasitic habit in cowbirds removes much of the value of territorial defense for them; development of co-operative group aggressiveness may replace the need for individual aggressiveness to a considerable extent; advantages apparently incompatible with excessive aggressiveness, such as the prevention of undue fatigue, may lead to a compromise like threatening, bluffing, or formal combat; while other characteristics may be preadapted to the service or control of aggressive behavior, such as the cerebral cortex in higher mammals.

EVOLUTIONARY TRENDS IN AGGRESSIVE BEHAVIOR AND RELATED SOCIAL PHENOMENA

Certain major trends of evolution related to aggressive behavior can be described. These trends are probably just as complex and ramifying in their effects as any influence on the integration of the animal community is likely to be; but, as yet, only the simpler or more obvious interrelationships can be followed with much assurance.

The origin of aggressive behavior is obscure. One possibility is that aggressive competition for food may have preceded aggressive competition in relation to reproduction. Cannibalism of smaller, especially of young, individuals is a widespread phenomenon in vertebrates.[32, 34] Groups of immature jewel fish[39c] and immature black-crowned night herons in the nest[43] have a nip-order or a peck-order which is later disrupted by the development of the instinct to defend separate territories.

The Mating Relationship

There is a possibility that aggressive behavior among vertebrates may have arisen in evolution as a result of competition between males to fertilize eggs located in a definite place or nest. An interesting start is made even among the lowly cyclostomes. Sex recognition appears to require physical contact in the brook lamprey, which lays its eggs in nests. The lake lamprey is less social; it does not require physical contact for sex recognition, and the males are somewhat pugnacious; this has led to partial polygamy and the formation of incipient territories.[39b]

In the lake herring each female scatters her eggs widely; and, although several males may follow a female as she descends to the bottom to deposit her eggs, there is no fighting, nor is there any restricted territory.[39b] Many of the marine teleosts breed in large swarms, and the females lay an enormous number of eggs; the eggs, which are shed at intervals, float and are dispersed widely by currents. It would seem that there is comparatively small opportunity for selective fertilization, such as would be necessary to give much point to antagonistic competition between males for females. As a rule, however, the female has a male in close attendance, and more data on possible presence or absence of aggressive competition between males for females is desirable. Courtship is rare among marine fishes, but the male of the common dragonet *(Collionymus)* has a brilliant nuptial display and establishes close contact with the female; eggs and milt are extruded at the same moment, and the males attempt to frighten away rivals. No care is given to the pelagic eggs or young.[44]

In some fish in which the eggs are fertilized externally, they are grouped and hence provide more of a chance for selective fertilization by the males. Some marine fishes which breed in shallow water and many fresh-water fishes lay demersal eggs which commonly adhere in a mass on the bottom. Aggressive competition between males for females or territory is common; often the male builds a nest and guards the eggs.[44]

Another way of making possible selective fertilization has been the method of internal fertilization. This is generally associated with terrestrial life, or among fishes with the bearing of live young, as in the case of many elasmobranch fishes and some teleosts. It may be worth noting that the elasmobranchs are relatively primitive among fish. In many of the rays the males have a patch of sharp spines on each pectoral fin above; and it is known that several males will pursue a female, fighting and buffeting each other with their fins.[44] The males of live-bearing teleosts, like the guppy and swordtail, are very pugnacious.[39b]

Aggressive competition, as observed in terrestrial vertebrates, may be keener in cases of polygyny or promiscuous polygyny than in cases of monogamy. In the sage grouse on its mating grounds J. W. Scott[49, 49a] observed that 3 percent of the males did 87 percent of the mating. In the house wren, which as a rule is monogamous while raising a given brood, there are about 15 percent more unmated males than females.[29] An intermediate example is that of ducks, which form their comparatively loose and temporary pairs while migrating in the spring flock. In bluewinged teals extensive data indicate that at this time there are ordinarily about 50 percent more males than females; and each female may be attended by two or more competing males.[5] Lack of aggressiveness is associated with sexual promiscuity in certain fish,[39b] amphibians,[39] most snakes,[39a] and certain bats.[2]

In the case of polygyny, selection appears to emphasize the individual male; and there may be only a very loose limit to evolutionary trends in characteristics that aid aggressive competition for females. Increase in size of polygynous males of terrestrial vertebrates is a good example, with such extreme cases as that of the very pugnacious fur seal, in which the male may be from six to twelve times larger than the mature female. Large size, while perhaps not generally of primary importance within the species,[10] except where size differences are extreme, has been found to favor high social position in certain laboratory groups of fish,[39b] turtles,[18d] lizards,[18] chickens,[47] mice (if differences are large enough),[22] and various primates.[36]

Sex differences in aggressiveness are connected with the type of mating system characteristic of a given species. In polygynous or promiscuous polygynous species the females tend to be relatively more social and in most cases fight much less than the males, if at all—for example, in viviparous fishes, red deer and other ungulates, and the fur seal. In the case of territorial polygyny in birds the females may defend small subterritories against each other within the larger territory of the male, as in the case of the corn bunting;[46] such defense may be very lax and occasional in some species, like the tricolored red-wing.[31] The female in many monogamous species is almost or quite as aggressive as the male—for example, in jewel fish,[42] in certain birds,[38] and in gibbons.[9a] Defense of the mate against rivals in these cases is characteristic of both sexes, and the female may aid in the defense of the territory of the sex pair. In the few polyandrous birds, such as tinamous, button quail, painted snipe, and perhaps phalaropes, the female is the conspicuous displaying sex;[30b] but precise and sufficient data on relative aggressiveness of the sexes in these species seem to be scarce. In the suggestive phalarope case the female is known to be very aggressive.[52]

The evolution of territorial defense among vertebrates has been closely associated with that of the mating relationship. While territory may at times be unconnected with reproduction, as in the case of roosting or winter territories of birds, in general it is especially associated with nests and eggs among vertebrates,[39c] at least in its more rigid aspects. Many fresh-water fish,[39b, 7] many lizards,[41, 18b, 18c] and the great majority of birds[38] furnish examples. Territorial defense is absent or relaxed in viviparous and school-breeding fish[39b] and in the parasitic cowbirds,[38] and during the non-breeding season in fish, lizards, and birds in general. The functions of territorial defense in birds may be extended, specialized, or elaborated to subserve mating, nesting, and feeding uses, details of which have been summarized by Nice.[38]

Territorial organization results in dispersion within populations. Wide dispersion of individuals within a species may be caused by a dispersed food supply and a need for increased safety from predators while breeding. Small land birds seem especially subject to these difficulties. Of some 67 living families of passerine or perching birds, gregarious breeding is found in only 9.[19] The presence of an abundant and concentrated food supply, together with relatively safe breeding places, makes possible gregarious breeding in most sea birds[19, 27] and, for example, in the marine iguanas of the Galapagos,[48] among other animals; and their individual territories are very small.

Increased formalization of combats is an example of an evolutionary trend apparently determined by opposed selection pressures. Formal combat by means of special display may in turn stimulate formal combat by the opponent. Adult male blackcocks will violently attack other males; but, if instead of running the latter displays, the attack promptly changes over to display fighting.[30a] The presumed advantage is the avoidance of undue fatigue, and therefore conservation of energy for reproduction and increased safety from predators. The matter may be complicated by special factors in particular instances, but the general trend seems clear. In general, vertebrates bluff or threaten before they resort to fighting to settle conflicts, and a given individual will frequently not face an obviously superior foe.

Huxley[28a] has extended Hingston's[26] views on the biological antagonism between threat coloration and concealing coloration to all characters whose function it is to make the organism less conspicuous and all whose function it is to make it more conspicuous. For example, even the male ruff *(Philomachus pugnax)* is a cryptic bird when its conspicuous ruff is folded. There are many cases among birds in which special characters or colors are developed only for use in the breeding season and which are employed only for intermittent display. During formal combat the body color of fish and lizards may become much brighter or darker; the loser quickly becomes dull or pale again, whereas the winner may remain bright for some time.[18b, 39b, 44]

Evidence has been presented for different species of fish[39b] and especially for lizards[41] that the greater the development of threat coloration and behavior the less does actual fighting occur. The same thing has been noted for birds.[50] In the tiny blue tit, fighting is said to be entirely psychological.[11] This is what one might expect in small birds, since such birds have many enemies and would fall ready prey to a passing predator should they become very fatigued. However, active combat involving physical contact is not uncommon in its close relative, the black-capped chickadee.[23]

The robin redbreast displays its conspicuous breast to frighten intruding robins off its territory. Other species of birds of approximate robin size and shape which display some red in their plumage seem especially prone to attack.[30] Such an attack on birds with a superficial resemblance to the species concerned, apparently without much regard for the biological usefulness of the attack, seems to be widespread among birds.[13, 30, 52]

Males, as a rule, are much more aggressive than females; and this is correlated with the occurrence of sex dichromatism in many species of fish, lizards, and birds. Noble[39b] has reviewed the case among fish. In most territory-guarding fish the males are conspicuously colored, and the females are conspicuous in species in which they defend the nest or young. The nuptial colors of the males of many viviparous fish may serve, in part at least, as a warning for other males to keep away. In most fish which breed in schools there is no sex dimorphism in color and little or no sex rivalry. In lizards and birds bright colors of the male also frequently seem to be displayed during defense of territory. In phalaropes the female vigorously defends territory and the male incubates alone; this reversal of normal sex relations is correlated with brighter, more conspicuous coloration of the female.

Most amphibians show little or no sexual dichromatism,[39] and aggressive behavior seems to be very poorly developed in the amphibians, aside from infant cannibalism. If two or more male wood frogs get a good hold on the same female, they try to dislodge each other by strong kicks of the hind legs;[3] but no male frogs are known to fight with their teeth for the possession of a female,[39] despite the existence of sex differences in teeth of some forms. Noble,[39] who has summarized an extensive literature on the subject, states (p. 115) that

in all Salientia where the courtship and mating has been adequately analyzed, sight has been found to play almost no part in sex recognition, other than to inform the male of the approach of another object of suitable size or movement.

Sex dichromatism among snakes is rare and is correlated with fighting between males for the females, as in the European adder. Most snakes resemble amphibians in that sex recognition is effected largely by sensory modalities other than vision, and fighting between males for females appears to be uncommon.[39a] Sex dichromatism is not very common among mammals, and this fact is associated with their usually nocturnal habits or relatively large size.

There is no implication here that formal combat by males is the only factor responsible for sexual dichromatism. For example, while sexual dichromatism among birds is associated with vulnerability to predation,[37] this association may be due either to formalization of fighting tendencies or to need for inconspicuous coloration of the incubating sex or both. Among birds the less the male shares incubation and feeding of the young, the more he differs from the female with respect to conspicuous display characters.[28]

In species among which, because of nocturnal or skulking habits or other reasons, conspicuous coloration would be of limited usefulness, if not detrimental, the mode of fighting may be very vigorous, or else formal combat acts through other sensory channels than vision. *Ctenops vittatus,* a close relative of the fighting fish *(Betta),* as if to compensate for its somber tones, replaces the brilliant threat display of its relative by growling loudly as a challenge to passing females.[39b] The mode of fighting is quite vicious in nocturnal reptiles, such as geckos and alligators; and often fights end in the death of one of the combatants. The nocturnal geckos lack intimidating structures or bright colors, depending instead upon vocal signals.[18a] However, Greenberg[22a] noted that in the peculiar western banded gecko of North America fighting is not very intense and voice does not enter directly into the fight pattern but is only heard when one of the geckos is bitten. Male house wrens, which are dull- colored birds and very similar to the female in appearance, largely compete for territory and females by means of vigorous singing contests.[29] Fighting may be vicious in mammals, many of which, while they have good vision, are more active by night. On the whole, most mammals seem to be comparatively inconspicuous in coloration. The use of threat sounds is widespread among mammals. About half the sounds made by wolves are said to express anger.[2] Vocal combat may also be important in diurnal mammals. Battles between groups of howler monkeys are largely vocal, and this is often the case between family groups of gibbons.[9, 9a]

The same display is used by males in threat and in courtship, as a rule, only in species of birds like the raven, in which the sexes appear alike; in such cases one function of the display is to serve as a method of sex diagnosis, since a male will depart or respond similarly and a fight may ensue, while a female will either depart or respond with behavior which may eventually lead to mating.[28a] Aggressive behavior is also used as a method of sex diagnosis by males of some fish, like the red horse and hog sucker, in which the sexes appear alike.[39b] (Noble, 1938). Courtship behavior may in part have originated as extraneous or substitute activity, presumably serving in a tension-releasing capacity for a highly emotional situation—for example, as when different drives conflict, such as the sex drive versus the urge to attack the approaching partner in a newly mated European blue heron.[52a]

A complex and important evolutionary trend is that determined by dominance relations between the sexes of a mated pair. In the case of monogamous pairs, where both parents help in the care of eggs or young, the mated pair must maintain its stability for some time. Sex pairs have the strongest and most enduring bonds in those species of fish[39b] and of birds[28] in which there is most elaborate or reciprocal courtship. It is in such mated pairs that greatest tolerance, deference, or protection is given to the female by the male—for example, in pairs of night herons, geese, and canaries, as compared with the loose, temporary unions of sage grouse, red deer, and rhesus monkeys. The female out of oestrus or out of the breeding season may lose much of her attractiveness to the male, and the male may lose much of his tolerance or "chivalry" for the female. This would appear to place the female at a serious disadvantage in the struggle for existence, especially, in polygynous forms where the male is generally much larger and stronger than the female and often equipped with special weapons. But close competition is usually avoided, because such males, when not breeding, frequently keep apart from the females and young; and they may, especially in mammals, form unisexual male groups.[2]

The Family

The family in vertebrates may have had its roots in the sex jealousy of males competing to fertilize eggs, since this was apparently followed in many fresh-water fishes by extension of the defense reactions of the male to include guarding of the fertilized eggs and young.

Since in all classes of vertebrates the male, as a rule, is the more aggressive sex, his sex jealousy is a more effective block to the prolonged extension of family ties than is that of the female. This difficulty has been circumvented in certain species, like the red deer, by excluding the male from the family group, except during the relatively brief mating period. In other species, like the promiscuous howler monkeys, the difficulty is met by apparently eliminating aggressive competition for females. In other species, as in the higher primates, the slow physical maturation of the young may be an important factor. The relatively less aggressive female plays a much more important family role in the higher, than in the lower, vertebrates. Among fish the female often merely lays the eggs over the spawning grounds or in the nest built and guarded by the male. In some species she may help guard the eggs, as in the jewel fish. Some female fish also have developed ovovivipary. In many amphibians the female may desert the eggs after laying, or she may stay near them and exhibit other types of parental care.[39] Although some salientians exhibit close parental care of highly specialized kinds, all in all, there is little, if any, advance over the parental care shown by some fish.

Female turtles often dig a burrow in which they bury their eggs. Many snakes are ovoviviparous,[14] and different species of reptiles exhibit more advanced parental care. Among many birds it is the female that is most active in incubation of the eggs and care of the young, and in the viviparous mammals she usually takes the leading role in rearing her offspring.

In birds and mammals the young do not usually become independent as early as do the young of lower vertebrates, and they are cared for by their parents for a longer period of time. There is a possibility that, accompanying the increase of parental care of young, there has been a decrease in the precocity of young with respect to the appearance of aggressive behavior. More data are needed to settle this point. Fighting behavior appears in the fish *Platypoecilus maculatus* almost from the day of birth (Braddock, personal communication), in chickens roughly from 3 weeks (males) to 3 months (females),[2] while the young of man are quite helpless and unaggressive for many months.

It has been suggested that the prolonged education and association of the young with their parents may be the important basis for the greater social development of the higher, as compared with the lower, primates.[57] The higher social development of red deer, as compared with roe deer,[12] and of jackdaws, as compared with most other birds,[19] is also associated with much greater overlapping of generations and greater tolerance of one or both parents for the young, even after the latter are well grown. However, the capacity to train the young may be very limited in lower vertebrates. It may be remarked that increase in size of organized groups which facilitates social advance does not necessarily depend upon the extension of family ties.

Acquaintanceship Groups

Judging from the examples which have been reviewed in the preceding pages, the degree of dominance exerted by a group of vertebrate animals depends on the numbers of individuals of which it is composed, on the size of individuals, on proximity to its territorial center, on degree of integration, and on general level of aggressiveness of its members.

The number included in a stable and organized group depends, in large part, on memory for individuals and probably tends to increase with rise in the vertebrate series. In the viviparous fish *P. maculatus*, groups as large as 4 fish are not usually able to maintain stable hierarchies for much longer than 1 or 2 days; and most groups of this size cannot maintain a straight-line hierarchy, although groups of 3 usually do so.[6] However, it has been stated that the related *Xiphophorus* can maintain stable hierarchies in groups of 4 for months.[40] Flocks of domestic hens with less than 10 birds can maintain stable hierarchies for many months, and straight-line hierarchies are common. Stable, organized groups of various primates in the field may often be considerably larger and may have a high degree of constancy from season to season and even from year to year—a constancy which is affected by increments due to reproduction, maturation, and group splittings or additions.[9b] Among laboratory mice the capacity to recognize individuals is apparently very poor;[22] Uhrich[53] observed that albino mice caged in groups of generally 3-8 individuals would maintain a given social order from a few days to several months.

While more study with special reference to the problem is needed, co-operation in attack and defense reactions above the level of the sex pair seems to be rare, if it has been described at all, for fish or lizards in which the sex pairs are comparatively unstable. Co-operative defense of territories by stable, organized groups other than by a simple sex pair has been described for a number of birds and mammals.

The evolution of co-operative competition involving attack or defense by the group as a unit has been greatly facilitated by such attractive forces as sex and parental drive; but often the competing unit has been increased by attraction of unrelated acquaintances, and it may even be based merely on acquaintanceship. Increasing tolerance within groups not only has operated to make possible increase in size of group but directly facilitates (and probably is facilitated by) development of co-operative defense reactions. In general, the sequence of development of highly social groups was probably as follows: (1) continual, individualistic fighting without formation of a stable hierarchy; (2) inhibition of domination behavior between subordinates by the group despot; (3) tolerance of aggressive behavior of subordinates (at first merely the mate); and (4) extension of such tolerance to the immediate vicinity of the despot—a tolerance which permits more or less simultaneous attack of strangers by both despots and subordinates. Such co-operative attacks would permit dominance over large and powerful strangers capable of easy victory in single combat; they would therefore be expected to be preserved by selection.

All this gives us some insight from a biological point of view as to why primitive groups of peoples have two codes of conduct—one of peace for fellow-members of the group, and usually one of aggression for strangers and other groups.[15] Aggressiveness in the sense of belligerence, is related to human warfare. The directness of this relationship is a matter of some conflict. It depends in large part on the definition used for war, and the matter is too complicated to be reviewed here. Different aspects of the subject are presented by Durbin and Bowlby,[15] Quincy Wright,[55] and Malinowski.[35] The fighting tendencies of man are based in part on the selection pressures that have played upon his ancestors, and an attempt has been made to clarify these selection pressures in the foregoing pages. Beyond the existence of leaders, sentinels, and the predominant roles of males in aggression by heterosexual groups, there does not appear to be much special organization for group defense in small, stable, organized groups of infrahuman vertebrates; and, except for the use of missile weapons, the most primitive groups of man do not appear to be very superior in this respect.

Compound Groups

Groups compounded from smaller groups of the same species may react more or less as a unit. These groups are often of very large size; and the congregation of individuals is made possible by a concentrated food supply, by movement of the group from one feeding ground to another, as in the case of migratory flocks of birds, or by the group's scattering over a wide area while feeding, as in the case of many seabirds, jackdaws, rooks, red deer, and baboons, and coming together while breeding, sleeping, or if alarmed. These large groups, as a rule are more or less open to newcomers, and the compound organization tends to be rather loose.[2a] Among baboons the leaders and sentinels are often the largest and strongest males; and, when danger threatens, they meet it with organized defense reactions as a group.[1]

Below the human level there seems to be no present evidence of intraspecies fighting between large compound groups as competing units. Division of labor between subgroups, especially in relation to food supply and to warfare, has been increasingly important in the history of man. The whole process reaches its climax in civilized, modern man, where millions of individuals are enabled to fight together with cognizance of a common cause and territory and in whom the foreshortening of time and space by various inventions is rapidly forcing a global organization for the first time in any species.

Physiological Aspects of Social Evolution

The evolution of social life among vertebrates requires, and is made possible by, some reorganization at the physiological level. There is a progressive encephalization of nervous mechanisms which control individual aggressiveness and social behavior among the vertebrates. The basic fighting patterns are organized into a coherent whole below the forebrain level in fish, but mainly by the hypothalamus in the few mammals which have been investigated. Noble[42] has pointed out that the forebrain mechanisms essential for social behavior have shifted from the corpus striatum of fish and birds to the cerebral cortex of mammals; and, while the influence of the basal ganglia of mammals on social behavior is inadequately known, this statement is evidently true for the most important neural mechanisms of social control. Excessive dependence of aggressive or reproductive behavior on particular sensory modalities, such as vision or audition, is paralleled by increased sensitivity or development of the sensory and central nervous mechanisms concerned.[18c]

Increase in size of well-integrated groups which would facilitate group or tribal dominance requires better memory for individuals and may have been one of the reasons for selection favoring the development of the cerebral cortex in mammals, possibly including early man. The gradual appearance of human intelligence profoundly changed, in some respects, the very rules of evolution for the species *Homo sapiens*. The growth of tradition, including tools, weapons, and language, amounts to the inheritance of characters acquired by direct environmental influence. This does not imply the complete absence of these tendencies below the human level. Rapid social evolution, based on accretion of culture, replaces the comparatively extremely slow organic evolution of subhuman animals. While tradition not infrequently facilitated and was facilitated by success in intergroup conflict, it should be noted that absence of survival value for an individual in battle no longer has very much influence on the elimination or preservation of his ideas.

In the higher vertebrates, dominance orders based on despotism may lead into dominance orders based on leadership as well. While there may be dominance orders not based on despotism in infrahuman vertebrates, especially in some of the higher primates, these do not compare with the great variety of such dominance orders among men which are based on appreciation of special abilities, training, advantages, or prejudices, all in relation to special objectives. To a certain extent, the more primitive forms of competition have merely been replaced by more subtle means of coercion. But self-conscious evolution, combined with the consistent application of scientific method to further our understanding, gives us greatly increased possibilities of control over the less desirable forms of competition.

To summarize, inhibition of aggressive and egocentric competition, increased social tolerance within groups, smoothing of inherited reactions, increased memory for individuals, and better judgment, based on experience, represent contributions of the higher brain levels, and especially of the cerebral cortex in mammals, to harmonious social life of animals in which each individual tends to recognize, find and keep its appropriate place. Arbitration and insight into the benefits of co-operation, imaginative powers and profound elaboration of instinctive reactions, language and the capacity for cultural growth, are additional contributions of the cerebral cortex with special reference to the human effort.

SUMMARY

The general advantage of groups over individuals as competing units has led to the selection of individuals in terms of social values. Furthermore, competition at one functional level of social organization may be considered as co-operation at a higher level, and vice versa. Co-operation within the group means increased efficiency in intergroup competition.

Examples are cited which indicate that evolutionary trends in aggressive behavior are related in a complex way to evolutionary trends in various social phenomena. Trends in social evolution are paralleled by trends in evolution of physiological adjustments. The most important of these is the progressive encephalization of neural mechanisms of social control with increased subjugation of primitive, more aggressive levels to the control of higher, more social brain levels. Temporary physiological regression may occur at any level of evolution. The most striking fact of endocrine physiology in relation to aggressive behavior has been the persistent association in the vertebrate series of male hormone with aggressive behavior. The appearance of man, with a cumulative social inheritance based on tradition, removed one of the principal impediments to rapid progress in adaptive evolution and also leads to greatly increased possibilities with respect to the effectiveness, control, or elimination of excessive and harmful aggressiveness.

REFERENCES

1. Allee, W. C. 1931. *Animal Aggregations: A Study in General Sociology.* Chicago: University of Chicago Press. 431 pp.

1a. ———. 1938. *The Social Life of Animals.* New York: Norton. 293 pp.

1b. ———. 1940. Concerning the origin of sociality in animals. *Scientia,* April. Pp. 154–60.

1c. ———. 1941. Integration of problems concerning Protozoa populations with those of general biology. *Amer. Nat.,* **75**: 473–87.

1d. ———. 1942. Social dominance and subordination among vertebrates. A chapter in *Levels of Integration in Biological and Social Systems.* Edited by R. Redfield. Lancaster, Pa.: Jacques Cattell Press.

1e. ———. 1943. Where angels fear to tread: a contribution from general sociology to human ethics. *Science,* **97**: 517–25.

2. Alverdes, F. 1935. The behavior of mammalian herds and packs. A chapter in Murchison's *Handbook of Social Psychology.* Worcester, Mass.: Clark University Press.

2a. ———. 1927 *Social Life in the Animal World.* New York: Harcourt Brace. 216 pp.

3. Banta, A. M. 1914. Sex recognition and the mating behavior of the wood frog, *Rana sylvaticus.* *Biol. Bull.,* **26**: 71–183.

4. Bayer, E. 1929. Beitrage zur Zweicomponenttheorie des Hungers. *Zeitschr. f. Psychol.,* **112**: 1–54.

5. Bennett, L. J. 1938. *The Blue-winged Teal.* Ames, Iowa: Collegiate Press. 144 pp.

6. Braddock, J. C. 1942. Some aspects of the dominance-subordination relationship in *Platypoecilus maculatus.* Thesis on file in University of Chicago library.

7. Breder, C. M., Jr. 1936. The reproductive habits of the North American sunfishes (family Centrarchidae). *Zoologica,* **21**: 1–48.

8. Burt, W. H. 1940. Territorial behavior and populations of some small mammals in southern Michigan. *Univ. Mich., Misc. Pub. Zool.,* **45**: 1–58.

9. Carpenter, C. R. 1934. A field study of the behavior and social relations of howling monkeys. *Comp. Psychol. Monog.,* **10**(2): 1–168.

9a. ———. 1940. A field study in Siam of the behavior and social relations of the gibbon, *Hylobates lar.* *Ibid.,* **16**(5):1–212.

9b. ———. 1942. Societies of monkeys and apes. A chapter in *Levels of Integration in Biological and Social Systems.* Edited by R. Redfield. Pp. 177–204. Lancaster, Pa.: Jacques Cattell Press.

10. Collias, N. E. 1943. Statistical analysis of factors which make for success in initial encounters between hens. *Amer. Nat.,* **77**: 519–38.

11. Colquhoun, M. K. 1942. Notes on the social behavior of blue tits. *Brit. Birds,* **35**: 234–40.

12. Darling, F. F. 1937. *A Herd of Red Deer.* London: Oxford University Press. 215 pp.
13. Davis, D. E. 1942. The phylogeny of social nesting habits in the Crotaphaginae. *Quart. Rev. Biol.*, **17**: 115–34.
14. Ditmars, R. L. 1936. *The Reptiles of North America.* New York: Doubleday, Doran. 476 pp.
15. Durbin, E. F. M., and Bowlby, J. 1939. *Personal Aggressiveness and War.* New York: Columbia University Press. 154 pp.
16. Emerson, A. E. 1939. Social coordination and the superorganism. *Amer. Midl. Nat.*, **21**: 182–209.
17. Errington, P. L. 1941. An eight-winter study of central Iowa bobwhites. *Wilson Bull.*, **53**: 91–102.
17a. Errington, P. L. and Hamerstrom, F. N., Jr. 1936. The northern bob-white's winter territory. *Iowa Agric. Exper. Sta. Res. Bull.*, **201**: 301–443.
18. Evans, L. T. 1936. A study of a social hierarchy in the lizard, *Anolis carolinensis. Jour. Genet. Psychol.*, **48**: 88–111.
18a. ———. 1936. The development of the cochlea in the gecko with special reference to the cochlea-lagena ratio and its bearing on vocality and social behavior. *Anat. Rec.*, **64**: 187–201.
18b. ———. 1938. Cuban field studies on territory of the lizard, *Anolis sagrei. Jour. Comp. Psychol.*, **25**: 97–125.
18c. ———. 1938. Courtship behavior and sexual selection of *Anolis. Ibid.*, **26**: 475–98.
18d. ———. 1940. Effects of testosterone proprionate upon social dominance in young turtles, *Chrysema picta. Biol. Bull.*, **79**: 371.
19. Friedman, H. 1935. Bird societies. A chapter in Murchison's *Handbook of social psychology.* Pp. 142–85. Worcester, Mass.: Clark University Press.
20. Gerard, R. W. 1940. Organism, society and science. *Sci. Monthly*, **50**: 340–50, 403–12, 530–35.
21. Gerstell, R. 1939. Certain mechanisms of winter quail losses revealed by laboratory experimentation. *Trans. Fourth North Amer. Wildlife Conf.*, Washington. Pp. 462–68.
22. Ginsburg, B., and Allee, W. C. 1942. Some effects of conditioning on social dominance and subordination in inbred strains of mice. *Physiol. Zool.*, **15**: 485–506.
22a. Greenberg, B. 1943. Social behavior of the western banded Gecko, *Coleonyx variegatus* Baird. *Physiol. Zool.*, **16**: 110–22.
23. Hamerstrom, F. 1942. Dominance in winter flocks of chickadees. *Wilson Bull.*, **54**: 32–42.
24. Heape, W. 1931. *Emigration, Immigration and Nomadism.* Cambridge, England: Heffer & Sons. 369 pp.
25. Hesse, R., Allee, W. C., and Schmidt, K. P. 1937. *Ecological Animal Geography.* New York: Wiley. 597 pp.
26. Hingston, R. W. G. 1933. *The Meaning of Animal Colour and Adornment.* London: E. Arnold & Co. 411 pp.
27. Howard, H. E. 1920. *Territory in Bird Life.* London: John Murray. 308 pp.

28. Huxley, J. S. 1930. Biology of bird courtship. *Proc. Seventh Intl. Ornith. Cong.*, Amsterdam. Pp. 107–8.

28a. ———. 1934. Threat and warning coloration in birds with a general discussion of the biological functions of colour. *Proc. Eighth Intl. Ornith. Cong.*, Oxford. Pp. 430–55.

29. Kendeigh, S. C. 1941. Territorial and mating behavior of the house wren. *Ill. Biol. Mono.*, **18**(3): 1–120.

30. Lack, D. 1939. The behaviour of the robin. *Proc. Zool. Soc. London, A*, **109**: 169–219.

30a. ———. 1939. The display of the blackcock. *Brit. Birds*, **32**: 290–303.

30b. ———. 1939. Pair formation in birds. *Condor*, **42**: 269–86.

31. Lack, D. and Emlen, J. T., Jr. 1939. Observations on breeding behavior in tri-colored red-wings. *Condor*, **41**: 225–30.

32. Langlois, T. H. 1937. Sociological succession. *Ecology*, **18**: 458–61.

33. Leopold, A. 1933. *Game Management*. New York: Scribner's. 481 pp.

34. McAtee, W. L. 1936. The Malthusian principle in nature. *Sci. Monthly*, **42**: 444–56.

35. Malinowski, B. 1937. Culture as a determinant of behavior. *Harvard Tercentenary Conference on Factors Determining Human Behavior*. Cambridge, Mass.: Harvard University Press. 168 pp.

36. Maslow, A. H. 1940. Dominance quality and social behavior in infrahuman primates. *Jour. Soc. Psychol.*, **11**: 313–24.

37. Mottram, J. C. 1915. The distribution of secondary sexual characters amongst birds with relation to their liability to the attack of enemies. *Proc. Zool. Soc. London*, pp. 663–78

38. Nice, M. M. 1941. The role of territory in bird life. *Amer. Midl. Nat.*, **26**: 441–87.

39. Noble, G. K. 1931. *The Biology of the Amphibia*. New York: McGraw-Hill. 577 pp.

39a. ———. 1937. The sense organs involved in the courtship of *Storeria, Thamnophis* and other snakes. *Bull. Amer. Mus. Nat. Hist.*, **63**: 673–725.

39b. ———. 1938. Sexual selection among fishes. *Biol. Rev.*, **13**: 133–58.

39c. ———. 1939. The experimental animal from the naturalist's point of view. *Amer. Nat.*, **73**: 113–26.

40. Noble, G. K., and Borne, R. 1940. The effect of sex hormones on the social hierarchy of *Xiphophorus helleri*. *Anat. Rec. Suppl.*, **78**: 147.

41. Noble, G. K., and Bradley, H. T. 1933. The mating behavior of lizards; its bearing on the theory of sexual selection. *Ann. N. Y. Acad. Sci.*, **35**: 25–100.

42. Noble, G. K., and Curtis, B. 1939. The social behavior of the jewel fish, *Hemichromis bimaculatus*. *Bull. Amer. Mus. Nat. Hist.*, **76**: 1–76.

43. Noble, G. K.; Wurm, M., and Schmidt, A. 1938. Social behavior of the blackcrowned night heron. *Auk.*, **55**: 7–40.

44. Norman, J. R. 1931. *A History of Fishes*. London: Ernest Benn. 463 pp.

45. Park, Thomas. 1941. The laboratory population as a test of a comprehensive ecological system. *Quart. Rev. Biol.*, **16**: 274–93, 440–61.

46. Ryves, B. H., and Ryves, Mrs. 1934. The breeding habits of the corn-

bunting as observed in North Cornwall: with special reference to its polygamous habit. *Brit. Birds,* **28**: 2–26.

47. Schjelderup-Ebbe, T. 1922. Beitrage zur Sozialpsycholgie des Haushuhns. *Zeitschr. f. Psychol.,* **88**: 225–52.
48. Schmidt, K. P. 1935. Notes on the breeding behavior of lizards. *Field Mus. Nat. Hist., Zool. Ser.,* **20**(9): 71–6.
49. Scott, J. W. 1941. Sexual selection in the sage grouse. *Anat. Rec., Suppl.,* **81**: 51.

49a. ———. 1942. Mating behavior of the sage grouse. *Auk,* **59**: 477–98.

50. Selous, E. 1933. *Evolution of Habit in Birds.* London: Constable. 296 pp.
51. Swarth, H. S. 1934. The bird fauna of the Galapagos Islands in relation to species formation. *Biol. Rev.,* **9**: 213–34.
52. Tinbergen, N. 1935. Field observations of East Greenland birds. I. The behavior of the rednecked phalarope, *Phalaropus lobatus* L. in spring. *Ardea,* **24**: 1–42.

52a. ———. 1939. On the analysis of social organization among vertebrates, with special reference to birds. *Amer. Midl. Nat.,* **21**: 210–34.

53. Uhrich, J. 1938. The social hierarchy in albino mice. *Jour. Comp. Psychol.,* **25**: 373–413.
54. Wing, L. 1941. Size of bird flocks in winter. *Auk,* **58**: 188–94.
55. Wright, Q. 1942. *A Study of War,* Vol. I. Chicago: University of Chicago Press. 679 pp.
56. Wright, S. 1931. Evolution in Mendelian populations. *Genetics,* **16**: 97–159.

56a. ———. 1932. The roles of mutation, inbreeding, crossbreeding and selection in evolution. *Proc. Sixth Intl. Cong. Genet. (Ithaca, N.Y.),* **I**: 356–66.

56b. ———. 1940. Breeding structure of populations in relation to speciation. *Amer. Nat.,* **74**: 232–48.

57. Yerkes, R. M., and Yerkes, A. W. 1935. Social behavior in infrahuman primates. A chapter in Murchison's *Handbook of Social Psychology.* Worcester, Mass.: Clark University Press.

4

FIGHTING

N. TINBERGEN
University of Oxford

When an animal is cornered by a predator, it will often fight. This type of fighting, the defence against a predator, will not however concern us here, because it usually does not involve animals of the same species. Nor is it as common as the fighting of animals which is directed at individuals of their own species. Most of this intraspecific fighting is done in the breeding season, and is therefore called reproductive fighting. Some fighting has to do with dominance relationships in the group and is not linked with the breeding season.

REPRODUCTIVE FIGHTING

Different species fight in different ways.[1] Firstly, the weapons used are different. Dogs bite each other, and so do gulls, and various fish. To that end alone the male Salmon develops a formidable jaw. Horses and many other hoofed animals try to kick each other with the forelegs. Deer measure their relative strength by pushing against each other with their antlers. Waterhens can be seen to fight all through the spring in many parks. They throw themselves halfway on their backs, and fight with their long-toed feet. Many fish fight by sending a strong water-jet towards the opponent by means of vigorous

Figure 1 Fighting red deer

sideways tail-beats. Although they do not actually touch each other, the movement in the water caused by the tail-beats gives a powerful stimulus to the opponent's highly sensitive lateral-line organs (Fig. 2). Male Bitterlings develop horny warts on the head in spring, and try to butt each other with the head.

Secondly, although so much fighting goes on all through the spring, it is relatively rare to see two animals actually engaged in "mortal combat" and wounding each other.[2] Most fights take the form of "bluff" or threat. The effect of threat is much the same as that of actual fighting: it tends to space individuals out because they mutually repel each other. Some instances of threat display were given in Chapter I. Its variety is almost endless. Great Tits threaten by facing each other, stretching the head upward, and swinging slowly from side to side, thus displaying the black-and-white head pattern.[3] Robins threaten by displaying the red breast, turning it to the opponent and then turning slowly right and left alternately (Fig. 3). Some Cichlids display the gill covers by raising them while facing the enemy. In *Cychlasoma meeki* and in *Hemichromis bimaculatus* these gill covers are adorned with very marked black spots, bordered by a golden ring; the threat display shows them off beautifully (Fig. 4).

Not all threat is visual. Many mammals deposit "scent signals" at

Figure 2 Tail-fighting in fish (*after* *Tinbergen, 1951*)

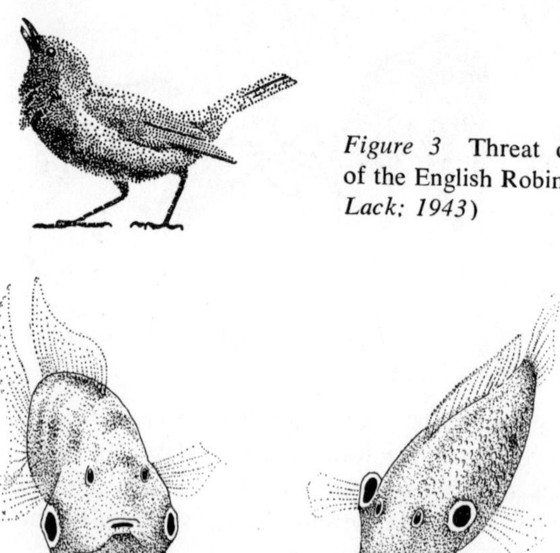

Figure 3 Threat display of the English Robin (*after Lack; 1943*)

Figure 4 Frontal threat display in *Cychlasoma meeki (left)* and *Hemichromis bimaculatus (after Tinbergen, 1951)*

Figure 5 Male *Antelope cervicapra* marking a tree with the secretion of the scent-gland located in front of the eye (*after Hediger, 1949*)

places where they meet or expect rivals.[4] Dogs urinate to that purpose; Hyaenas, Martens, Chamois, various Antelopes and many other species have special glands, the secreta of which are deposited on the ground, on bushes, tree stumps, rock, etc. (Fig. 5). The Brown Bear rubs its back against a tree, urinating while it does so.

Sounds may also have a threat function. All the calls, mentioned in Chapter II under the collective heading "song", do not merely attract females, but serve to repel males as well.

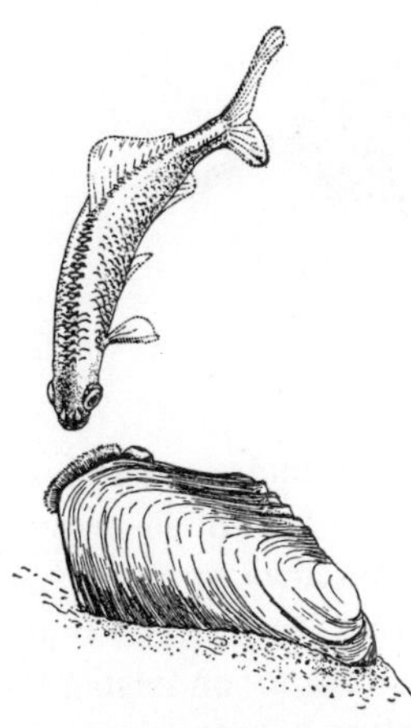

Figure 6 Bitterling male with Mussel (*after Boeseman et al., 1938*)

THE FUNCTIONS OF REPRODUCTIVE FIGHTING

Reproductive fighting is always aimed at a special category of individuals. In most species it is the males which fight, and they attack exclusively, or mainly, other males of the same species. Sometimes male and female both fight; when that happens there is often a double fight; male attacking male, and female fighting female. In the Phalaropes and some other species of birds it is the females who fight, and they again attack mainly other females. This all shows that fighting is aimed at reproductive rivals.

Further, fighting, and threat as well, tend to prevent two rivals or competitors from settling at the same spot; mutual hostility makes them space out, and thus reserve part of the available space for themselves. An examination of what is essential in this reserved space will help us understand the significance of fighting.

The fighting of each individual is usually restricted to a limited area.[5, 6] This may be the area round the female(s) as it is in Deer and many other animals. Bitterling males defend the area around a Freshwater Mussel against other males (Fig. 6); to this Mussel they attract a female. They induce her to lay her eggs in its mantle cavity, where they will develop, leading a parasitic life. Carrion Beetles of the genus *Necrophorus* defend carrion against rivals. The defence in all these cases not only concerns the central object itself, but also a certain area round it; rivals are kept at a considerable distance. In the species mentioned it is easy to see what the central object is: when a doe moves and walks off the male will go with her; it always fights in her vicinity. When the Mussel moves, the male Bitterling shifts the area it defends along with it. In most species however the

Figure 7 Fighting male Chaffinches

defended area does not move; the male settles down on a chosen spot, and defends a territory. This is known in many animals; territorial fighting and threat can be watched in every garden, for Robins, Chaffinches (Fig. 7), and Wrens, to mention only a few species, are renowned fighters. It is possible to understand the significance of such a territory when the fighting is centred on one particular part of it. Thus in many hole-breeding birds the fighting is particularly furious when intruders come near the hole. In most species, however, there is no such concentration on a particular part of the territory, and here the significance of territory is less easy to understand. It has been suggested that the territory of many songbirds might be useful as a reservoir of food for the young. This would enable the parents to collect a certain basic quantity of food near the nest, which would mean that the foraging trips could be short. Since newly hatched songbirds have to be brooded in order to remain warm and ready to gape for food, the territory might be a help in keeping foraging trips, and thus intervals between bouts of brooding, as short as possible. The length of the intervals between bouts of brooding might, on unfavourable days, be critical. Opinions about the value of this argument differ, however.

In ground-breeding birds such as Gulls, Terns, Lapwings, etc., spacing-out appears to be part of the defence of the brood against predators. There is evidence to show that too dense a concentration of prey such as eggs or chicks makes predators specialize on them; that is the main reason why camouflaged animals are as a rule solitary and well spaced out.[7] In birds like Gulls, where the brood is camouflaged, territorial fighting has the effect of keeping the individual broods reasonably far apart. Here again the conflict between two interests has resulted in compromise: social nesting has certain advantages; so has spacing-out. The various species of Gulls and Terns have each arrived at a compromise which give them some, though not complete, benefit of both tendencies.

Concluding, it is clear that reproductive fighting serves a function.

It results in a spacing-out of individuals, thus ensuring each of them the possession of some object, or a territory, which is indispensable for reproduction. It thus prevents individuals sharing such objects, which would in many cases be disastrous, or at least inefficient. Too many Bitterling eggs in a Mussel will result in a low ration for each. When many males would mate with one female instead of securing females of their own this would be a waste of germ cells. Two broods of Starling in one hole may be fatal to both broods. Spacing out makes the individuals utilize the available opportunities.

THE CAUSES OF FIGHTING

Our next problem is: what makes the animals fight in such a way as to promote these functions? What makes them fight only when it is necessary, and only at the place where it is necessary? How does the animal select its potential rival amongst the multitude of other animals it meets? Since fighting endangers the individual (because it makes it vulnerable to attack by predators), and since it may endanger success in reproduction because unlimited fighting might leave the animal little time to do anything else, restriction of fighting to situations in which it can serve its functions is of vital importance. These problems are rather similar to those discussed in relation to mating. In order to confine fighting to the actual defence of territory, the Mussel, the female, etc., the animal will have to react specifically to these situations. Further, fighting must be timed, that is, confined to those moments when there is a rival to be driven off. Finally, it must not be wasted on other species, except when these are rivals. As we will see, many of the outside stimuli responsible for these various aspects of co-ordination are provided by the rival. Since, moreover, most of these stimuli serve more than one of these functions, I will not divide this treatment into sections according to the function served as rigidly as I did in the chapter on mating.

As we have seen, restriction to a certain locality is one of the most obvious characteristics of fighting. When a male Stickleback meets another male in spring, it will by no means always fight. Whether it does depend entirely on where it is. When in its own territory, it attacks all trespassing rivals. When outside its territory, it will flee from the very same male which it would attack when 'at home'. This can be nicely demonstrated in an aquarium, provided it is large enough to hold two territories. Male A attacks male B when the latter comes into A's territory; B attacks A when A trespasses. Usu-

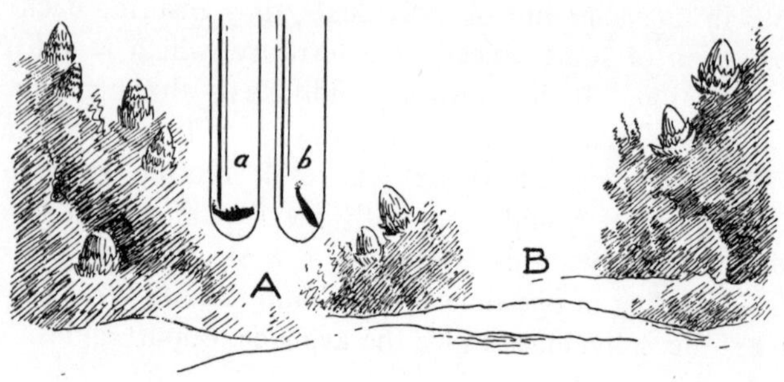

Figure 8a. A test on the dependence of attack on territory: Male *b*, owner of territory B, is brought in a glass tube into territory A of male *a*; the latter attacks while the former tries to escape.

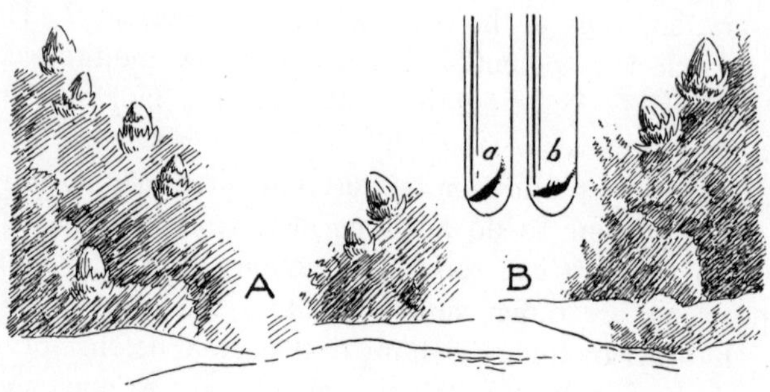

Figure 8b The same males in territory B: male *b* attacks while male *a* flees

ally neither male trespasses voluntarily on to strange territory, but one can easily provoke the situation by capturing the males and putting each of them in a wide glass tube. When both tubes are lowered into territory A, A will try to attack B through the double glass wall, and B will frantically try to escape. When both tubes are moved into territory B, the situation is completely reversed (Fig. 8).

How the territory stimulates the male to fight has rarely been studied in any detail. It can of course only be found out by experimentally moving the territory or parts of it and seeing whether the male adjusts its fighting to the changed situation. This is of course difficult in birds because of their large territories, but small fish that can be kept in aquaria offer unique opportunities for study. Several cases have been reported of birds extending their territory after the female had started to build a nest outside the territory originally staked out by the male.

It seems certain that territories are selected mainly on the basis of properties to which the animals react innately. This makes all animals of the same species, or at least of the same population, select the same general type of habitat. However, the personal binding of a male to its own territory—a particular representative of the species' breeding habitat—is the result of a learning process. A male Stickleback is born with a general tendency to select a habitat in shallow water with liberal vegetation, but it is not born with the tendency to react to a particular plant here and a pebble there. It shifts its territory when we move these landmarks because it has been conditioned to them. This can be seen from the fact that when it breeds two or three times in succession, it often moves to new territories. In each of them it orients itself to landmarks.

Species which react to a special object, such as a hole, or, as the Bitterling does, to a Mussel, probably react innately to it, and as a consequence react to only few "sign stimuli" provided by it. The Bitterling,[8] for instance, reacts only to a minor extent to the visual stimuli provided by the Mussel; the main stimulus is the exhalation current sent out by the Mussel; the fish reacts both to the movement of the water and to its chemical properties (Fig. 9).

Stimuli from the territory to which the animal reacts either in-

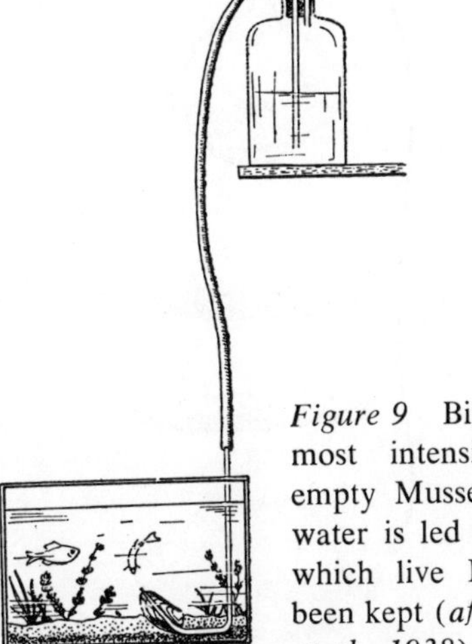

Figure 9 Bitterlings react most intensively to an empty Mussel shell when water is led through it in which live Mussels have been kept (*after Boeseman et al., 1938*)

nately or as an added result of conditioning, makes the animal confine its fighting to the territory.

The gross timing of the attack is again a matter of outside factors. As in mating, the first, very crude timing depends on sex hormones. Fighting appears as a consequence of gonadal growth which, in its turn, through the pituitary gland, depends on rhythmic factors such as day lengthening in the case of many animals of the northern temperate zone. The more accurate timing however is again a matter of reaction to signals. Signals from the rival release fighting when the latter comes too near the territory, or whatever the defended object may be. These signals always have a curious double function. When displayed by a stranger, they draw the attacker to it. When displayed by an attacker on its own ground, they intimidate the stranger. When experimenting with models one can release both responses, dependent on the place—inside or outside the territory—where they are presented. In both cases they serve to space out the species, and, since the responses are specifically released by these displays, not by threat displays of other species, they tend to confine hostilities within one species.

These stimuli have been analysed in various species by experiments with models. The male three-spined Stickleback, while show-

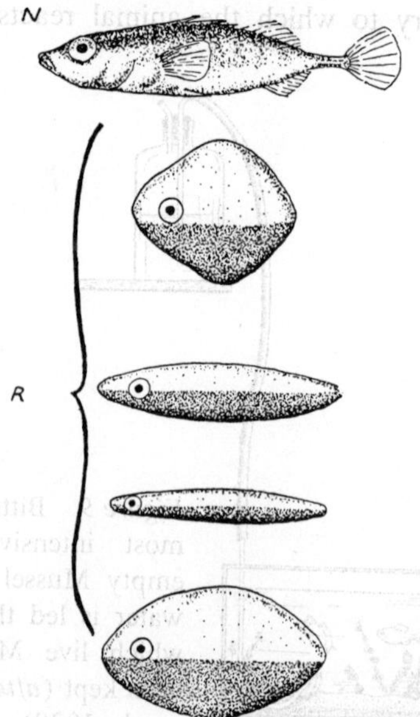

Figure 10 Models used in experiments on the release of fighting in male Three-spined Stickleback. A perfectly shaped silvery model (N) is rarely attacked, while crude models with red undersides (R) are strongly attacked (*after Tinbergen, 1951*)

ing some hostility towards any trespassing fish, concentrates on males of its own species. Models of males release the same response, provided they are red underneath. A bright blue eye and a light bluish back add a little to the model's effectiveness, but shape and size do not matter within very wide limits. A cigar-shaped model with just an eye and a red underside releases much more intensive attack than a perfectly shaped model or even a freshly killed Stickleback which is not red (Fig. 10). Size has so little influence that all males which I observed even "attacked" the red mail vans passing about a hundred yards away; that is to say they raised their dorsal spines and made frantic attempts to reach them, which of course was prevented by the glass wall of the aquarium. When a van passed the laboratory, where a row of twenty aquaria were situated along the large windows, all males dashed towards the window side of their tanks and followed the van from one corner of their tank to the other. Because models of three times stickleback size, although releasing a similar attack as long as they were not too close, were not actually attacked when brought into the territory, it seems that the angle subtended by the object is important and this must be the reason why the distant mail vans were attacked.

Apart from colour, behaviour may release the attack. A male Stickleback viewing a neighbor from afar often adopts a threat posture, a curious vertical attitude, head downward (Fig. 11). The side, or even the underside, is turned towards the opponent, and one or both ventral spines are erected. This posture has an infuriating effect on other males, and we can intensify a male's attack on a dummy by presenting it in this posture.

Similar observations have been made on the Robin. When a male Robin has staked out his territory, the sight of another Robin in this territory releases attack or threat. Lack showed that the red breast

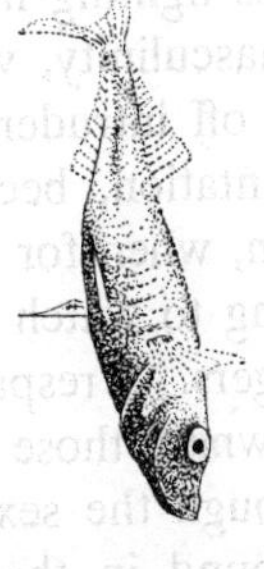

Figure 11 Threat posture of male Three-spined Stickleback (*after Tinbergen, 1951*)

Figure 12 An experiment on fight-releasing stimuli in the Robin: a mounted immature Robin, which has brown breast feathers (*left*) is rarely attacked, while an isolated tuft of red feathers (*right*) is postured at (*after Lack, 1943*)

is the releasing factor more than anything else.[9] When he put up a mounted Robin in an occupied territory, this was postured at by the owner. Even a small cluster of red feathers was sufficient to evoke posturing (Fig. 12). And, just as in the Stickleback a very crude red model was more effective than a perfectly shaped but silvery model, so to the Robin these few red feathers had more meaning than an entire mounted immature Robin, which had all the form-feathers of its species but had a brown instead of a red breast. It is remarkable how similar are the functions of the red breast of the male Stickleback and those of the Robin's red breast. We will see that comparable signalling systems have convergently developed in animals of other groups as well.

In the Robin, the signalling is not entirely visual however. Robins hear each other over far greater distances than they see each other. In particular, the song of a Robin arouses the owner of a territory and sets him off to find the singer. The real attack therefore occurs in at least two steps; a male first flies in the direction from which it hears another male singing; it then looks round and is roused by the red breast of the intruder to posture or attack.

In many other species song has this same function; it is a "badge of masculinity" and releases fighting in territory holders. As I said earlier, such a badge of masculinity, when demonstrated by a male on its own territory, drives off intruders. This can easily be seen in the field without experimentation, because it often happens that a singing male cannot be seen, when for instance it is hidden by a tree or a shrub. It is fascinating to watch the intense reactions of other birds to such concealed singers. Trespassers are personifications of a bad conscience; territory owners those of righteous indignation.

In the Herring Gull, though the sexes have the same coloration, aggressiveness is mainly found in the males, and directed against

Figure 13 Female *(left)* and male American Flicker *(after Noble, 1936)*

other Herring Gull males. Male Herring Gulls however do not sing, nor does any of their calls particularly arouse other males. Nor do the males have conspicuously coloured parts that release fighting in other males. Their behaviour however does. Threat postures and nest building movements particularly draw the attention of other males and elicit a hostile response from them.

Other species again resemble the Stickleback in that the male's bright colours act as their badge. This for instance was found to be the case in the American Flicker *(Colaptes auratus)*, a Woodpecker in which the male has a patch at the corner of the mouth (the so-called moustache) which the female has not (Fig. 13). When the female of a pair was captured and given an artificial black moustache she was attacked by her own mate. After recapture and removal of the moustache she was again accepted.[10]

Male Shell Parrakeets *(Melopsittacus undulatus)* differ from females in the colour of the cere, which is blue in males, brown in females (Fig. 14). Females with the cere painted blue were attacked by males.[11]

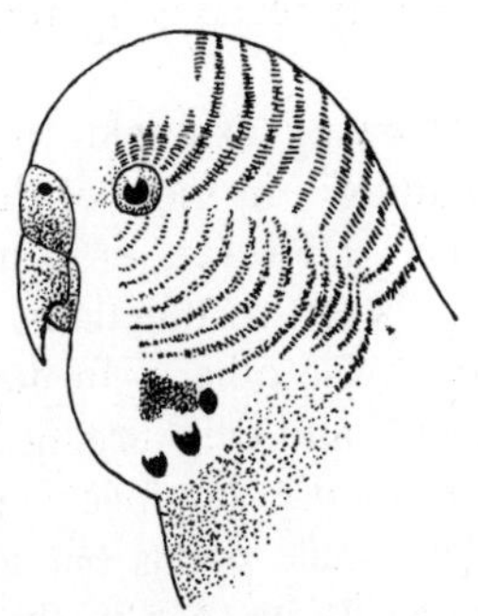

Figure 14 Head of Shell Parrakeet *(after Tinbergen, 1951)*

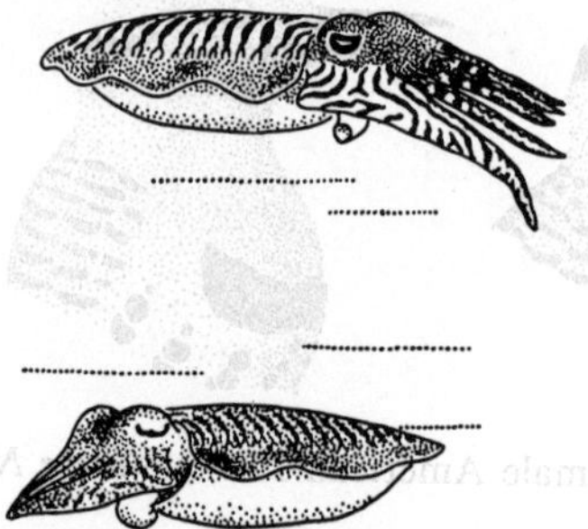

Figure 15 Male Cuttlefish at rest (*below*) and displaying (*above*) (*after L. Tinbergen, 1939*)

A most remarkable parallel was found in a group as different as the Cephalopods. Males of the Common Cuttlefish, *Sepia officinalis,* have a brilliant visual display at the mating time. On meeting another Sepia they show the broadside of their arms, and by co-ordinated action of their chromatophores develop a conspicuous pattern of very dark purple and white (Fig. 15). The fighting of the males is a response to this male display; experiments with plaster models showed that the display acts visually; both shape and colour pattern contributing to the release of attack.[12]

Lizards behave much as Cuttlefish do.[13, 14, 15, 16] The males have special movements which serve to display specific male colours. The American Fence Lizard *(Sceloporus undulatus)* has procryptic colours on the back. The underside of the males, however, is a clear blue. This colour is not visible until the male displays, as it does in spring upon meeting another Fence Lizard. It then takes up a position in front of the other and at right angles to it, and compresses its body laterally so that the blue underside becomes visible from the side (Fig. 16). By changing the colour of males and females with lacquers, Noble showed that the blue belly releases fighting in territory holding males.[15, 16]

So far, I have been reviewing examples of stimuli responsible mainly for the timing of fighting. In most of these cases they direct the fighting at the same time. However, as in mating behaviour, we have to distinguish between these two functions, for there are stimuli contributing to one and not to the other. In ducks, for instance, females make special movements and calls urging their mates to attack other males. The calls merely raise the male's aggressiveness, but by special head movements the female points out to her mate the male to be attacked.[17] This can easily be seen in the tame and half-tame

Figure 16 Male Fence Lizard in display (*after Noble, 1934*)

Mallards living in our parks: the female swims from an "accosting" male to her own mate, repeatedly pointing her head with a sideways movement over her shoulder in the direction of the stranger.

The third problem, related to reproductive isolation, that of confining the fighting to members of the same species, has also been covered by the examples given. Again, as with the signals which play a part in mating behaviour, the fight-evoking signals are specific, and very different even in closely related species if they are living in something like the same habitat. Yet one gets the impression that interspecific fighting is not as rigorously eliminated in evolution as interspecific mating. It seems, so far as the evidence goes, that what little interspecific fighting occurs is directed at species superficially resembling the species of the attacking animal. "Erroneous" attacks occur because a strange species happens to present some of the sign stimuli normally releasing attack. In some cases, however, fighting is clearly aimed at other species because they are competitors for the same "indispensable object." Thus Starlings and Tree Sparrows are known to drive other species from nesting holes.

THE PECK-ORDER

Animal species living in groups sometimes fight over other issues than females or territories. Individuals may clash over food, over a favourite perch, or possibly for other reasons. In such cases, learning often reduces the amount of fighting. Each individual learns, by pleasant or bitter experience, which of its companions are stronger and must be avoided, and which are weaker and can be intimidated. In this way the "peck-order" originates, in which each individual in the group knows its own place. One individual is the tyrant; it dominates all the others. One is subordinate to nobody but the tyrant. Number three dominates all except the two above it, and so on. This has been found in various birds, mammals, and fish. It can easily be seen in a hen-pen.

The peck-order is another means of reducing the amount of actual fighting. Individuals that do not learn quickly to avoid their "superiors" are at a disadvantage both because they receive more beatings and because they are an easier prey to predators during fights.

The behaviour leading to peck-orders has some interesting aspects. Lorenz found in Jackdaws that when a female of low "rank" got engaged to a male high up in the scale, this female immediately rose to the same rank as the male, that is to say that all the individuals inferior to the male avoided her though several of them had been of higher rank than she before.

The American literature contains many valuable contributions on the problems of peck-order.[18, 19] In many of these papers, however, peck-order is claimed to be the only principle of social organization. This leads to distorted views; peck-order relationships form only one category among the numerous types of social relationships in existence.

REFERENCES

1. Meisenheimer, J. 1921. Geschlecht und Geschlecter im Tierreich. Jena.
2. Tinbergen, N. 1951. A note on the origin and evolution of threat display. *The Ibis,* **94**: 160–2.
3. ———. 1937. Über das Verhalten Kämpfender Kohlmeisen, *Parus m. major* L. *Ardea,* **26**: 222–3.
4. Hediger, H. 1949. Säugetier-Territorien und ihre Markierung. *Bijdr. tot de Dierk.,* **28**: 172–84.
5. Howard, H. E. 1920. *Territory in Bird Life.* London: John Murray.
6. Tinbergen, N. 1936. The function of sexual fighting in birds, and the problem of the origin of territory. *Bird Banding,* **7**: 1–8.
7. ———. 1951. On the significance of territory in the Herring gull. *The Ibis,* **94**: 158–9.
8. Boeseman, M., Van Der Drift, J., Van Roon, J. M., Tinbergen, N., and Ter Pelkwijk, J. 1938. De bittervoorns en hun Mossels. *De Lev. Nat.,* **43**: 129–236.
9. Lack, D. 1943. *The Life of the Robin.* London: H. F. and G. Witherby.

10. Noble, G. K. 1936. Courtship and sexual selection of the flicker, *Colaptes auratus luteus*. *The Auk,* **53**: 269–82.
11. Cinat-Tomson, H. 1926. Die geschlechtliche Zuchtwahl beim Wellensittich, *Melopsittacus undulatus Shaw*. *Biol. Zbl.,* **46**: 543–52.
12. Tinbergen, L. 1939. Zur Fortpflansungsethologie von *Sepia officinalis* L. *Arch. neerl. Zool.,* **3**: 323–64.
13. Kitzler, G. 1941. Die Paarungsbiologie einiger Eidechsenarten. *Zs. f. Tierpsychol.,* **4**: 353–402.
14. Kramer, G. 1937. Beobachtungen über Paarungsbiologie und soziales Verhalten von Mauereidechsen. *Zs. Morphol. Oekol. Tiere,* **32**: 752–84.
15. Noble, G. K. 1934. Experimenting with the courtship of lizards. *Nat. Hist.,* **34**: 1–15.
16. Noble, G. K., and Bradley, H. T. 1933. The mating behavior of lizards. *Am. N. Y. Acad. Sci.,* **35**: 25–100.
17. Lorenz, K. 1941. Vergleichende Bewegungsstudien an Anatinen. *Jour. f. Ornithol.* **89** (Festschrift Heinroth), 194–294.
18. Allee, W. C. 1931. *Animal Aggregations.* Chicago: University of Chicago Press. 431 pp.
19. ———. 1938. *The Social Life of Animals.* New York: Norton. 293 pp.

5

WHAT AGGRESSION IS GOOD FOR

KONRAD LORENZ
Max Planck Institut für Verhaltenphysiologie

What is the value of all this fighting? In nature, fighting is such an ever-present process, its behavior mechanisms and weapons are so highly developed and have so obviously arisen under the selection pressure of a species-preserving function, that it is our duty to ask this Darwinian question.

The layman, misguided by sensationalism in press and film, imagines the relationship between the various "wild beasts of the jungle" to be a bloodthirsty struggle, all against all. In a widely shown film, a Bengal tiger was seen fighting with a python, and immediately afterward the python with a crocodile. With a clear conscience I can assert that such things never occur under natural conditions. What advantage would one of these animals gain from exterminating the other? Neither of them interferes with the other's vital interests.

Darwin's expression, "the struggle for existence," is sometimes erroneously interpreted as the struggle between different species. In reality, the struggle Darwin was thinking of and which drives evolution forward is the competition between near relations. What causes a species to disappear or become transformed into a different species is the profitable "invention" that falls by chance to one or a few of its members in the everlasting gamble of hereditary change. The descendants of these lucky ones gradually outstrip all others until the particular species consists only of individuals who possess the new "invention."

There are, however, fightlike contests between members of different species: at night an owl kills and eats even well-armed birds of prey, in spite of their vigorous defense, and when these birds meet the owl by day they attack it ferociously. Almost every animal capable of self-defense, from the smallest rodent upward, fights furiously when it is cornered and has no means of escape. Besides these three particular types of inter-specific fighting, there are other, less typical cases; for instance, two cave-nesting birds of different species may fight for a nesting cavity. Something must be said here about these three types of inter-specific fighting in order to explain their peculiarity and to distinguish them from the intra-specific aggression which is really the subject of this book.

The survival value of inter-specific fights is much more evident than that of intra-specific contests. The way in which a predatory animal and its prey influence each other's evolution is a classical example of how the selection pressure of a certain function causes corresponding adaptations. The swiftness of the hunted ungulate forces its feline pursuers to evolve enormous leaping power and sharply armed toes. Paleontological discoveries have shown impressive examples of such evolutionary competition between weapons of attack and those of defense. The teeth of grazing animals have achieved better and better grinding power, while, in their parallel evolution, nutritional plants have devised means of protecting themselves against being eaten, as by the storage of silicates and the development of hard, wooden thorns. This kind of "fight" between the eater and the eaten never goes so far that the predator causes extinction of the prey: a state of equilibrium is always established between them, endurable by both species. The last lions would have died of hunger long before they had killed the last pair of antelopes or zebras; or, in terms of human commercialism, the whaling industry would go bankrupt before the last whales became extinct. What directly threatens the existence of an animal species is never the "eating enemy" but the competitor. In prehistoric times man took the Dingo, a primitive domestic dog, to Australia It ran wild there, but it did not exterminate a single species of its quarry; instead, it destroyed the large marsupial beasts of prey which ate the same animals as it did itself. The large marsupial predators, the Tasmanian Devil and the Marsupial Wolf, were far superior to the Dingo in strength, but the hunting methods of these "old-fashioned," relatively stupid and slow creatures were inferior to those of the "modern" mammal. The Dingo reduced the marsupial population to such a degree that their methods no longer "paid," and today they exist only in Tasmania, where the Dingo has never penetrated.

In yet another respect the fight between predator and prey is not a fight in the real sense of the word: the stroke of the paw with which a lion kills his prey may resemble the movements that he makes when he strikes his rival, just as a shotgun and a rifle resemble each other outwardly; but the inner motives of the hunter are basically different from those of the fighter. The buffalo which the lion fells provokes his aggression as little as the appetizing turkey which I have just seen hanging in the larder provokes mine. The differences in these inner drives can clearly be seen in the expression movements of the animal: a dog about to catch a hunted rabbit has the same kind of excitedly happy expression as he has when he greets his master or awaits some longed-for treat. From many excellent photographs it can be seen that the lion, in the dramatic moment before he springs, is in no way angry. Growling, laying the ears back, and other well-known expression movements of fighting behavior are seen in predatory animals only when they are very afraid of a wildly resisting prey, and even then the expressions are only suggested.

The opposite process, the "counteroffensive" of the prey against the predator, is more nearly related to genuine aggression. Social animals in particular take every possible chance to attack the "eating enemy" that threatens their safety. This process is called "mobbing." Crows or other birds "mob" a cat or any other nocturnal predator, if they catch sight of it by day.

The survival value of this attack on the eating enemy is self-evident. Even if the attacker is small and defenseless, he may do his enemy considerable harm. All animals which hunt singly have a chance of success only if they take their prey by surprise. If a fox is followed through the wood by a loudly screaming jay, or a sparrow hawk is pursued by a flock of warning wagtails, his hunting is spoiled for the time being. Many birds will mob an owl, if they find one in the daytime, and drive it so far away that it will hunt somewhere else the next night. In some social animals such as jackdaws and many kinds of geese, the function of mobbing is particularly interesting. In jackdaws, its most important survival value is to teach the young, inexperienced birds what a dangerous eating enemy looks like, which they do not know instinctively. Among birds, this is a unique case of traditionally acquired knowledge.

Geese and ducks "know" by very selective, innate releasing mechanisms that anything furry, red-brown, long-shaped, and slinking is extremely dangerous, but nonetheless mobbing, with its intense excitement and the gathering together of geese from far and wide, has an essentially educational character as well as a survival value; anyone who did not know it already learns: foxes may be found here! At a time when only part of the shore of our lake was protected by a foxproof fence, the geese kept ten or fifteen yards clear of all unfenced cover likely to conceal a fox, but in the fenced-in area they penetrated fearlessly into the thickets of young fir trees. Besides this didactic function, mobbing of predators by jackdaws and geese still has the basic, original one of making the enemy's life a burden. Jackdaws actively attack their enemy, and geese apparently intimidate it with their cries, their thronging, and their fearless advance. The great Canada geese will even follow a fox over land in a close phalanx, and I have never known a fox in this situation try to catch one of his tormentors. With ears laid back and a disgusted expression on his face, he glances back over his shoulder at the trumpeting flock and trots slowly—so as not to lose face—away from them.

Among the larger, more defense-minded herbivores which, en masse, are a match for even the biggest predators, mobbing is particularly effective; according to reliable reports, zebras will molest even a leopard if they catch him on a veldt where cover is sparse. The reaction of social attack against the wolf is still so ingrained in domestic cattle and pigs that one can sometimes land oneself in-danger by going through a field of cows with a nervous dog which, instead of barking at them or at least fleeing independently, seeks refuge between the legs of its owner. Once, when I was out with my bitch Stasi, I was obliged to jump into a lake and swim for safety when a herd of young cattle half encircled us and advanced threateningly; and when he was in southern Hungary during the First World War my brother spent a pleasant afternoon up a tree with his Scotch terrier under his arm, because a herd of half-wild Hungarian swine, disturbed while grazing in the wood, encircled them, and with bared tusks and unmistakable intentions began to close in on them.

Much more could be said about these effective attacks on the real or supposed enemy. In some birds and fishes, to serve this special purpose brightly colored "aposematic" or warning colors have evolved, which predators notice and associate with unpleasant experiences with the particular species. Poisonous, evil-tasting, or otherwise specially protected animals have, in many cases, "chosen" for these warning signals the combination of red, white, and black; and it is remarkable that the Common Sheldrake and the Sumatra Barb, two creatures which have nothing in common either with each other or the above-named groups, should have done the same thing. It has long been known that Common Sheldrake mob predatory animals and that they so disgust the fox with the sight of their brightly colored plumage that they can nest safely in inhabited foxholes. I bought some Sumatra Barbs because I had asked myself why these fishes looked so poisonous; in a large communal aquarium, they immediately answered my question by mobbing big Cichlids so persistently that I had to save the giant predators from the only apparently harmless dwarfs.

There is a third form of fighting behavior, and its survival value is as easily demonstrated as that of the predator's attack on its prey or the mobbing by the prey of the eating enemy. With H. Hediger,[2] we call this third behavior pattern the *critical reaction*. The expression "fighting like a cornered rat" has become symbolic of the desperate struggle in which the fighter stakes his all, because he cannot escape and can expect no mercy. This most violent form of fighting behavior is motivated by fear, by the most intense flight impulses whose natural outlet is prevented by the fact that the danger is too near; so the animal, not daring to turn its back on it, fights with the proverbial courage of desperation. Such a contingency may also occur when, as with the cornered rat, flight is prevented by lack of space, or by strong social ties, like those which forbid an animal to desert its brood or family. The attack which a hen or goose makes on everything that goes too near her chicks or goslings can also be classified as a critical reaction. Many animals will attack desperately when surprised by an enemy at less than a certain critical distance, whereas they would have fled if they had noticed his coming from farther away. As Hediger has described, lion tamers maneuver their great beasts of prey into their positions in the arena by playing a dangerous game with the margin between flight distance and critical distance; and thousands of big game hunting stories testify to the dangerousness of large beasts of prey in dense cover. The reason is that in such circumstances the flight distance is particularly small, because the animal feels safe, imagining that it will not be noticed by a man even if he should penetrate the cover and get quite close; but if in so doing the man oversteps the animal's critical distance, a so-called hunting accident happens quickly and disastrously.

All the cases described above, in which animals of different species fight against each other, have one thing in common: every one of the fighters gains an obvious advantage by its behavior or, at least, in the interests of preserving the species it "ought to" gain one. But intra-specific aggression, aggression in the proper and narrower sense of the word, also fulfills a species-preserving function. Here, too, the Darwinian question "What for?" may and must be asked. Many people will not see the obvious justification for this question, and those accustomed to the classical psychoanalytical way of thinking will probably regard it as a frivolous attempt to vindicate the life-destroying principle or, purely, and simply, evil. The average normal civilized human being witnesses aggression only when two of his fellow citizens or two of his domestic animals fight, and therefore sees only its evil effects. In addition there is the alarming progression of aggressive actions ranging from cocks fighting in the barnyard to dogs biting each other, boys thrashing each other, young men throwing beer mugs at each other's heads, and so on to bar-room brawls about politics, and finally to wars and atom bombs.

With humanity in its present cultural and technological situation, we have good reason to consider intra-specific aggression the greatest of all dangers. We shall not improve our chances of counteracting it if we accept it as something metaphysical and inevitable, but on the other hand, we shall perhaps succeed in finding remedies if we investigate the chain of its natural causation. Wherever man has achieved the power of voluntarily guiding a natural phenomenon in a certain direction, he has owed it to his understanding of the chain of causes which formed it. Physiology, the science concerned with the normal life processes and how they fulfill their species-preserving function, forms the essential foundation for pathology, the science investigating their disturbances. Let us forget for a moment that the aggression drive has become derailed under conditions of civilization, and let us inquire impartially into its natural causes. For the reasons already given, as good Darwinians we must inquire into the species-preserving function which, under natural—or rather precultural—conditions, is fulfilled by fights within the species, and which by the process of selection has caused the advanced development of intra-specific fighting behavior in so many higher animals. It is not only fishes that fight their own species: the majority of vertebrates do so too, man included.

Darwin had already raised the question of the survival value of fighting, and he has given us an enlightening answer: It is always favorable to the future of a species if the stronger of two rivals takes possession either of the territory or of the desired female. As so often, this truth of yesterday is not the untruth of today but only a special case; ecologists have recently demonstrated a much more essential function of aggression. Ecology—derived from the Greek oikos, the house—is the branch of biology that deals with the manifold reciprocal relations of the organism to its natural surroundings—its "household"—which of course includes all other animals and plants native to the environment. Unless the special interests of a social organization demand close aggregation of its members, it is obviously most expedient to spread the individuals of an animal species as evenly as possible over the available habitat.

The danger of too dense a population of an animal species settling in one part of the available biotope and exhausting all its sources of nutrition and so starving can be obviated by a mutual repulsion acting on the animals of the same species, effecting their regular spacing out, in much the same manner as electrical charges are regularly distributed all over the surface of a spherical conductor. This, in plain terms, is the most important survival value of intra-specific aggression.

Now we can understand why the sedentary coral fish in particular are so crazily colored. There are few biotopes on earth that provide so much and such varied nutrition as a coral reef. Here fish species can, in an evolutionary sense, take up very different professions: one can support itself as an "unskilled laborer," doing what any average fish can do, hunting creatures that are neither poisonous nor armorplated nor prickly, in other words hunting all the defenseless organisms approaching the reef from the open sea, some as "plankton," others as active swimmers "intending" to settle on the reef, as millions of free-swimming larvae of all coral-dwelling organisms do. On the other hand, another fish species may specialize in eating forms of life that live on the reef itself and are therefore equipped with some sort of protective mechanism which the hunting fish must render harmless. Corals themselves provide many different kinds of nourishment for a whole series of fish species. Pointed-jawed butterfly fish get their food parasitically from corals and other stinging animals. They search continuously in the coral stems for small prey caught in the stinging tentacles of coral polyps. As soon as they see these, they produce, by fanning with their pectoral fins, a current so directly aimed at the prey that at the required point a "parting" is made between the polyps, pressing their tentacles flat on all sides and thus enabling the fish to seize the prey almost without getting its nose stung. It always gets it just a little stung and can be seen "sneezing" and shaking its nose, but, like pepper, the sting seems to act as an agreeable stimulant. My beautiful yellow and brown butterfly fishes prefer a prey, such as a piece of fish, stuck in the tentacles of a stinging sea anemone, to the same prey swimming free in the water. Other related species have developed a stronger immunity to stings and they devour the prey together with the coral animal that has caught it. Yet other species disregard the stinging capsules of coelenterates altogether, and eat coral animals, hydroid polyps, and even big, strong, stinging sea anemones, as placidly as a cow eats grass. As well as this immunity to poison, parrot fish have evolved a strong chisellike dentition and they eat whole branches of coral including their calcareous skeleton. If you dive near a grazing herd of these beautiful, rainbow-colored fish, you can hear a cracking and crunching as though a little gravel mill were at work—and this actually corresponds with the facts, for when such a fish excretes, it rains a little shower of white sand, and the observer realizes with astonishment that most of the snow-clean coral sand covering the glades of the coral forest has obviously passed through parrot fish.

Other fish, plectognaths, to which the comical puffers, trunk, and porcupine fish belong, have specialized in cracking hard-shelled mollusks, crabs, and sea urchins; and others again, such as angelfish, specialize in snatching the lovely feather crowns that certain feather worms thrust out of their hard, calcareous tubes. Their capacity for quick retraction acts as a protection again slower predators, but some angelfish have a way of sidling up and, with a lightning sideways jerk of the mouth, seizing the worm's head at a speed surpassing its capacity for withdrawal. Even in the aquarium, where they seize prey which has no such quick reactions, these fish cannot do otherwise than snap like this.

The reef offers many other "openings" for specialized fish. There are some which remove parasites from others and which are therefore left unharmed by the fiercest predators, even when they penetrate right into the mouth cavities of their hosts to perform their hygienic work. There are others which live as parasites on large fish, punching pieces from their epidermis, and among these are the oddest fish of all: they resemble the cleaner fish so closely in color, form, and movement that, under false pretenses, they can safely approach their victims.

It is essential to consider the fact that all these opportunities for special careers, known as ecological niches, are often provided by the same cubic yard of ocean water. Because of the enormous nutritional possibilities, every fish, whatever its specialty, requires only a few square yards of sea bottom for its support, so in this small area there can be as many fish as there are ecological niches, and anyone who has watched with amazement the thronging traffic on a coral reef knows that these are legion. However, every one of this crowd is determined that no other fish of his species should settle in his territory.

In less densely populated biotopes where the same unit of space can support three or four species only, a resident fish or bird can "afford" to drive away all living beings, even members of species that are no real threat to his existence; but if a sedentary coral fish tried to do the same thing, it would be utterly exhausted and, moreover, would never manage to keep its territory free from the swarms of noncompetitors of different "professions." It is in the occupational interests of all sedentary species that each should determine the spatial distriution that will benefit its own individuals, entirely without consideration for other species. The colorful "poster" patterns, and the fighting reactions elicited by them, have the effect that the fish of each species keep a measured distance only from nutritional competitors of the same species. This is the very simple answer to the much discussed question of the function of the colors of coral fish.

As I have already mentioned, the species-typical song of birds has a very similar survival value to that of the visual signals of fishes. From the song of a certain bird, other birds not yet in possession of a territory recognize that in this particular place a male is proclaiming territorial rights. It is remarkable that in many species the song indicates how strong and possibly how old the singer is, in other words, how much the listener has to fear him. Among several species of birds that mark their territory acoustically, there is great individual difference of sound expression, and some observers are of the opinion that, in such species, the personal visiting card is of special significance. While Heinroth[3] interpreted the crowing of the cock with the words, "Here is a cock!" Baeumer,[1] the most knowledgeable of all domestic fowl experts, heard in it the far more special announcement, "Here is the cock Balthazar!"

Among mammals, which mostly "think through their noses," it is not surprising that marking of the territory by scent plays a big role. Many methods have been tried; various scent glands have been evolved, and the most remarkable ceremonies developed around the depositing of urine and feces; of these the leg-lifting of the domestic dog is the most familiar. The objection has been raised by some students of mammals that such scent marks cannot have anything to do with territorial ownership because they are found not only in socially living mammals which do not defend single territories, but also in animals that wander far and wide; but this opinion is only partly correct. First, it has been proved that dogs and other pack-living animals recognize each other by the scent of the marks, and it would at once be apparent to the members of a pack if a non-member presumed to lift its leg in their hunting grounds. Secondly, Leyhausen and Wolf[4] have demonstrated the very interesting possibility that the distribution of animals of a certain species over the available biotope can be effected not only by a space plan but also by a time plan. They found that, in domestic cats living free in open country, several individuals could make use of the same hunting ground without ever coming into conflict, by using it according to a definite timetable, in the same way as our Seewiesen housewives use our communal washhouse. An additional safeguard against undesirable encounters is the scent marks which these animals—the cats, not the housewives—deposit at regular intervals wherever they go. These act like railway signals whose aim is to prevent collision between two trains. A cat finding another cat's signal on its hunting path assesses its age, and if it is very fresh it hesitates, or chooses another path; if it is a few hours old it proceeds calmly on its way.

Even in the case of animals whose territory is governed by space only, the hunting ground must not be imagined as a property determined by geographical confines; it is determined by the fact that in every individual the readiness to fight is greatest in the most familiar place, that is, in the middle of its territory. In other words, the threshold value of fight-eliciting stimuli is at its lowest where the animal feels safest, that is, where its readiness to fight is least diminished by its readiness to escape. As the distance from this "headquarter" increases, the readiness to fight decreases proportionately as the surroundings become stranger and more intimidating to the animal. If one plotted the graph of this decrease the curve would not be equally steep for all directions in space. In fish, the center of whose territory is nearly always on the bottom, the decline in readiness to fight is most marked in the vertical direction because the fish is threatened by special dangers from above.

The territory which an animal apparently possesses is thus only a matter of variations in readiness to fight, depending on the place and on various local factors inhibiting the fighting urge. In nearing the center of the territory the aggressive urge increases in geometrical ratio to the decrease in distance from this center. This increase in aggression is so great that it compensates for all differences ever to be found in adult, sexually mature animals of a species. If we know the territorial centers of two conflicting animals, such as two garden redstarts or two aquarium sticklebacks, all other things being equal, we can predict, from the place of encounter, which one will win: the one that is nearer home.

When the loser flees, the inertia of reaction of both animals leads to that phenomenon which always occurs when a time lag enters into a self-regulating process—to an oscillation. The courage of the fugitive returns as he nears his own headquarters, while that of the pursuer sinks in proportion to the distance covered in enemy territory. Finally the fugitive turns and attacks the former pursuer vigorously and unexpectedly and, as was predictable, he in his turn is beaten and driven away. The whole performance is repeated several times till both fighters come to a standstill at a certain point of balance where they threaten each other without fighting.

We can safely assume that the most important function of intra-specific aggression is the even distribution of the animals of a particular species over an inhabitable area, but it is certainly not its only one. Charles Darwin had already observed that sexual selection, the selection of the best and strongest animals for reproduction, was furthered by the fighting of rival animals, particularly males. The strength of the father directly affects the welfare of the children in those species in which he plays an active part in their care and defense. The correlation between male parental care and rival fighting is clear, particularly in those animals which are not territorial in the sense which the Cichlids demonstrate but which wander more or less nomadically, as, for example, large ungulates, ground apes, and many others. In such animals, intra-specific aggression plays no essential part in the "spacing out" of the species. Bisons, antelopes, horses, etc., form large herds, and territorial borders and territorial jealousy are unknown to them since there is enough food for all. Nevertheless the males of these species fight each other violently and dramatically, and there is no doubt that the selection resulting from this aggressive behavior leads to the evolution of particularly strong and courageous defenders of family and herd; conversely, there is just as little doubt that the survival value of herd defense has resulted in selective breeding for hard rival fights. This interaction has produced impressive fighters such as bull bison or the males of the large baboon species; at every threat to the community, these valiantly surround and protect the weaker members of the herd.

In connection with rival fights attention must be drawn to a fact which, though it seems paradoxical to the nonbiologist, is, as we shall show later on in this book, of the very greatest importance: purely intra-specific selective breeding can lead to the development of forms and behavior patterns which are not only nonadaptive but can even have adverse effects on species preservation. That is why, in the last paragraph, I emphasized the fact that family defense, a form of strife with the extra-specific environment, has evolved the rival fight, and this in its turn has developed the powerful males. If sexual rivalry, or any other form of intra-specific competition, exerts selection pressure uninfluenced by any environmental exigencies, it may develop in a direction which is quite unadaptive to environment, and irrelevant, if not positively detrimental, to survival. This process may give rise to bizarre physical forms of no use to the species. The antlers of stags, for example, were developed in the service of rival fights, and a stag without them has little hope of producing progeny. Otherwise antlers are useless, for male stags defend themselves against beasts of prey with their fore-hoofs only and never with their antlers. Only the reindeer has based an invention on this necessity and "learned" to shovel snow with a widened point of its antlers.

Sexual selection by the female often has the same results as the rival fights. Wherever we find exaggerated development of colorful feathers, bizarre forms, etc., in the male, we may suspect that the males no longer fight but that the last word in the choice of a mate is spoken by the female, and that the male has no means of contesting this decision. Birds of Paradise, the Ruff, the Mandarin Duck, and the Argus Pheasant show examples of such behavior. The Argus hen pheasant reacts to the large secondary wing feathers of the cock; they are decorated with beautiful eye spots and the cock spreads them before her during courtship. They are so huge that the cock can scarcely fly, and the bigger they are the more they stimulate the hen. The number of progeny produced by a cock in a certain period of time is in direct proportion to the length of these feathers, and, even if their extreme development is unfavorable in other ways—his unwieldiness may cause him to be eaten by a predator while a rival with less absurdly exaggerated wings may escape—he will nevertheless leave more descendants than will a plainer cock. So the predisposition to huge wing feathers is preserved, quite against the interests of the species. One could well imagine an Argus hen that reacted to a small red spot on the wings of the male, which would disappear when he folded his wings and interfere neither with his flying capacity nor with his protective color, but the evolution of the Argus pheasant has run itself into a blind alley. The males continue to compete in producing the largest possible wing feathers.

My teacher, Oskar Heinroth, used to say jokingly, "Next to the wings of the Argus pheasant, the hectic life of Western civilized man is the most stupid product of intra-specific selection!" The rushed existence into which industrialized, commercialized man has precipitated himself is actually a good example of an inexpedient development caused entirely by competition between members of the same species. Human beings of today are attacked by so-called manager diseases, high blood pressure, renal atrophy, gastric ulcers, and torturing neuroses; they succumb to barbarism because they have no more time for cultural interest. And all this is unnecessary, for they could easily agree to take things more easily; theoretically they could, but in practice it is just as impossible for them as it is for the Argus pheasant to grow shorter wing feathers.

There are still worse consequences of intra-specific selection, and for obvious reasons man is particularly exposed to them: unlike any creature before him, he has mastered all hostile powers in his environment, he has exterminated the bear and the wolf and now, as the Latin proverb says, *"Homo homini lupus."* Striking support for this view comes from the work of modern American sociologists, and in his book *The Hidden Persuaders* Vance Packard gives an impressive picture of the grotesque state of affairs to which commercial competition can lead. Reading this book, one is tempted to believe that intra-specific competition is the "root of all evil" in a more direct sense than aggression can ever be.

In this chapter on the survival value of aggression, I have laid special stress on the potentially destructive effects of intra-specific selection: because of them, aggressive behavior can, more than other qualities and functions, become exaggerated to the point of the grotesque and inexpedient. It is more than probable that the destructive intensity of the aggression drive, still a hereditary evil of mankind, is the consequence of a process of intra-specific selection which worked on our forefathers for roughly forty thousand years, that is, throughout the Early Stone Age. When man had reached the stage of having weapons, clothing, and social organization, so overcoming the dangers of starving, freezing, and being eaten by wild animals, and these dangers ceased to be the essential factors influencing selection, an evil intra-specific selection must have set in. The factor influencing selection was now the wars waged between hostile neighboring tribes. These must have evolved in an extreme form of all those so-called "warrior virtues" which unfortunately many people still regard as desirable ideals.

I return to the theme of the survival value of the rival fight, with the statement that this only leads to useful selection where it breeds fighters fitted for combat with extra-specific enemies as well as for intra-specific duels. The most important function of rival fighting is the selection of an aggressive family defender, and this presupposes a further function of intra-specific aggression: brood defense. This is so obvious that it requires no further comment. If it should be doubted, its truth can be demonstrated by the fact that in many animals, where only one sex cares for the brood, only that sex is really aggressive toward fellow members of the species. Among sticklebacks it is the male, in several dwarf cichlids the female. In many gallinaceous birds, only the females tend the brood, and these are often far more aggressive than the males. The same thing is said to be true of human beings.

It would be wrong to believe that the three functions of aggressive behavior dealt with in the last three chapters—namely, balanced distribution of animals of the same species over the available environment, selection of the strongest by rival fights, and defense of the young—are its only important functions in the preservation of the species. We shall see later what an indispensable part in the great complex of drives is played by aggression; it is one of those driving powers which students of behavior call "motivation"; it lies behind behavior patterns that outwardly have nothing to do with aggression, and even appear to be its very opposite. It is hard to say whether it is a paradox or a commonplace that, in the most intimate bonds between living creatures, there is a certain measure of aggression. Much more remains to be said before discussing this central problem in our natural history of aggression. The important part played by aggression in the inter-action of drives within the organism is not easy to understand and still less easy to expound.

We can, however, here describe the part played by aggression in the structure of society among highly developed animals. Though many individuals interact in a social system, its inner workings are often easier to understand than the interaction of drives within the individual. A principle of organization without which a more advanced social life cannot develop in higher vertebrates is the so-called ranking order. Under this rule every individual in the society knows which one is stronger and which weaker than itself, so that everyone can retreat from the stronger and expect submission from the weaker, if they should get in each other's way. Schjelderup-Ebbe was the first to examine the ranking order in the domestic fowl and to speak of the "pecking order," an expression used to this day by writers. It seems a little odd though, to me, to speak of a pecking order even for large animals which certainly do not peck, but bite or ram. However, its wide distribution speaks for its great survival value, and therefore we must ask wherein this lies.

The most obvious answer is that it limits fighting between the members of a society, but here in contrast one may ask: Would it not have been better if aggression among members of a society were utterly inhibited? To this, a whole series of answers can be given. First, the case may arise that a society, for example, a wolf pack or monkey herd, urgently need aggression against other societies of the same species, therefore aggression should be inhibited only inside the horde. Secondly, a society may derive a beneficial firmness of structure from the state of tension arising inside the community from the aggression drive and its result, ranking order. In jackdaws, and in many other very social birds, ranking order leads directly to protection of the weaker ones. All social animals are "status seekers," hence there is always particularly high tension between individuals who hold immediately adjoining positions in the ranking order; conversely, this tension diminishes the further apart the two animals are in rank. Since high-ranking jackjaws, particularly males, interfere in every quarrel between two inferiors, this graduation of social tension has the desirable effect that the higher-ranking birds always intervene in favor of the losing party.

In jackdaws, another form of "authority" is already linked with the ranking position which the individual has acquired by its aggressive drive. The expression movements of a high-ranking jackdaw, particularly of an old male, are given much more attention by the colony members than those of a low-ranking, young bird. For example, if a young bird shows fright at some meaningless stimulus, the others, especially the older ones, pay almost no attention to his expressions of fear. But if the same sort of alarm proceeds from one of the old males, all the jackdaws within sight and earshot immediately take flight. Since, in jackdaws, recognition of predatory enemies is not innate but is learned by every individual from the behavior of experienced old birds, it is probably of considerable importance that great store is set by the "opinion" of old, high-ranking and experienced birds.

With the higher evolution of an animal species, the significance of the role played by individual experience and learning generally increases, while innate behavior, though not losing importance, becomes reduced to simpler though not less numerous elements. With this general trend in evolution, the significance attached to the experienced old animal becomes greater all the time, and it may even be said that the social coexistence of intelligent mammals has achieved a new survival value by the use it makes of the handing down of individually acquired information. Conversely, it may be said that social coexistence exerts selection pressure in the direction of better learning capacity, because in social animals this faculty benefits not only the individual but also the community. Thus longevity far beyond the age of reproductive capacity has considerable species-preserving value. We know from Fraser Darling and Margaret Altmann that in many species of deer the herd is led by an aged female, no longer hampered in her social duties by the obligations of motherhood.

All other conditions being equal, the age of an animal is, very consistently, in direct proportion to the position it holds in the ranking order of its society. It is thus advantageous if the "constructors" of behavior rely upon this consistency and if the members of the community—who cannot read the age of the experienced leader animal in its birth certificate—rate its reliability by its rank. Some time ago, collaborators of Robert M. Yerkes made the extraordinarily interesting observation that chimpanzees, animals well known to be capable of learning by imitation, copy only higher-ranking members of their species. From a group of these apes, a low-ranking individual was taken and taught to remove bananas from a specially constructed feeding apparatus by very complicated manipulations. When this ape, together with his feeding apparatus, was brought back to the group, the higher-ranking animals tried to take away the bananas which he had acquired for himself, but none of them thought of watching their inferior at work and learning something from him. Then the highest-ranking chimpanzee was removed and taught to use the apparatus in the same way, and when he was put back in the group the other members watched him with great interest and soon learned to imitate him.

S. L. Washburn and Irven DeVore[6] observed that among free-living baboons the band was led not by a single animal but by a "senate" of several old males who maintained their superiority over the younger and physically stronger members by firmly sticking together and proving, as a united force, stronger than any single young male. In a more exactly observed case, one of the three "senators" was seen to be an almost toothless old creature while the other two were well past their prime. On one occasion when the band was in a treeless area and in danger of encountering a lion, the animals stopped and the young, strong males formed a defensive circle around the weaker animals. But the oldest male went forward alone, performed the dangerous task of finding out exactly where the lion was lying, without being seen by him, and then returned to the horde and led them, by a wide detour around the lion, to the safety of their sleeping trees. All followed him blindly, no one doubting his authority.

Let us look back on all that we have learned in this chapter from the objective observation of animals, and consider in what ways intra-specific aggression assists the preservation of an animal species. The environment is divided between the members of the species in such a way that, within the potentialities offered, everyone can exist. The best father, the best mother are chosen for the benefit of the progeny. The children are protected. The community is so organized that a few wise males, the "senate," acquire the authority essential for making and carrying out decisions for the good of the community. Though occasionally, in territorial or rival fights, by some mishap a horn may penetrate an eye or a tooth an artery, we have never found that the aim of aggression was the extermination of fellow members of the species concerned. This of course does not negate the fact that under unnatural circumstances, for example confinement, unforeseen by the "constructors" of evolution, aggressive behavior may have a destructive effect.

Summing up what has been said in this chapter, we find that

aggression, far from being the diabolical, destructive principle that classical psychoanalysis makes it out to be, is really an essential part of the life-preserving organization of instincts. Though by accident it may function in the wrong way and cause destruction, the same is true of practically any functional part of any system.

REFERENCES

1. Baeumer, E. 1964. Das dumme Huhn: Verhalten des Haushuhns. *Kosmos-Bibliothek,* 242.
2. Hediger, H. 1955. *Studies of the Psychology and Behaviour of Captive Animals in Zoos and Circuses.* London: Butterworth.
3. Heinroth, O. 1910. Beitrage zur Biologie, insbesondere Psychologie und Ethologie der Anatiden. *Verh. d. 5. Intern. Ornithol. Kongr. Berlin.*
4. Leyhausen, P. and R. Wolff. 1959. Das Revier einer Hauskatze. *Zur Tierpsychol.,* **16**: 66–70.
5. Lorenz, K. 1959. Methods of approach to the problems of behavior. *The Harvey Lectures,* **Ser. 54**: 60–103. New York: Academic Press.

5a. ———. 1962. The Function of Colour in Coral Reef Fishes. *Proc. Roy. Inst. of Great Britain,* **39**: 282–96.

6. Washburn, S. L., and DeVore, I. 1961. The social life of baboons. *Sci. Am.,* **204**(6): 62–71.
7. Yerkes, R. M. 1943. *Chimpanzees: A Laboratory Colony.* New Haven: Yale University Press.

6

AGGRESSION IN SOCIAL INSECTS

D. I. WALLIS
University of Aberdeen, Scotland

Reprinted from The Natural History of Aggression, *edited by J. D. Carthy and F. J. Ebling, pp. 15–22, with permission of the Institute of Biology. London and New York: Academic Press.*

INTRODUCTION

By definition, social insects are those which live together in colonies. Aggressive behaviour is part of the fundamental mechanism which maintains a colony as a separate entity. The colony is kept distinct from other colonies of the same and different species. Thus, aggression is primarily outwardly directed, i.e. extra-colonial. However, the extent to which aggression is inhibited between colony members does vary and examination of this aspect can help to elucidate the factors which normally evoke aggressive behaviour.

The functions of aggressive behaviour can be summarized as:

(a) an agent maintaining colony cohesion;
(b) an agent in intraspecific competition. A territory is often marked out by a particular colony, so ensuring colony cohesion, a food supply and a nest-site;
(c) in interspecific competition, which may again be for food-sources and nest sites;
(d) in hunting behaviour. Some of the components of aggressive

behaviour are shown in the killing of other insects, including ants, for prey.

The basis of colony distinctiveness and the reasons why aggression is primarily extra-colonial have long puzzled workers in the field and received much attention in the literature. In considering ants, bees and wasps, I shall survey, albeit briefly, three aspects of the subject: the components of aggressive behaviour; current views on the basis of colony distinctiveness; and the factors which influence aggression.

COMPONENTS OF AGGRESSIVE BEHAVIOUR

Examples from various species may be given. My own work on *Formica fusca*[12] illustrates the components of aggressive behaviour seem to be shown by most social insects.

In *fusca,* aggression may consist of adoption of a "threat" posture, or of attack by "seizing" or "dragging." Seizing and dragging function to destroy or remove an alien ant from the nest. Seizing consists of gripping part of the attacked ant with the mandibles. Short, sharp rushes followed by seizing are often observed and puncture of the head or epinotum, or loss of a limb or antenna, may result. Dragging consists of seizing plus a locomotory element. The attacked ant is usually dragged out of the nest. In the threat posture, the head is raised and directed towards the other ant. The mandibles are held wide open with the labial mouthparts tightly withdrawn. Threat is classified as such because it is shown in association with seizing and dragging, and its components suggest it is an intention or incomplete seizing movement. Thus, when the reaction of a colony towards an alien is studied,[12a] it is found that as scores for seizing rise so do scores for threat. However, at the highest frequency of seizing, threat scores have started to decline. This and other evidence indicates that threat is shown most frequently at a moderate intensity of aggressive motivation.

When the response sequences of individuals are analysed, the frequency of transition from one response to another is a further way of demonstrating that responses are similarly motivated—Fig. 1. On the assumption that over short periods of time motivation does not alter greatly, responses linked by the highest transition frequencies are the expression of similar motivation. Fig. 1 supports the view that threat is linked with seizing. It suggests that licking (a response that will be considered later), threat, seizing and dragging, respec-

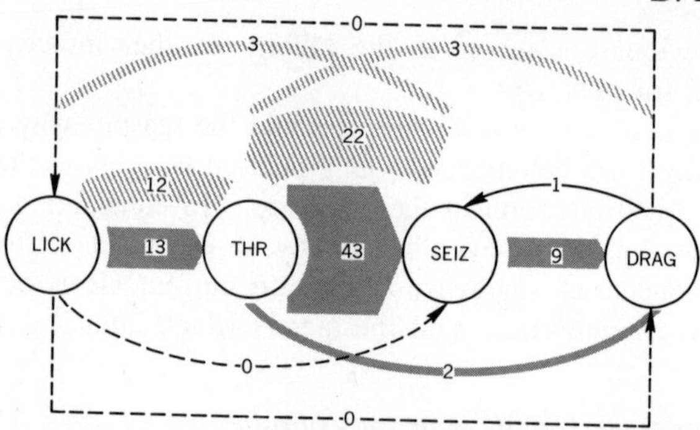

Figure 1 The frequency of transitions from one response to another observed in ants encountering an alien. The line thickness and the figures indicate the frequency of the transition. Black indicates transitions in the direction of increasing aggressive motivation. Dashed lines show possible transitions which were not observed. THR = Threat; SEIZ = Seize.

tively, represent a gradual increase in a common motivation. Transitions from licking to dragging and vice versa are not observed, but dragging is most clearly associated with seizing, licking with threat. Significantly, dragging tends to show a negative rather than a positive correlation with threat when frequencies of the two responses are plotted against each other. Probably when dragging is evoked, motivation is so high as to inhibit a "low motivation" response such as threat.

Only two other responses are shown at all frequently towards alien ants—examining and licking. In "examining," the head and antennae are oriented towards another ant and may touch it. Information is probably obtained through the chemoreceptors on the antennae. "Licking" consists of cleaning another ant with the labial mouthparts. In part this serves merely to clean areas of an ant's body which it cannot clean for itself, but a more significant function is possibly that of removing exudates from the body surface which are the basis of the specific odour of the ant and of the colony. Much licking occurs of areas that the ant can clean for itself.

An aggressive response not seen in *fusca* is shown by *Formica rufa.* The gaster is brought forward between the legs and formic acid is squirted at an opponent. Many ants show a stinging response. In the evolution of the Hymenoptera, two trends are apparent. Some species possess a painful sting, e.g. honeybee, wasp, and some ants; a second trend has been towards the functional reduction and replacement of the sting by other defensive mechanisms, e.g. many ants including the genus *Formica*. The stinging response seems to be a high threshold one, only evoked at high levels of aggressive motivation.

Butler and Free[1] have described aggressive behaviour in the honeybee. Bees show examining, licking, seizing, dragging and probably threat responses. A stinging response is shown. Bees, termed "guards," are frequently stationed at the nest entrance. They adopt a typical posture, frequently standing with forelegs off the ground and antennae held forwards. When more excited, they open their mandibles—presumably this is equivalent to threat—and open their wings. Bees flying near the hive are watched carefully and bees landing are examined. If from another colony they are usually attacked. When fighting occurs, two bees often lie on their sides, holding on to one another's legs with their mandibles and attempting to sting each other. Often they buzz round and round extremely fast like a catherine wheel.

Bumblebees show similar behaviour. Free[3a] reports that guard bees are present, at least in large colonies. If the colony is disturbed, a guard may adopt a typical defensive posture by rolling over on to its side with the mid- and hind-legs of one side raised.

Sakagami[10] describes the primitive social bee *Allodape* defending the nest entrance first by narrowing it with masticated pith and then by blocking it completely with the dorsal surface of the abdomen. Stinging is readily elicited. Similarly among *Halictid* bees, *Chloralictus* plugs the nest-entrance with her head. Michener and Lange[8] report that guard bees back into the nest, where the tunnel diameter is greater, to allow nest-mates to enter. When an intruder appears, they may turn and block the entrance with the abdomen or they may face the intruder and show seizing. Disturbance of the nest may cause the bees to push dirt into the entrance and plug it.

Among wasps, Rau[9] has described aggressive behaviour in *Polistes*. Surprisingly, some species of this genus show great tolerance towards workers from other colonies of the same species but attack workers of other species. Seizing, dragging, stinging and licking occur. Lin[7] in describing the territorial behaviour of the cicada-killer wasp, *Sphecius speciosus*, gives an interesting account of the aggressive behaviour. The initial response is to fly straight at an intruder. "Threat" may be shown when the wasp gains on the intruder but then slows and returns to its territory. Increased aggressive motivation is reflected in the wasp "butting" the intruder and finally "grappling" with it. In grappling the wasp grasps the opponent only to separate almost immediately or falls to the ground and then separates. Loud buzzing is heard during grappling. Interestingly, only the males show this territorial aggressiveness.

THE BASIS OF COLONY COHESION

A colony is maintained as a distinct unit because individuals are able to recognize colony members and differentiate them from non-colony members. The latter evoke aggressive behaviour. There seems little doubt that the basis of this colony distinctiveness is a specific colony odour, a conclusion supported by the work of McCook, Bethe and Fielde on ants and Kalmus and Ribbands[5] on bees. There is little evidence that the odour is a result of definite secretions. It may be nothing more than odours absorbed selectively into the epicuticle. The origin of the odour has been the subject of controversy. Fielde[2] concluded that colony odour is genetically controlled and, thus, a function of the foundress queen. She also postulated odour changes as a result of acquisition of new odours, presumably by surface adsorption. Her theories are complex and other authorities such as Wheeler have questioned them. On the other hand, Kalmus and Ribbands[5] have shown that colony odour in bees is not wholly genetically controlled. Distinctive odours develop quickly if colony-halves receive different diets. Normally colony distinctiveness would result from differences in diet caused by colonies feeding on various crops in varying proportions. A similar non-hereditary mechanism might be expected in all social insects and some recent work of mine on ants attempted to investigate colony odour in this group.[12a] Three groups of about 50 *fusca* workers from the same colony were cultured separately. Groups A and B were fed on the normal culture diet; C was fed on black treacle. The odours of these foods are quite distinct (to man), much more so than the mixture of foods which two colonies might be expected to receive if they foraged naturally in different areas. The groups were kept in identical nests under the same conditions of light, temperature and humidity for seven months. Aggression shown by A to individuals of group C, to individuals of control group B, and, as a further control, to individuals from a different colony X was recorded. Colony X was fed like groups A and B. Results are given in Table 1.

Table 1. *Effect of Differential Feeding in Producing Distinct Colony Odours*

	n	Mean no. of aggr. responses	Significance	Lick	Threat	Seize	Drag
A against B	16	1.2	$P<0.05$	5.6	1.1	0.1	0
A " C	16	3.5	$P<0.001$	9.9	3.2	0.3	0
A " X	16	19.7		1.1	13.6	4.4	1.7
A " B				82%	16%	2%	0%
A " C		Percentages of total		74%	24%	2%	0%
A " X				5%	66%	21%	8%

A against B shows the aggression resulting simply from separation. In fact, an ant returning to its own colony often evokes slight aggression in ants guarding the nest entrance. The causes of this aggression, which is always much less than that shown to aliens, are discussed in the last section. The result of differential feeding (A against C) is to increase the aggression shown, since the mean number of aggressive responses rises from 1.2 to 3.5. Yet far greater aggression is shown towards alien ants from colony X. Further, proportionally more seizing and dragging is shown towards X. In fact, the response pattern to B and C ants is more like that shown towards returning nestmates, where the commonest response is licking.

Thus, metabolic differences induced by different diets may play only a small role in producing distinct colony odours in ants, although more experiments need to be done on this question. Clearly, dietary differences can affect colony odour, but these results suggest genetic influences may be important. Possibly the mechanism in ants is somewhat different from that operating in bees.

FACTORS AFFECTING AGGRESSION: APPARENT BREAKDOWN OF COLONY COHESION

Although alien colony odour is the principal stimulus evoking aggression in social insects, it is certainly not the only one. Visual cues may evoke aggression in bees, ants, and probably wasps. For example, the bobbing flight of bees about to rob another colony acts as a visual releaser and this is reinforced when the bee gets nearer by the alien odour releaser, as Free[3] has shown. Dark colour or movement of any sort evoke more aggression in bees than light colours and still forms, according to Lecomte.[6] Tactile cues may be of some, but generally slight, importance. Free[3b] reports that stinging in bees is more readily evoked by rough than smooth textures. Other chemical cues include formic acid which elicits attack in the ant *Camponotus* as Vowles[11] has found, and the scent of mammals which Free[3b] states encourages stinging in the honeybee.

Other factors influencing the degree or type of aggression are territory, temperature, the degree of hunger and probably the presence of brood. In addition, my results show that different colonies, although cultured under the same conditions, may vary considerably in the amount of aggression they show to intruders.[12a] In any one colony, individuals vary in aggressiveness and the most active ants may also be the most belligerent.

Some observations on *Formica fusca* suggest that situation may be important in influencing aggression.[12a] Various results made it clear that an ant appearing at the nest entrance constituted a situation which alerted guard ants and might evoke aggression in them. Whether the ant is an alien or a nest-mate is clearly a separate factor and determines the subsequent response to the entering ant. Table 2 shows the response of a colony to entering ants. The entrants were either aliens or ants of the same colony which had been away from the colony (a) for 24 hours or (b) for less than a minute. Ants within the colony acted as controls to see whether any aggression is normally shown to ants within the nest.

Table 2. *Response to Aliens and Nest-Mates by a Colony*

Ant towards which responses were made	*n*	Mean aggr. responses	Significance	Mean responses			
				Lick	Threat	Seize	Drag
A. Alien	15	15.5	A & B: P<.001	8.3	13	2.4	0.1
B. Nest-mate away 24 hrs.	15	5.4	B & C: Not sig.	9.8	5.2	0.2	0
C. Nest-mate away <1 min.	20	4.1	C & D: P<.001	6.2	4.0	0.1	0
D. Nest-mate within nest	10	0.1		0.1	0.1	0	0

What is surprising about these results is the amount of aggression evoked by ants returning to their own nests—an apparent breakdown in colony cohesion. Of course, the response pattern to aliens is different from that to returning nest-mates. Very little seizing and fewer threat responses are shown towards the latter, although they evoke a considerable amount of licking. However, some aggressive responses are evoked fairly consistently by ants returning to their own nests. Note that virtually no aggression is shown towards a nest-mate within the nest.

The length of time for which a nest-mate is away does not affect the aggression shown towards it. On the basis of odour alone, it seems doubtful whether there can be any odour difference between an ant within the nest and one which is away for less than a minute. The factor eliciting aggression in these circumstances seems to be the situation "ant-entering-the-nest." Foragers, too, evoke aggression on re-entering their nests. Aggression is shown on entry but not later. The factor here is one of orientation to a particular part of the nest. The entrance is probably detectable visually as an area of higher light intensity.

The association of licking with aggressive behaviour is interesting. Licking, as Table 2 shows, is rarely shown towards ants within the nest, but returning nest-mates are often licked for considerable periods. The mean duration of licking bouts shown towards returned nest-mates isolated for 24 hours is 30 seconds ($n = 147$), but towards aliens is only 6½ seconds ($n = 125$). Response sequences show that licking tends to be linked with threat rather than with seizing or dragging. But licking and threat probably do not share causal factors to a great extent, for threat scores show a negative correlation with licking scores. Licking seems to be elicited by some of the factors evoking aggression, e.g. "ant-entering-nest," but also by other, quite different factors. Ants outside the nest would be likely to adsorb foreign odours on to their body surfaces and this odour difference may evoke both licking and aggression in other ants. The function of licking in this context may be to reincorporate a returned ant into the colony by removing any adventitious odours. Aggression shown towards a returned ant, on the other hand, tends to disrupt the colony. The fact that much licking and little aggression is shown towards returned nest-mates, but much aggression and less licking towards aliens, indicates that the total response pattern tends to reincorporate nest-mates but exclude aliens from the colony.

Colony odour seems to be learned by nest members. An individual seems to learn the collective odour of the colony by a rapid learning process similar to "imprinting" soon after emergence from the cocoon. Thus pupae can be transferred to other nests and the adults which emerge show allegiance to the nest in which they find themselves. In this way, *fusca* slave-ants develop an allegiance to the *Formica sanguinea* colony into which they emerge. However, some experiments I did on the ant *Lasius flavus* suggest that some further learning of colony odour is possible, since one colony may be habituated to some extent to the odour of another, if exposed to an airstream which has passed through the other colony. Ants are probably continually habituating to the slight variations in the odour of their nest-mates. If an ant is separated from its nest-mates, the habituation decays and it may show a few aggressive responses itself when it returns to the nest. In very primitive ponerine ants, Haskins and Haskins[4] found evidence that unless all members of a given community are in relatively continuous contact schisms will develop so that isolated colony-portions become permanently hostile to the rest. This may be due simply to a decay in habituation or to metabolic changes altering individual odours to which all ants would normally habituate.

SUMMARY

It is clear that aggression is primarily channelled into extra-colonial encounters by the development of distinct colony odours, but that the complexity of the factors governing aggressiveness results in apparent exceptions to this. This complexity is the result of the nature of the colony odour itself with its probable tendency to vary with time and the likelihood of small differences occurring between individuals.

REFERENCES

1. Butler, C. G., and Free, J. B. 1952. *Behaviour,* **4**: 262–92.
2. Fielde, A. 1904. *Biol. Bull.,* **7**: 227–50.
3. Free, J. B. 1955. *Behaviour,* **7**: 233–40.
3a. ———. 1958. *Behaviour,* **12**: 233–42.
3b. ———. 1961. *Anim. Behav.,* **9**: 193–6.
4. Haskins, C. P., and Haskins, E. F. 1950. *Ann. Ent. Soc. Amer.,* **43**: 461–91.
5. Kalmus, H., and Ribbands, C. R. 1952. *Proc. Roy. Soc., Lond., B.,* **140**: 50–9.
6. Lecomte, J. 1952. *Behavior,* **4**: 60–67.
7. Lin, N. 1963. *Behavior,* **20**: 115–33.
8. Michener, C. D., and Lange, R. B. 1958. *Insectes Sociaux,* **5**: 379–401.
9. Rau, P. 1930. *J. compar. Psychol.* **10**: 267–86.
10. Sakagami, S. F. 1960. *Insectes Sociaux,* **7**: 231–49.
11. Vowles, D. M. 1952. *Adv. Sci.,* **10**: 18–21.
12. Wallis, D. I. 1962. *Anim. Behav.,* **10**: 105–11.
12a. ———. 1962. *Anim. Behav.,* **10**: 267–74.

7

AGONISTIC BEHAVIOR OF MICE AND RATS: A REVIEW

J. P. SCOTT
Department of Psychology, Bowling Green State University

This article originally appeared in the American Zoologist, **6**: *683–701, 1966 (excerpted). It is reprinted with the permission of the American Society of Zoologists.*

This paper might very well be called "Aggression Revisited." In 1951 Fredericson and I published a review, "The Causes of Fighting in Mice and Rats," and in 1958 I expanded that material into a book, "Aggression," which outlined the causes and consequences of fighting behavior and its implications for human affairs. As I pointed out then, aggression is a poor scientific term and chiefly functions as a convenient handle to relate phenomena described in more objective terms to practical human problems. What we are really concerned with is agonistic behavior, a behavioral system composed of behavior patterns having the common function of adaptation to situations involving physical conflict between members of the same species. We cannot analyze fighting behavior without also studying the alternate behavior patterns of escape, threat, "freezing," defensive posture, dominance and subordination, etc.

Since we wrote these two general papers there has been much new research. Some of the original material has been confirmed, or even rediscovered, and some questions raised in our original paper still remain unanswered. However, in rereading the 1951 paper, which reviewed all the work done on mice and rats up to that time, I find that, although much has been added, very little needs to be revised in the light of subsequent work.

The principal advances which have been made since 1951 include much additional material on the fighting behavior of wild rats, which have been studied by Calhoun,[18a] Barnett,[6a, 6b] and Eibl-Eibesfeldt.[23a] Ulrich[58] has conducted a long series of experiments on pain-elicited fighting in laboratory rats, using the foot-shock technique developed by O'Kelly and Steckle.[48]

Additional observations have been made on the behavior of wild house mice by Brown.[16] King[35, 35a, 36, 37] did a series of experiments on early experience in relation to fighting, and Denenberg[22] has recently added some important discoveries. Bronson and Eleftheriou[14, 14a, 14b] have been concerned with the physiological effects of fighting, and other authors have experimented with the modification of fighting behavior by drugs. Finally, there has been some evidence and considerable speculation about the effects of fighting in a broad sense, in relation to dispersal and evolution.

BASIC BEHAVIOR PATTERNS

Comparison of patterns in mice and rats. At the time of our original review, the patterns of agonistic behavior of the rat had been studied in only a very superficial fashion, and almost entirely in laboratory strains. Since then Calhoun's[18a] detailed monograph of the behavior of wild rats in a semi-natural enclosure and Barnett's[6, 6b] excellent studies of the fighting of caged wild rats have appeared. It is now possible to make a meaningful comparison between the behavior of this species and that of the house mouse. This material is summarized in Table 1.

To begin with, the behavior of wild rats is considerably more elaborate than that previously reported for the laboratory strains, while that of wild mice is essentially the same as that originally described for the laboratory strains. The result is to emphasize certain major behavioral differences between the two species which in turn are reflected in their respective societies formed under semi-natural conditions.

Perhaps the most fundamental of these differences is the complete absence of playful fighting in young mice. In rats this begins at about 17 days of age[12] and continues up through the juvenile period, when it is replaced by serious fighting.[30] Adult rats, but not mice, show a special pattern of behavior toward juveniles which Calhoun has called "psychological drubbing." The old rat pounces on the young one and knocks it down, striking it with the feet but not biting. Females show this behavior toward their own young at the time of weaning, and adults of both sexes attack strange juveniles in this way.

Table 1. *Patterns of agonistic behavior in rats and mice*

Rats	Mice
Whirling of head and/or body toward other animals	
"Prancing" approach	"Mincing"
Extending heads and necks	
Tooth chattering	
Supersonic cries	
Sidewise approach and hip throwing	
Rearing and pushing ("boxing"), biting	
Force other rat onto back	
Striking with teeth	Striking with teeth
Chasing	Chasing
Squealing (when bitten)	Squealing (when bitten or threatened)
Rearing and holding other rat off (defensive posture)	Rearing upright, forepaws rigidly extended (defensive posture)
Rolling and tumbling (two animals)	Rolling and scratching (two animals)
Hair fluffing	Hair fluffing
	Tail rattling
Running away	Running away
	Freezing
Roll on back	Roll on back, feet outstretched
Move forward, neck and tail outstretched, forefeet crouching (subordinate posture)	
"Drubbing" (directed toward young)	
Playful fighting	
Pouncing	
Nipping	
Rolling on back	

The result is that the young rat has considerable experience with these two kinds of fighting by the time it is old enough to exhibit serious fighting. Playful fighting should lead to the improvement of skill in fighting, although we have no experimental evidence on this point, and the attacks on juveniles should lead to pressure for dispersal. Since neither of these behavior patterns is present in mice, one would expect (a) that mice would acquire skill in fighting at a later age, and (b) that there would be less pressure for dispersal of the juveniles.

One of the characteristic patterns of mouse behavior is the defensive posture assumed by a beaten mouse, in which the animal rears up and sits still with the forepaws rigidly extended toward the attacker, who rushes in and attacks with the teeth, sometimes rearing in a hunched posture before striking but never assuming the same posture as the defensive animal. Rats, on the other hand, frequently rear up and face each other, appearing to push each other with their paws and sometimes striking with their teeth. They also utter supersonic cries.[1, 23b] The result is an ambiguous situation from the viewpoint of the observer, there being three different possibilities of interpretation: (1) both rats assume a defensive posture, (2) both rats attack, and (3) one assumes a defensive posture while the other attacks. This ambiguity has some importance when the results of pain-induced aggression are assessed, as will be seen later, as well as being a qualitative difference in the behavior exhibited by the two species. The only condition in which two mice rear up together is when both are given foot-shock.[56]

Another distinct difference is tail-rattling (or tail-switching) which is commonly heard and seen in mice which are hesitating before an attack. This behavior pattern has never been reported in rats. It suggests a signal conveying a warning or threat, similar to growling in carnivores, but there is no evidence that other mice react to it in this way.

Dominance and subordination. Both species are alike in that they appear to be incapable of developing dominance-subordination relationships which permit animals to live together without injury. The typical organization is one in which there is one dominant and uninjured animal in the group, with all the rest subordinate to him and bearing wounds. The subordinate animals avoid each other and do not develop any rank toward each other.

This contrasts with the dominance-subordination hierarchies developed in many animals which normally live together in groups. In chickens or dogs, for example, fighting is reduced to threat and avoidance, with no serious injury in most cases. While fighting is reduced in repeated conflicts between rats and mice, each fight usually ends with the beaten animal being bitten. The behavioral repertories of the two species thus seem to be deficient in harmless threat signals.

Grant and Chance[30] have attempted to analyze the playful fighting of young albino rats in terms of dominance and subordination. In most pairs, one member will consistently beat another a majority of times, but the differences in the win ratios are often slight (e.g., 48:42), and there is no evidence that a consistent habit of dominance-subordination is being formed. Furthermore, these playful fights end with one rat being held on its back. In the adult fights, the beaten rat rolls over on its feet and is bitten in the sacral region as he attempts to escape. Playful fighting does not lead to the formation of stable adult dominance order in which injurious fighting is controlled. In Calhoun's[18a] colony, almost every adult animal showed bite wounds.

DEVELOPMENT OF FIGHTING

Mice. It was long discovered that young mice would begin to fight a stranger between 32 and 36 days of age, but that mice reared together in the same litter would not begin to fight until much later, and sometimes not for very long periods.[50] This delay was attributed to the phenomenon of passive inhibition. Since then, Brown[16] has found that when wild mice are reared by a single pair of animals in a cage, the fighting is of low intensity, with few bite wounds, and that usually, but not always, the original male dominates the younger ones. The earliest instance of fighting occurred when a young male was 55 days of age, confirming observations on the domestic strains.

Rats. Bolles and Woods[12] have described the origin of playful fighting in groups of albino rats as beginning at 21 days, and Grant and Chance[30] have studied the further development of playful fighting in groups of albinos. It is more common between 3 and 6 weeks of age than it is between 9 and 12 weeks, and toward the end of the period the fights become more severe with a greater likelihood of biting.

Calhoun[18a] has confirmed the importance of playful fighting in young wild rats and describes a similar course of development. Adults begin "trouncing" attacks upon the young juveniles when they are about 45 days of age, and this is also the time when females begin to drive their own young away from their burrows. The young rats are never bitten by adults while under 50 days of age and are rarely bitten until 86 days, when they become adults themselves and begin to take part in sexual behavior. Thereafter the number of wounds suffered by the adults increases until they reach maximum levels at approximately 266 days in males and 368 days in females. The average number of bite wounds on any adult male in Calhoun's colony was 9.5. Females averaged 7.5, an almost equally large number. These figures suggest a high incidence of injurious fighting in the population.

Finally, Hutchinson *et al.*[32] tested the response of albino rats to foot shock at various ages. They got no reaction at 24 days but obtained a small amount at 33 days. From this point on the incidence rose to a maximum at 93 days, when rats respond by fighting almost 90% of the time.

We may conclude that playful fighting and serious fighting are two different phenomena, and that during the period between weaning at 3 weeks and adulthood at 12 weeks the incidence of playful fighting decreases and that of serious fighting increases, although it by no means reaches a maximum at this point. These results give guidelines for future experiments, in that rats should not be considered to be adults with respect to the development of fighting behavior until they are approximately 12 weeks of age.

STIMULI ELICITING FIGHTING

In a recent publication Lorenz[44] stated "If we put together, into the same container, two sticklebacks, lizards, robins, rats, monkeys, or boys, who have not had any previous experience with each other, they will fight." This statement would be literally true only if we insert the word "sometimes" before "fight." It is very rare in any experimental situation that 100% of the paired individuals can be induced to fight. To begin with, fighting occurs much more frequently if males are involved than females. In addition, there are for every species certain situations and stimuli which are effective in producing fighting behavior, and others which produce no effect. In our earlier work with fighting mice we discovered only one stimulus which would reliably induce fighting in an inexperienced mouse; namely, an attack by another mouse, and we concluded that pain was a major component in this sort of stimulation.[50]

Pain-elicited aggression. This reaction, which is almost reflex in nature, appears very early in development. As soon as a young mouse develops teeth it will turn around and bite at anything which pinches its tail. As an adult a mouse will turn and strike at an attacker which bites it. Similarly, the pain of electric shock is highly effective in causing two rats to fight.[59] Pain therefore acts as a primary stimulus or releaser which stimulates fighting in an almost reflex fashion. In our original paper I stated that other eliciting stimuli, including the sight of another animal running away, were also possible and might be defined by careful study. Eibl-Eibesfeldt[23b] misinterpreted these findings and attributed to me a theory that a rat or mouse reacts aggressively "toward another rat or mouse because of pain inflicted by a nestmate early in life" and that "rats that have had no early experience of pain inflicted by another rat should be completely unaggressive." Eibl-Eibesfeldt then 'disproved' this statement by raising rats together and noting that they seldom fought each other but still attacked strangers vigorously. I thus had the interesting experience of having a theory attributed to me that I had not made, and disproved by experiments which I had already done. I later corresponded with Eibl-Eibesfeldt and discovered that the initial misunderstanding was based on the use of the word "primary" in different senses in German and English. This does, however, bring up the problem of what primary stimuli or releasers other than pain may elicit fighting.

Visual Stimuli. In an extensive series of cinematographic analyses Banks[4] was unable to find any reliable indices of behavior preceding a fight (except that it was often preceded by investigation), indicating that visual signals have no importance. Beeman had already shown that fighting could take place in the absence of visual stimuli by working with blinded mice. Recently it has been discovered that many of the inbred mouse strains are congenitally blind, and indeed the C3H strain on which Ginsburg and I based some of our early conclusions about strain differences was probably blind. This strain was characteristically aggressive in the sense that fighting was easily elicited but tended to be inefficient in winning a fight.

Lagerspetz and Mettala[39] have recently induced fighting in mice by the use of a bottle brush. Using 34 albino mice more than 12 months of age, they found that these unusually aggressive animals would attack even a motionless brush and increased their attacks if the brush was rotated and still more if it was swung against the fighters similarly to the technique used in dangling live mice. Adding painful stimulation through foot shock to this situation tended to reduce the amount of attacking, if anything, with perhaps some tendency for more attacks with greater intensity of shock. The painful stimulation from a different direction thus seemed to distract the animals rather than cause them to attack.

These results indicate that purely visual stimuli are effective under certain conditions, since the animals are more likely to attack an object in motion.

Sex. Mice, whether wild or domestic, do not appear to fight more frequently because of the presence of the opposite sex, and males do not fight for the possession of females. Indeed, the presence of a female may serve to inhibit fighting between a pair of males with a well-established habit of fighting.[29]

In rats, sexual behavior indirectly increases the frequency of fighting in the following way.[18a] A female in estrus marks the area around the entrance to her nest or burrow with urine and this attracts males, who likewise mark the area and roll on it. If two males are attracted at the same time, they are likely to fight, but once copulation has begun there is no interference by other males, and the same female may be mounted by numerous males in succession. Barnett[6b] similarly finds that caged wild rats do not fight over females.

Unlike appearance. Bauer[8] systematically stimulated mice of two inbred strains to fight, using the dangling method. These strains were albino and black in appearance, and a significantly greater number of attacks was elicited by the unlike animals. This probably resulted from the fact that the unlike animals presented a greater degree of change, and hence greater stimulation, and it is probable that there were differences in odor and behavior as well as differences in appearance.

This raises the problem of what it is about strangeness that elicits fighting, as strangeness is a relative condition dependent upon previous experience.

Other possibilities. It is possible that the supersonic cries emitted by rats act as eliciting stimuli. The presence of such cries in mice has not yet been verified. Another stimulus which is highly important to rodents is that of odor, and we are now beginning to be able to work with this stimulus effectively. Some of Beeman's unpublished work[50] indicates that males still fight when the olfactory nerves are cut, and in any case it is difficult to see how such a stimulus could act except to enable discrimination between strange and familiar animals.

TERRITORIALITY

Mice. In an early paper[49] I attempted to predict the social organization which should be developed by wild house mice on the basis of observed behavior patterns in the species. This prediction was made on the general theory that social behavior determines social organization. The data were based on naturally-formed populations of inbred mice observed in large multiple-escape pens. Each population started with a mated pair, and one pair from the first litter was permitted to survive. All other young were removed at weaning. Thus there were only two permanent couples in a relatively large area. Fighting appeared between the males, but there was no evidence that it was associated with any particular area. Males were frequently found in the same nest, although they may have been previously observed fighting. No males were ever found in nests in which there were females with young, and I concluded that the nest was guarded as a temporary territory by the females, and that if territoriality exists at all in males it should be extremely nebulous.

It should be remembered that these observations were made in a multiple-escape pen in which each box had at least three escape passages and that I was attempting to predict behavior as it would exist in mice in a free population. I did not see how mice, as nocturnal animals and living in a situation in which there were large natural objects on every hand, could effectively patrol large territorial boundaries.

Since, then, territoriality has been reported to develop in certain situations by various authors. Eibl-Eibesfeldt[23] reported that house mice observed in a barracks developed group territories, and stated that mice which were closely related formed a "Grossfamilie" whose members did not fight with each other but attacked strange individuals, this resulting in a territorial arrangement. This observation has been confirmed at least once by Crowcroft,[20] who described a case in which a group of one male, two females, and fourteen young of various ages lived peacefully together for a period of 12 months, although they would attack strangers of either sex. Crowcroft[20a] also reported a case of territoriality which developed in a large pen about 18 ft. in diameter. In this were 14 nest boxes, and he introduced 28 male and 28 female mice so that there was one box available for each 4 animals, or two pairs. The mice actually arranged themselves in the following way. Thirteen of the males and 19 of the females lived in one box with considerable fighting among themselves. Another 8 males lived in another box. Finally, 7 of the males occupied one or two boxes and defended the area around them as a territory. Each of these territories contained one or two females. What would have developed if the females had begun to bear young and ejected the males was not reported. In any case the size of the territories defended was very small, being limited to the nest boxes and a space two or three feet around them.

Anderson and Hill[3] find that if mice are placed in a row of connecting pens with only one small passage between them, the male resident in one of these pens may guard the opening and thus set up a territory with effective boundaries.

In all these cases, the territory is quite small compared to the home range as established by trapping of wild mice under free conditions. While mice do not move far from their home localities, they do frequently roam over distances as long as 30 ft.[16] The ability of a mouse to guard effectively a territory other than a nest is dependent upon the presence of physical barriers, and in no case extends more than a few feet. It may, therefore, be concluded that house mice do have the capacity to develop territories under special conditions, but this is done in no regular fashion. Territories developed by the females are based on nests, are only defended by lactating females, and thus are temporary in nature.

Rats. Eibl-Eibesfeldt[23b] states that wild Norway rats live together peacefully in large packs and attack any rat not a member of the group. This does not agree with Calhoun's[18a] observations of wild Norway rats over a period of approximately 2½ years. Young rats in this group regularly became involved in serious fights as soon as they became mature. Bite wounds were regularly found on the adult males of the colony. Territoriality was almost entirely confined to nests and harborage boxes. Lactating females would eject other females from their nests, and animals were almost invariably attacked and ejected if they attempted to enter a nest box occupied by another animal. Rats would be submissive in a strange burrow although they might be dominant outside, but the low ranking individuals were more frequently ejected. In some cases the males would defend a territory around the mouth of a burrow and would permit no other male to enter. In other cases, a group of males would show dominance-subordination relationships in an area, but no defense of territory.

Evidence of territoriality varied a great deal from year to year. In one year one male dominated most of the pen and none of the other males born in the same year ever showed any territorial defense or clear-cut dominance relationships. In another year some seven males showed a degree of territorial defense around the burrows that they inhabited.

As with mice, the territorial defense appears to be highly irregular except in the defense of nests by lactating females. On the basis of experiments with caged wild rats Barnett[6b] concludes that the fighting between males is territorial because when a strange male is introduced into a cage the home male attacks and usually wins. The situation probably corresponds to the defense of nests seen in Calhoun's rats. Barnett states that the relationship between territory and home range is unknown, but all the evidence indicates that the effectively defended territory is very small compared to the home range. In any case, there is no evidence of rats defending precisely defined boundaries outside burrows and nests as is the case in prairie dogs and many species of birds.

HEREDITY AND AGONISTIC BEHAVIOR

Differences between the sexes. There are large differences in fighting behavior between males and females in both mice and rats, presumably caused by the male sex hormone.[50] Fighting between females is more common in wild rats and mice than it is between females of domestic strains, in which it is often difficult to elicit. In mice there is some evidence that castrated males and females respond differentially to injections of the male hormone. The fact that this has no effect on fighting behavior of a female,[57] although it modifies sexual behavior, indicates that the nervous system is essentially different in the two sexes. Modification of adult sexual behavior by injections of hormones in early infancy has been established, but no systematic work has been reported on its effects on fighting.

Differences between strains and individuals. Heredity produces important differences in fighting behavior between mouse strains, some being more easily excited to fight than others and some strains being more capable of winning than others.[50] This conclusion still stands, and much evidence has been added since.

For several years the C57B1/10 and BALB/C strains of inbred

mice were used at the Jackson Laboratory as the standard strains for experimental work on fighting.[53, 53a] Whenever the two strains were compared, differences in agonistic behavior were found, no matter whether the testing technique was dangling,[8] latency to initiation of fighting,[29, 35] or competition for food.[27] However, the differences took quite different and sometimes opposite forms, depending on the test used and the previous experience of the animals. The C57BI/10 strain showed more attacking and less acquiescent behavior when subjected to the simulated mild attacks of the dangling technique,[8] but when Fredericson and Birnbaum[27] left pairs of the two strains together overnight, the BALB/C's killed their opponents in 8 out of 10 cases.

Using two entirely different strains, Levine[41] found large differences in reaction to early social experience. Lindzey[43] obtained a linear order of dominance between strains in their tube competition test. C3H's decisively defeated DBA/8's and these were in turn decisively defeated by the A/alb strain. Bevan[11] found differences between castrated SWR and C3H males in response to androgens. In a selection experiment based on a rating scale of fighting between pairs of Swiss albinos, Lagerspetz[38] found a significant separation between strains in the first three generations, although there was considerable overlap. The aggressive strain also showed higher activity in a running wheel, higher ambulation in an open-field test, and lower defecation scores. This indicates that aggressive performance involves a number of different traits. On the negative side, Martin and Andrewartha[45] found no effect of the tailless gene on fighting success in wild mice.

Not as much detailed work has been done with rats, but Ulrich[58] and his colleagues have found large strain differences using the footshock technique. Uyeno[60] obtained large differences between the F_1's in a selection experiment involving food competition. Genetic differences in agonistic behavior are therefore important, ubiquitous, and complex. Any experiment on agonistic behavior should be repeated on at least two different strains, if at all possible, in order to obtain some idea of the generality of results.

Despite all these reports of important strain differences, agonistic behavior is yet to be analyzed in breeding experiments in rats and mice, although results have been reported for both playful fighting and dominance-subordination relationships in dogs.[51] Nor has any attempt been made to look for extreme differences between strains of rats and mice.

MOTIVATION AND PHYSIOLOGY

After reviewing the evidence then available[49a] I concluded that there was no physiological evidence of any spontaneous stimulation for fighting arising within the body. I further concluded that there was no such thing as a simple "instinct for fighting." There is, however, an internal physiological mechanism which has only to be stimulated to produce fighting. This finding has important theoretical implications because it means that under the proper environmental conditions an animal is not driven to fight, nor will he suffer from emotional disturbances because of repression.

While the physiology of fighting has not been thoroughly explored, and most of our facts come from a few species of mammals, it is clear that the two hormones associated with fighting, adrenalin and cortisone, are the results of fighting rather than its causes. Injection of adrenalin does not produce anger, although it accompanies it, and the secretion of cortisone is the result of almost any sort of stressful situation, including fighting. The only remaining possibility is that the sex hormone, testosterone, could directly stimulate brain cells controlling fighting behavior. Injections of this hormone into the brain will produce sexual and maternal behavior in rats[25] but there is no report that it produces fighting. It must be concluded that the male hormone simply lowers the threshold to external stimulation. Injection of estrogen into intact male mice has no effect on fighting.[31]

Some recent experiments by Everett and Wiegand[24] indicate that if mice are treated with drugs which act as inhibitors of monoamine-oxidase, and are then given dopa, these animals will become irritated and aggressive, accompanied by a marked rise of dopa and dopamine in the brain. While these amines are the precursors of norepinephrine, Everett believes that they themselves produce the primary effect, since norepinephrine rises only to the normal level. In order to demonstrate that this effect mimics a normal mechanism for the origin of spontaneous internal stimulation it would have to be shown that the body in some way produces inhibitors of monoamineoxidase which permit the accumulation of the above amines. It would also be necessary to demonstrate that the effects observed in Everett's experiment were not the side effects of the administration of excessive amounts of protein. These findings do, however, give some interesting leads regarding the biochemistry of fighting behavior.

In a recent paper, Myer and White[47] showed that rats learned to run faster through a T-maze in order to attack and kill mice, and implied that these animals were satisfying an inner drive. Aside from the fact that this behavior is much more likely to be predation (rats sometimes eat mice) than it is to be a distortion of normal agonistic behavior directed against a member of the same species, Fredericson[26a] long ago demonstrated that mice would learn to attack more rapidly provided they were separated immediately so that neither mouse was defeated. In this symposium Thompson has shown that fighting can be used as a reinforcer for operant behavior in the Siamese fighting fish. These experiments show that fighting (and winning) is rewarding, but they give no information regarding the antecedent physiological state of the animal.

The fact that fighting is a rewarding activity does not demonstrate the existence of spontaneous internal stimulation any more than the fact that most people find the odor of roses pleasant indicates that there is spontaneous internal stimulation to go out and smell the flowers. This confusion arises from the fact that "drive" has been operationally defined by behavioral results based on the physiology of ingestive behavior which have no relevance to the physiology of fighting behavior.

In the case of eating, a decline in blood sugar will induce hunger contractions and also stimulate an appetite control center in the brain, with the result that an elevation of blood sugar under these conditions will produce a rewarding effect. A similar physiological mechanism involving physiological changes arising without external stimulation would have to be discovered in agonistic behavior in order to demonstrate spontaneous internal stimulation.

A second line of evidence which is sometimes used as an argument for the existence of "spontaneous drive" is the fact that fighting behavior can be elicited by electrical stimulation of brain centers, particularly those in the hypothalamus. The stimulation in this case actually comes from the outside through the electrodes inserted by the experimenter and no more indicates the existence of spontaneous stimulation than does the electrical stimulation of movement in a frog's leg in a nerve muscle preparation.

This evidence does, however, give us information about the neural organization of agonistic behavior. With a few exceptions, most of this work has been done on the cat, and an excellent recent review is given by Kaada.[33] He concludes that the hypothalamus is an important structure for the excitation and integration of autonomic somatomotor and endocrine effects seen in agonistic behavior.

The chief advances from brain ablation studies have come through the further localization of excitatory and inhibitory areas in the brain. Contrary to the early work of Bard and Mountcastle,[5] recent evidence shows that the amygdala has an excitatory function and that the inhibitory area of the forebrain is located in the septum, the latter results being based on rats. It is still clear that there is a balance between excitatory and inhibitory areas in the brain, and Delgado in this symposium has emphasized the point that many areas of the brain affect agonistic behavior.

Supporting the importance of external stimulation, recent work with electrical stimulation has shown a convergence of cutaneous, auditory and visual sensory input to the regions of the hypothalamus controlling the defense reactions in cats.

As pointed out above, our evidence concerning physiological reactions connected with agonistic behavior is quite limited, but all of it is in the direction that there is no physiological mechanism providing for spontaneous internal stimulation, but, on the contrary, much evidence of neural-mechanisms which permit the magnification and prolongation of the effects of external stimulation. This is not to deny the possibility that some species may someday be discovered in which physiological mechanisms for spontaneous internal stimulation can be demonstrated, but only to argue that theories concerning physiological processes must be based on physiological evidence. As Brown and Hunsperger[15] put it in their review on the motivation of agonistic behavior, "non-neural concepts of drive or tendency are considered to be superfluous and misleading."

While we still have relatively little neurological evidence regarding agonistic behavior in rats and mice, the behavioral evidence is that these animals can either live for long periods in a relatively peaceful manner without evidence of behavioral disturbance, or they can live in a condition of constant fighting and turmoil, depending on their previous history.

From an evolutionary viewpoint, almost any sort of physiological mechanism would be possible provided it led to the survival of the species concerned. It is difficult to see how an internal drive for fighting behavior could be adaptive, since it would result in both the individual and the species being unnecessarily put into danger. Agonistic behavior primarily serves as an adaptation to the external circumstances rather than to a universal inner need. Other species of animals should be investigated, not only behaviorally (it is impossible to determine physiological mechanisms by behavioral evidence alone) but physiologically. These should include a wide range of rodents, from the highly aggressive woodchucks which normally do not tolerate members of their own species except briefly during mating and the rearing of the young, to the prairie dogs which are capable of living in large colonies in a reasonably peaceful manner. It is possible that a quite different picture of physiological mechanisms would emerge from these additional data.

Physiological effects of fighting. In contrast to the lack of physiological changes preceding fighting, physiological effects following fighting are well established. In rats, Barnett[6] has shown that males living in groups in which fighting takes place have adrenals about one-third larger than animals living under peaceful conditions. Enlarged adrenals occur in both dominant and subordinate animals. In another experiment Barnett[7] showed that fighting has the effect of lowering the amount of liver glycogen and elevating the amount of blood glucose. The effects were greatest in rats which were consistently attacked by a superior fighter.

In mice, Bronson and Eleftheriou[14, 14a, 14b] find that repeated defeats by a trained fighter cause the defeated animal to lose weight, to increase the adrenal size in proportion to the body length, and to increase the amount of corticosterone in the blood plasma. The weight of the seminal vesicles also decreases, indicating a diminution of the animal's capacity for mating behavior. Similarly, Vandenberg[61] found that CFW mice placed in groups of four showed lowered eosinophil counts, with subordinate animals lower than dominant ones.

Bronson and Eleftheriou find that the maximum effect on corticosterone occurs within one hour after the fight, but its effects may last over 24 hours. If the animal is attacked daily, recovery occurs faster and faster so that a chronically-defeated animal comes back to normal within a few hours. Furthermore, if a mouse is attacked for several days in succession and thereafter is exposed only to the sight of a fighter, the hormonal level remains high and, in fact, stays somewhat higher than that of mice which are actually attacked. This demonstrates that the threat of injury has greater physiological effect than injury itself, once injury has taken place. Since it is well known that these physiological reactions are part of the reparatory process following injury, but that prolonged stress is physiologically harmful, this result has strong implications for the existence of physiological damage resulting from psychological stress. Prolonged experiences of this kind might well result in psychosomatic symptoms.

Corticosterone itself has little effect on the fighting of males when liberated by injections of ACTH.[13] If it has an effect, it is to increase "neural excitability" slightly and thus make the animal more responsive to all sorts of stimulation.

EFFECTS OF EARLY SOCIAL EXPERIENCE

Non-competitive fighting. All experimenters agree that mice and rats raised in groups, whether in experimental situations or naturally-formed colonies, fight very little compared to animals brought together after being reared separately. Kahn[34a] found that males which had been raised with their mothers and littermates until 59 days of age showed much less fighting than mice which had been isolated at 21 days of age. The isolated animals showed three times as much attacking behavior and much less running away.

Using still another technique, the round robin method of fighting until dominance is determined, Levine[41] found that group-reared mice which were tested against a different strain showed less fighting than did isolated animals treated in the same way. These mice were not tested against their own strain, but each strain was affected somewhat differently by early social experience, although always in the direction of reduction of fighting.

The effects of early social experience upon fighting in mice thus appear to be complex, depending on the kind of early social experience, its length, and the kind of test situation that is used. On balance, most of the results are consistent with the finding that mice raised in groups for long periods are not only more peaceable among themselves, but are less aggressive towards strange animals than are mice which have been isolated since approximately 20 days. This effect can be explained by the process of passive inhibition,[49a] i.e., a habit of not-fighting can be built up simply by not fighting, and that this habit becomes associated with certain environmental situations.

An even more dramatic effect of early experience is produced by fostering mice on rats a few days after birth and rearing them with young albino rats.[22] Twelve pairs of mice reared in this way until 85 days or older showed no fighting when given the latency test. This suggests that the mice have become socialized (imprinted) on rats and no longer recognize their own species as suitable objects for attack. It is also possible that the non-aggressiveness is the result of living with much larger animals which normally exhibit playful fighting.

In contrast, cross-fostering between strains of aggressive and non-aggressive mice produced little effect, except that fostering appeared to reduce aggressiveness in both strains.[40]

Competition over food. Fredericson[26] demonstrated that either male or female mice would compete for food when hungry, provided the piece of food could be held by one mouse.[28] This competition is object-directed, and involves none of the prolonged violence associated with other forms of fighting. If young mice of 29 to 35 days (the age when males normally begin to attack strangers) were given experience with food competition, they would compete for food even when not hungry at 72 days of age. By contrast, control animals given no early experience would compete for food only after they were made hungry. Thus, there is a definite carry-over of early reactions associated with food to a later period in development.[26b]

Uyeno[60] found that a dominant strain of rats became more dominant if fostered on parents from a submissive strain, in a competition for food.

Effects of severe defeat. Kahn[34] subjected male mice to a severe defeat by trained fighters at three different ages: 21, 35, and 60 days. Thirty days after being defeated they were tested by the dangling method and compared with littermate controls which had not been previously defeated. All the groups showed less attacking, more escape behavior, more squeaking, and more tendency to adopt the defense posture than did the controls. However, the adult group was much less severely affected, and showed behavior which was significantly different from controls only in the defense posture.

With respect to the animals defeated at younger ages, there were no significant differences between the two, and it may be concluded that severe defeat has a pronounced effect either at 21 days, when the animals are still unweaned, or at 35 days, when mice normally begin to attack strangers. It is difficult to evaluate the results completely because the effects of the attacks on the younger animals were much more severe, and the differential results might indicate only greater primary injuries rather than greater sensitivity at the younger ages. Nevertheless, the older animals do seem to be more resistant to defeat, and show less aftereffects.

SOCIAL DISORGANIZATION

The factor of social disorganization is now recognized as a major cause of destructive violence, not only among rodents but in other mammalian societies and even among human beings.[49b]

Calhoun's[18] original experiment in rats produced a disorganized population by introducing a large number of strange Norway rats into the resident population of a Baltimore city block. The result was a greatly increased mortality, both among the residents and the strangers, with the result that the population sank to a level below that before the strangers were introduced.

Most of the studies of fighting in populations of wild rats involve groups of more or less strange individuals trapped and brought together in an enclosure. Even Calhoun's[18a] experimental population reared under semi-natural conditions was started with five pairs of wild rats trapped on a small island. While these animals may have been acquainted with each other previously, it is possible that even this experiment started with a partially-disorganized population, which may account for the high frequency of fighting and wounding observed.

Calhoun's[18b] experiment on population density and social pathology utilized a deliberately-disorganized population composed of 32 or more albino rats. Since tame strains are much more tolerant of each other than wild rats, he was able to maintain a density of 80 adults in a room 10 x 14 ft. Even in these albinos constant fighting occurred, along with many sorts of pathological behavior which could be attributed to social disorganization.

Among mice, Brown[16] worked with two sorts of caged populations of wild strains. When he developed a population from a single mated pair, he found that fighting was sporadic, of low intensity, and that the young males first fought when they were approximately 55 days old. Most of the populations were quite peaceful, there were very few bite wounds, and the original male became dominant over the younger ones. By contrast, when he assembled populations of strange wild mice he observed fierce fighting. Eventually one male became dominant and the rest subordinate, similar to results with groups of strange males in tame strains. In one such disorganized population, composed of four pregnant females and four males, the females attacked and killed three of the males, perhaps in defense of their nests.

These results are similar to the observations of Young[62] on a free population of house mice living in a frame building used as an animal house. They observed only infrequent chasing and squealing, and in their surveys of the population discovered many community nests, including several adults and young of several litters. The relative peacefulness of this organized population contrasts strongly with the severe fighting which breaks out in any group of strange wild or tame mice which are caged together.

We must conclude that social disorganization produced by forced contact between strange individuals is a major factor inducing destructive fighting in these two species. We must also conclude that the vast majority of experimental studies on the induction of fighting have been done under conditions which mimic those of a disorganized population. Hence these are somewhat suspect as a foundation for conclusions regarding normal behavior.

The most valid conclusion from them is that violent destructive fighting is abnormal. The usual situation in a wild population should be a center of food supply penetrated by one or two wandering animals which then populate the region close by with their offspring, and so form an organized society. Contact with strangers under these conditions should be extremely rare, and an occasional wandering individual would in most cases be frightened away without much fighting taking place.

Comparisons with other animals. From this review it is apparent that we have now accumulated a large body of consistent information concerning the causes and effects of agonistic behavior in mice and rats. Similar detailed information is available on only a very few other species, and while certain findings can be generalized, such as the evidence of Ulrich[59] that pain will elicit agonistic behavior in many different species of vertebrates, the patterns of agonistic behavior in mice and rats are limited and specialized in many ways, and it would be a mistake to generalize too widely.

As a general theory, each species of mammal has evolved patterns and physiological mechanisms of agonistic behavior which are related to its own social organization and population dynamics. The wild forms of both rats and mice possess patterns of behavior which do not permit the expression of harmless forms of fighting in permanent social groups. These species apparently cannot develop good dominance-subordination relationships nor have they forms of ritualized fighting. They either fight in a harmful fashion or not at all. Mice, in particular, are capable of living peaceably in large groups provided they have grown up together, and there are many reports of mouse plagues with very high concentrations of individuals. Contrary to the conclusions of Eibl-Eibesfeldt[23] and Steiniger,[54] Calhoun's[18a] observations indicate that wild Norway rats possess this ability to a much more limited degree, especially since the parents attack their juvenile young, and serious fighting goes on between adults with very few exceptions. The result is that populations of rats are definitely limited and rarely rise above levels of moderate density even in highly favorable conditions. Even if we assume that Calhoun's population was partially disorganized, the evidence indicates that the population growth of rats is limited by social fighting, whereas in mice predation is the major controlling mechanism, with social fighting playing a relatively minor role.

Both rats and mice show much simpler systems of agonistic behavior than those developed in many species of highly-social mammals. For example, dogs and wolves show highly-developed agonistic behavior in connection with competition over food and as adults develop definite territories around their dens or homes.[51] As puppies develop in a litter, they develop orders of dominance based on playful fighting and normally maintain these relationships as adults with no serious conflict. Fighting behavior is also related to mating, and Bronson[13] has even been able to develop experimentally the phenomenon of sibling rivalry in this species. Agonistic behavior is thus expressed in a wide variety of patterns, is elicited by many different factors, and can be organized into highly-elaborate relationships. This is also true of the highly-social primates and herd mammals. A thorough understanding of agonistic behavior must, therefore, be based on studies of a large number of different species, and we need more of this information before we can begin to make broad generalizations.

SUMMARY

1. Fighting first develops between strange individuals between 32 and 36 days in both rats and mice. Fighting appears between familiar individuals at much later ages, the earliest being approximately 55 days. Rats do not develop their full capacities for fighting until approximately 12 weeks of age.

2. Pain (either from an attack or an electric shock) is a major eliciting stimulus for fighting in both species. Visual signals are

relatively unimportant. Both food and the presence of an estrous female are distracting rather than eliciting stimuli under most situations.

3. Lactating females guard the nest as a territory in both species. Males may guard a small area with indefinite boundaries around the nest; this is usually smaller than the home range. Territories are unstable and fluctuate rapidly over short periods of time.

4. Genetically-determined differences in agonistic behavior are found between wild and tame strains, between tame strains, and between the sexes. One selection experiment has been reported, but no results from systematic crosses between different strains.

5. There is no evidence for the existence of a physiological mechanism that could produce spontaneous internal stimulation to fight. Rather, there is much evidence that neurophysiological mechanisms exist which magnify and prolong the results of external stimulation.

6. Fighting and the threat of attack modify endocrine responses, especially those connected with the adrenal stress response, over long periods of time. These effects can be psychogenic as well as physiogenic and confirm the possibility of damage due to psychological stress.

7. The effects of early social experience on fighting in mice are complex, depending on the kind of experience, its length, and the kind of test situation used. Mice reared from birth in groups for long periods are more peaceful toward each other and even toward strangers than are mice isolated at approximately 20 days. This is accounted for by the phenomenon of passive inhibition. The development of fighting in mice is strongly inhibited by fostering them on rat mothers and rearing with rat littermates.

8. Social disorganization is a major cause of destructive fighting and mortality in mice and rats. Naturally-formed populations are much more peaceful than those composed of strange animals artificially brought together.

REFERENCES

1. Anderson, J. W. 1952. A preliminary search for ultrasonic sounds produced by mammals. M.S. thesis, University of New Hampshire.
2. Anderson, P. K. 1964. Response of confined *Mus* populations to changes in effective density, and the role of social interaction in the regulation of free living mouse populations. *Am. Zoologist,* **4**: 270 (Abstr.)

3. Anderson, P. K., and Hill, J. L. 1965. *Mus musculus:* experimental induction of territory formation. *Science,* **148**: 1753–55.
4. Banks, E. M. 1962. A time and motion study of prefighting behavior in mice. *Jour. Genet. Psychol.,* **101**: 165–183.
5. Bard, P., and Mountcastle, V. B. 1948. Some forebrain mechanisms involved in expression of rage with special reference to the expression of angry behavior. *Proc. Assoc. Res. Nervous Mental Disease,* **27**: 362–404.
6. Barnett, S. A. 1958. Physiological effects of "social stress" in wild rats. I. The adrenal cortex. *Jour. Psychosomat. Res.,* **3**: 1–11.
6a. ———. 1958. An analysis of social behavior in wild rats. *Proc. Zool. Soc.,* London, **130**: 107–52.
6b. ———. 1963. *The Rat: A Study in Behaviour.* London: Methuen.
7. Barnett, S. A., Eaton, J. C. and McCallum, H. M. 1960. Physiological effects of "social stress" in wild rats. II. Liver glycogen and blood glucose. *Jour. Psychosomat. Res.,* **4**: 251–60.
8. Bauer, F. J. 1956. Genetic and experiential factors affecting social reactions in male mice. *Jour. Comp. and Physiol. Psychol.,* **49**: 359–64.
9. Bevan, J. M., Bevan, W. and Williams, B. F. 1958. Spontaneous aggressiveness in young castrate C3H male mice treated with three dose levels of testosterone. *Physiol. Zool.,* **31**: 284–8.
10. Bevan, W. D., Daves, W. F. and Levy, G. W. 1960. The relation of castration, androgen therapy and pre-test fighting experience to competitive aggression in male C57BL/10 mice. *Animal Behav.,* **8**: 6–12.
11. Bevan, W., Levy, G. W., Whitehouse, J. M. and Bevan, J. M. 1957. Spontaneous aggressiveness in two strains of mice castrated and treated with one of three androgens. *Physiol. Zool.,* **30**: 341–9.
12. Bolles, R. C., and Woods, P. J. 1964. The ontogeny of behavior in the albino rat. *Animal Behav.,* **12**: 427–41.
13. Bronson, F. H. 1966. Private communication.
14. Bronson, F. H., and Eleftheriou, B. E. 1964. Chronic physiological effects of fighting in mice. *Gen. Comp. Endocrinol.,* **4**: 9–14.
14a. ———. 1965. Adrenal response to fighting in mice: separation of physical and psychological causes. *Science,* **147**: 627–8.
14b. ———. 1965. Relative effects of fighting on bound and unbound corticosterone in mice. *Proc. Soc. Exptl. Biol. Med.,* **118**: 146–9.
15. Brown, J. L., and Hunsperger, R. W. 1963. Neuro-ethology and the motivation of agonistic behavior. *Animal Behav.,* **11**: 439–48.
16. Brown, R. Z. 1953. Social behavior, reproduction and population changes in the house mouse *Mus musculus L. Ecol. Monog.,* **23**: 217–40.
17. Cahn, J. 1966. *Private communication.*
18. Calhoun, J. B. 1948. Mortality and movement of brown rats *Rattus norvegicus* in artificially supersaturated populations. *Jour. Wildlife Management,* **12**: 167–72.
18a. ———. 1962. The ecology and sociology of the Norway rat. *Public Health Service Publication No. 1008.* Washington, D.C.
18b. ———. 1962. A "behavioral sink." In *Roots of Behavior.* Edited by E. L. Bliss. New York: Harper.
19. Catlett, R. H. 1961. An evaluation of methods for measuring fighting behavior with special reference to *Mus musculus. Animal Behav.,* **9**: 8–10.

20. Crowcroft, P. 1953. Aggressive behavior in wild house mice *Mus musculus* L. Research report #35, Ministry of Agriculture and Fisheries, Tolworth, Surbiton, Surrey. Mimeographed.

20a. ———. 1955. Territoriality in wild house mice, *Mus musculus*. *Jour. Mammal.,* **36**: 299–301.

21. Davis, D. E., Emlen, J. T. and Stokes, A. W. 1948. Studies on home range in the brown rat. *Jour. Mammal.,* **29**: 207–25.

22. Denenberg, V. H., Hudgens, G. A. and Zarrow, M. X. 1964. Mice reared with rats: modification of behavior by early experience with another species. *Science,* **143**: 380–1.

23. Eibl-Eibesfeldt, I. 1950. Beitrage zur Biologie der Haus- und der Ahrenmaus nebst einigen Beobachtungen an andere Nagern. *Z. Tierpsychol.,* **7**: 558–87.

23a. ———. 1952. Ethologische Unterschiede zwischen Hausratte und Wanderatte. *Verh. Deutsch. Zool. Ges. Freiburg, Zool. Anz., Suppl.,* **17**: 169–80.

23b. ———. 1961. The fighting behavior of animals. *Sci. Am.,* **205**: 112–22.

24. Everett, G. M., and Wiegand, R. G. 1962. Central amines and behavioral states: a critique and new data. *Proc. 1st Int. Pharmacol. Meeting,* **8**: 85–92.

25. Fisher, A. E. 1956. Maternal and sexual behavior induced by intracranial chemical stimulation. *Science,* **124**: 228–9.

26. Fredericson, E. 1950. The effects of food deprivation upon competitive and spontaneous combat in C57 black mice. *Jour. Psychol.,* **29**: 89–100.

26a. ———. 1951. Time and aggression. *Psychol. Rev.,* **58**: 41–51.

26b. ———. 1951. Competition: the effects of infantile experience upon adult behavior. *Jour. Abn. Social Psychol.,* **46**: 406–9.

26c. ———. 1952. Aggressiveness in female mice. *Jour. Comp. Physiol. Psychol.,* **45**: 254–7.

27. Fredericson, E., and Birnbaum, E. A. 1954. Competitive fighting between mice with different hereditary backgrounds. *Jour. Genet. Psychol.,* **85**: 271–80.

28. Fredericson, E., Fink, C. D., and Parker, J. R. 1955. Elicitation and inhibition of competitive fighting in food deprived mice. *Jour. Genet. Psychol.,* **86**: 131–41.

29. Fredericson, E., Story, A. W., Gurney, N. L., and Butterworth, K. 1955. The relationships between heredity, sex, and aggression in two inbred mouse strains. *Jour. Genet. Psychol.,* **87**: 121–30.

30. Grant, E. C., and Chance, M. R. H. 1958. Rank order in caged rats. *Animal Behav.,* **6**: 183–94.

31. Gustafson, J. E., and Winokur, G. 1960. The effect of sexual satiation and female hormone upon aggressivity in an inbred mouse strain. *Jour. Neuropsychiatry,* **1**: 182–4.

32. Hutchinson, R. R., Ulrich, R. E., and Azrin, N. H. 1965. Effects of age and related factors on the pain-aggression reaction. *Jour. Comp. Physiol. Psychol.* **59**: 365–9.

33. Kaada, B. 1966. Brain mechanisms related to aggressive behavior. In *Brain Mechanisms and Social Patterns of Aggression and Defense.* Edited

by C. D. Clemente and D. B. Lindsley. Los Angeles: University of California Press.

34. Kahn, M. W. 1951. The effect of severe defeat at various age levels on the aggressive behavior of mice. *Jour. Genet. Psychol.*, **79**: 117–30.

34a. ———. 1954. Infantile experience and mature aggressive behavior of mice: some maternal influences. *Jour Genet. Psychol.*, **84**: 65–76.

35. King, J. A. 1957. Relationship between early social experience and adult aggressive behavior in inbred mice. *Jour Genet. Psychol.*, **90**: 151–66.

35a. ———. 1958. Parameters relevant to determining the effects of early experience upon the adult behavior of animals. *Psychol. Bull.*, **55**: 46–58.

36. King, J. A., and Cannon, H. 1955. Effects of social relationships upon mortality in C57BL/10 mice. *Physiol. Zool.*, **28**: 233–9.

37. King, J. A., and Gurney, N. L. 1954. Effect of early social experience on adult aggressive behavior in C57BL/10 mice. *Jour. Comp. Physiol. Psychol.*, **47**: 326–30.

38. Lagerspetz, K. 1961. Genetic and social causes of aggressive behavior in mice. *Scand. Jour. Psychol.*, **2**: 167–73.

39. Lagerspetz, K., and Mettala, R. 1965. Simulation experiments on stimuli eliciting aggressive behavior in mice. *Inst. Psychol., Univ. Turku.* Report **13**: 1–9. Mimeographed.

40. Lagerspetz, K., and Wuorinen, K. 1965. A cross-fostering experiment with mice selectively bred for aggressiveness and non-aggressiveness. *Inst. Psychol., Univ. Turku.* Report **17**: 1–6. Mimeographed.

41. Levine, L., Diakow, C. A., and Barsel, G. E. 1965. Inter-strain fighting in male mice. *Animal Behav.*, **13**: 52–8.

42. Levine, S. 1959. Emotionality and aggressive behavior in the mouse as a function of infantile experience. *Jour. Genet. Psychol.*, **94**: 77–83.

43. Lindzey, G., Winston, H. and Manosevitz, M. 1961. Social dominance in inbred mouse strains. *Nature*, **191**: 474–6.

44. Lorenz, K. 1964. Ritualized fighting. In J. D. Carthy, and F. J. Ebling, (editors). *The Natural History of Aggression.* London: Academic Press.

45. Martin, P. G., and Andrewartha, H. G. 1962. Success in fighting of two varieties of mice. *Am. Nat.*, **96**: 375–6.

46. Mettala, R. 1965. A factorial study of the behavior of mice in simulation experiments eliciting aggressive responses. *Inst. Psychol., Univ. Turku.* Report **15**: 1–9. Mimeographed.

47. Myer, J. S., and White, R. T. 1965. Aggressive motivation in the rat. *Animal Behav.*, **13**: 430–3.

48. O'Kelly, L. E., and Steckle, L. C. 1939. A note on long enduring emotional responses in the rat. *Jour. Psychol.*, **8**: 125–31.

49. Scott, J. P. 1944. Social behavior, range and territoriality in domestic mice. *Proc. Indiana Acad. Sci.*, **53**: 188–95.

49a. ———. 1958. *Aggression.* Chicago: University of Chicago Press.

49b. ———. 1962. Hostility and aggression in animals. In *Roots of Behavior.* Edited by E. L. Bliss. New York: Harper.

50. Scott, J. P., and Fredericson, E. 1951. The causes of fighting in mice and rats. *Physiol. Zool.*, **24**: 273–309.

51. Scott, J. P., and Fuller, J. L. 1965. *Genetics and the Social Behavior of the Dog.* Chicago: University of Chicago Press.
52. Seward, J. P. 1945. Aggressive behavior in the rat. III. The role of frustration. *Jour. Comp. Psychol.*, **38**: 225–38.
53. Staats, J. 1958. Behavior studies on inbred mice: a selected bibliography. *Animal Behav.*, **6**: 77–84.
53a. ———. 1963. Behavior studies on inbred mice: a selected bibliography. II. *Animal Behav.*, **11**: 484–90.
54. Steiniger, F. 1950. Beitrage zur Soziologie und sonstigen Biologie der Wanderatte. *Z. Tierpsychol.*, **7**: 356–79.
55. Strecker, R. L., and Emlen, J. T. 1953. Regulatory mechanisms in house-mouse populations: the effect of limited food supply on a confined population. *Ecology*, **34**: 375–85.
56. Tedeschi, R. E., Tedeschi, D. H., Mucha, A., Cook, L., Mattis, P. A., and Fellows, E. J. 1959. Effects of various centrally acting drugs on fighting behavior of mice. *Jour. Pharm. Exptl. Therap.*, **125**: 28–34.
57. Tollman, J., and King, J. A. 1956. The effects of testosterone propionate on aggression in male and female C57BL/10 mice. *Brit. Jour. Animal Behav.*, **6**: 147–9.
58. Ulrich, R. E. 1966. Pain as a cause of aggression. *Am. Zool.*, **6**: 643–62.
59. Ulrich, R. E., Hutchinson, R. R., and Azrin, N. H. 1965. Pain-elicited aggression. *Psychol. Rec.*, **15**: 111–26.
60. Uyeno, E. T. 1960. Hereditary and environmental aspects of dominant behavior in the albino rat. *Jour. Comp. Physiol. Psychol.*, **53**: 138–41.
61. Vandenberg, J. G. 1960. Eosinophil response to aggressive behavior in CFW albino mice. *Animal Behav.*, **8**: 13–8.
62. Young, H., Strecker, R. L. and Emlen, J. T. 1950. Localization of activity in two indoor populations of house mice, *Mus musculus*. *Jour. Mammal.*, **31**: 403–10.

8
AGGRESSION IN MONKEY AND APE SOCIETIES

K. R. L. HALL
University of Bristol, England

Reprinted from The Natural History of Aggression, *edited by J. D. Carthy and F. J. Ebling, pp. 51–64, with permission of the Institute of Biology. London and New York: Academic Press.*

INTRODUCTION

The term "aggression" in its precise sense refers to fighting and means the act of initiating an attack.[23] However, as is clear from other contributions to this Symposium, the kinds of behaviour shown by different species of animal in trying to gain ascendancy over conspecifics often fall far short of actual fighting, at least in the natural environment, being expressed in ritualized displays and threat intention movements which are seemingly effective in furthering the survival of the species. In other words, aggressive behaviour is usually, under the ecological conditions of natural feeding, breeding, and defence, adaptive.

In considering the evidence on aggression in the nonhuman primates, no discussion on the Prosimiae will be included, and examples will be taken from those species of monkey and ape on which most systematic field data are now available. Even for these species, however, much remains to be learned about the factors which determine the forms and frequencies of aggression in the natural living groups or populations, the behavioural data being almost entirely at the essentially descriptive stage, with very few studies being taken further, by experiment or controlled observation, to the analysis of causes.

Monkeys and apes, in common with other animals including man, demonstrate aggressiveness by a variety of actions and expressions involving face, limbs, and the whole body. Threat, as the prelude to attack, is expressed in species-characteristic behaviour patterns, including vocalizations, the repertoire of these now being fairly well known for the rhesus macaque[11, 21] in a captive group situation, for baboons,[5, 8, 9, 15, 16] for patas monkeys,[10] for gorillas,[22] and for chimpanzees.[6] Other species that are or have been thoroughly studied in the wild, such as the common langurs, and the vervets, at present lack a detailed inventory of their attack-threat behaviour, and only very recently has an account appeared in English of the communication behaviour of the Japanese macaque.[12] In terms of thorough ethological description and analysis, all these studies are in some degree deficient, but, for the present purpose of attempting to work out the role of aggression in the natural populations, there is sufficient information for a broad assessment, though not for a detailed quantitative comparison.

Again as in other animals, we find that aggression is expressed not only in direct and seemingly unequivocal forms but in indirect ways where, as is very commonly the case, other motives than to attack are also aroused in the situation, or where direct attack is frustrated. Thus we see from field studies many instances in which a redirection of aggression occurs away from the primary objective or cause of aggressive arousal. For hamadryas baboons, this has been well described by Kummer,[15] and for other baboons by Hall and DeVore.[9] It probably occurs in all species, but the clearest examples, as in the baboon studies, are manifested when a dominant animal is inhibited from attacking another animal of its group of more or less equal status, and diverts its attack onto subordinates. Where, from the context of the behaviour, the motives of attack and escape are simultaneously aroused, both may receive expression in alternating behaviour patterns, or neither may receive expression, only signs of nervousness, such as increased scratching, food-fumbling, and possible yawning,[8a] being in evidence.

Elementary derivatives of threat-intention, or nervousness, or both, have been recorded for several species, as, for example, when branches, twigs, leaves, pebbles, or faeces, are dropped apparently with reference to the position of the human observer.[8b] Throwing, or even stick-brandishing, is not uncommon in captive monkeys and apes. Most of these acts seem to have the purpose, where purpose rather than the accidental outcome of agitation can be established, of getting rid of a disturbing stimulus, and not of attacking it. In trying to characterize the nature of aggression in these species, the behavioural "status" of such acts as these is not at issue, although it may later require brief discussion in considering certain implications for human evolution.

No discussion in detail will be included on one limited aspect of aggression, namely the killing of other animals for food. This propensity has been fully authenticated for baboons,[4, 27] and for chimpanzees,[6] the victims being buck of various species, sheep, and, on two occasions, other nonhuman primates (baboon eating a vervet monkey; chimpanzees eating a red colobus). The reasons for omitting further discussion of this interesting habit are, firstly, that far more evidence is required, and could fairly easily be gained, for regional variations in baboons in this respect; secondly, that it is not clear at what level of prey we need to look for some evolutionary significance—for example, patas monkeys hunt and eat lizards, vervets eat eggs and fledgeling birds, and so on; thirdly, it is not clear that this propensity has any bearing upon the major aspects of aggression with which we are concerned, namely aggression within and between groups of the same species.

It is similarly very difficult to know how any of these monkeys and apes deal with predators. Goodall[6] has no evidence that chimpanzees are attacked by leopards. Schaller,[22] though recording that mountain gorillas are occasionally killed by leopards, has no data as to how a gorilla group reacts on detecting their presence. Baboons have been described by Bolwig[2] as teasing lions. Washburn and DeVore[27a] have a film record of encounters between baboons and lions and cheetahs. Stevenson-Hamilton[26] observed a large cheetah being chased away by a large male baboon after the former had tried to cut out some juveniles from the group. Loveridge[17] describes the "mobbing" of a leopard by E. African baboons, "the four old baboons surrounding a leopard and striking at it with their hands" (p. 728). It is also widely known that baboons will turn on dogs that threaten their group. Except for baboons, however, there is so little evidence of defensive aggression in monkeys and apes that we cannot attempt any comparison on this basis as between species. The other large terrestrial monkeys, such as mandrills, drills, and the gelada, have not yet been studied in the wild, and the data on this aspect of aggression in the hamadryas is not yet available from the Kummer and Kurt study. All the evidence suggests that the terrestrial patas monkeys must rely on dispersal and concealment to avoid leopards or hyenas or hunting dogs,[8e] and it is difficult to imagine that this species would do otherwise if encountering cheetahs. Nothing seems to be known about the behaviour of macaque species towards predators.

It is usually supposed that the pronounced sexual dimorphism apparent in baboons (the adult male with well developed canines, being about twice as large and heavy as the adult female) is the consequence of selection pressures derived from their savannah-ranging habits and the need for defence against the large carnivores.[5a] Correlated with this is a highly-developed aggressive potential. Equally, if not more, important, however, from the point of view of group survival, would seem to be the very strong social facilitative effect amongst the males consequent upon aggressive arousal by one of their number against a predator-stimulus. All the males are likely to join in the attack if the intensity of arousal is high, but it seems that only the younger, peripheral males may initiate and maintain alarm and defensive behaviour on other occasions, the dominant males remaining in the background. A similar facilitative build-up of attack is reported for chimpanzees in captivity,[28] and is no doubt well documented for other species.

In patas, likewise, the sexual dimorphism of the adults is very pronounced, with comparable differences in the canine teeth development, but it seems probable that this functions very differently in the context of group survival. In each of the groups so far studied, there has been only a single full-grown male whose conspicuous size and colouration seemed, from his behaviour, to function in diverting attention from the group and in enabling the group itself to maintain contact in the long savannah grass by marking on him as he sat or stood high up in some tree. It is difficult to imagine, from the slender physique and the elusive habits of the patas, that this male alone or the group with him would resort to attacking any of the large carnivores as a means of defending themselves.

REVIEW OF FIELD DATA

The field study evidence will be discussed primarily in terms of the role of aggression within the group and between groups of the same species. On the whole, relationships between groups of different species of monkey or ape are characterized by tolerance or just ignoring each other. Multi-species aggregations are not uncommon in certain forested habitats,[7, 20] and Hall[8e] saw no instances of aggression as between groups of baboons, patas, and vervet monkeys when these encountered each other in the woodland savannah. It is, of course, likely that groups which encounter other species groups regularly in their habitat know very well the tolerance limits to be observed on such occasions. Between-species chases, or withdrawals by one species group from the vicinity of another, do occur, but inter-species group fights have only, it seems, been reported for geladas against hamadryas baboons in Ethiopia (quoted by Zuckerman,[29] p. 195), but such accounts need verification. It is difficult, likewise, to know how much truth there is in the many stories from different parts of Africa in which baboons are reported to have attacked and even killed human beings. Male baboons, in particular, may become quite fearless if conditioned to expect food from human beings, and may attack a person in trying to get food (as has occurred at the Cape, South Africa). No field observer has, however, reported being attacked by uncontaminated wild groups. On the contrary, these groups tend, initially, to be very shy, and only gradually, with habituation, allow of close approach.

(1) Baboons and Macaques

In dealing with all examples from the field literature, aggression within species groups and between species groups will be treated as two distinct but closely related aspects of the same social process. It has generally been considered that the baboon and macaque genera contain species which are more overtly aggressive in both within-group and between-group interactions than any other monkey or ape species. As has been already stated the ground-ranging habits, taking groups away from refuges of trees or cliffs, are suggested to have set a premium on the collective aggression of adult males. So far as the genera are concerned, however, it is to be noted that the species of macaques show, from the sampling of rhesus, Japanese, and bonnet, very considerable variations in the extent to which aggression seems to be expressed in the wild groups. Further, from captivity reports, both the stump-tailed macaque, *M. speciosa*[14] and the pig-tailed, *M. nemestrina,* are docile and easy to manage in captivity in comparison with *M. mulatta.*

In the baboon genus, systematic field studies are at present available on *hamadryas* in Ethiopia, on *cynocephalus* in Kenya, and on *ursinus* in Southern Africa. Other large terrestrial species sometimes included in *Papio,* but more usually given separate generic status, are the mandrill, drill, and gelada, on which no field data are available. In reviewing the evidence that is available, one cannot fail to be impressed by the apparent regional variability in aggressiveness shown by *Papio* groups, and it is necessary to be very careful in evaluating these differences in the light of ecological variants that may determine them.

The description concept that most nearly represents aggression in its various forms in these animals is that of dominance. The ordering of relationships within baboon groups of *ursinus* and *cynocephalus,* as outlined by Hall and DeVore,[9] indicates that the large adult males do, on occasions, behave aggressively to other members of their group in a variety of different situations, as where priority of access to a special food incentive or a fully-oestrous female is at issue, or where a female with a young infant has been molested by another female, or where there is a quarrel amongst subordinate members of the group. However, it is obvious from many days of observation of these groups that the routine behaviour of their members is controlled as much by a conditioned expectation of reprisal for what we may call a non-conformist action than by overt threat or attack. When dominance relationships amongst the adult males are clearly established, threat episodes amongst them will be rare, the subordinate simply keeping away from the superior, as in the food-test situation shown in the Washburn and DeVore film.[27a] Dominance is manifested aggressively as between the males when tension is aroused by the presence over a period of days of only one female in oestrus, "harassing" threat sequences occurring, as reported by DeVore.[9] Relative rank amongst the males is also complicated by temporary alliances between, for example, two males who act together in threatening another male who, individually, is described as superior to either of the other two. Fighting amongst the adult males is extremely rare, the demonstrations between them consisting mainly of, to the onlooker, impressive, noisy chases without physical contact being made. These "threat displays" are probably less stereotyped than those described for other nonprimate mammals, but are likely to have the same social significance. Discipline within the group is usually very adequately maintained by threat, or by beating and biting of the subordinate on the nape of the neck which very rarely result in any visible injury to the victim.

The overall picture of group organization in these animals is of a sensitive balancing of forces, the balance being achieved by the social learning of individuals in the group from time of birth to adulthood, so that infringements of the group norm are rare. When they occur, they may be severely punished *if* the victim is caught. Even changes in dominance rank amongst the males are reported to occur as a consequence of persistent harrying rather than by fighting. In other words, physical prowess may not be actually tested, the confident usurping animal achieving his end simply by some of the forms of threat display and moving towards the other animal. What exactly is the social context from which such a usurpment takes place is not yet known. From the Japanese macaque studies, it is likely that the confident attitude of the to-be-dominant male is engendered by his being the offspring of a female who is high in the female hierarchy and hence is closely associated with the already dominant males.

As no full account of the *hamadryas* study is yet available, it is possible only to point out that dominance relations amongst males are quite differently organized in this species. Because the social unit is the one-male party, the male having with him a few adult females and their offspring, dominance is manifested aggressively mainly in the adult male herding his females and preventing any from straying to other units. This exclusiveness is an alternative method of avoiding tension leading to fighting between the males.

Relationships between baboon groups are characterized by mutual tolerance or mutual avoidance according to the nature of the habitat. Where water needs have to be satisfied at a common source, as happens in Southwest Africa, Southern Rhodesia, and Kenya, groups may even intermingle temporarily, then divide up and go their separate ways into their home ranges. Where, as in the Cape of South Africa, or in Murchison Falls Park, Uganda, the need for congregating does not normally arise, groups very rarely meet. Although they overlap into each other's home ranges, and even use the same sleeping cliffs on different nights, they keep apart from one another. No aggressive interactions between groups have ever been recorded by Hall and DeVore[9] in over 2,000 hours of observation.

What has been said is not intended to imply that baboons are not potentially aggressive to one another. It is all too well known that, in the unnatural restriction of physical and social space of the usual captivity conditions, lethal aggressiveness may occur. As a recent example of this, fighting broke out in a group of 17 baboons at the Bloemfontein Zoo when an "alien" adult male and adult female were introduced into their midst, as a result of which most of the animals were killed or died of their injuries (van Ee, personal communication). The point, of course, is that the natural regulation of numbers within a baboon population, and within the groups that it comprises, is usually achieved entirely by means short of actual fighting. Animals so socially conditionable as baboons have a highly articulated system of appropriate behaviour patterns towards each other, within groups and between groups, so that this tremendous aggressive potential is rarely manifested toward species members.

The social system of the rhesus macaques and the Japanese macaques appears to be similarly constituted. According to Southwick *et al.*[25] the peculiar habitat of the Temple rhesus groups that they studied led to as much as an 80 or 90 percent overlap of the home ranges of adjacent groups but these usually avoided contact with each other, as Altmann[1] observed to be the case with the Cayo Santiago colony, and the "subordinate" group tended to move away as soon as it saw the approach of the more dominant group. Occasionally, however, fairly close contact was not quickly enough avoided, and severe fighting between the two groups would occur. In 85 days of observation, there were 24 severe fights between two of the groups and numerous minor scraps. Normally, the adult males began the fight, but females and juveniles would become involved. Severe wounds often resulted, and most adult males bore wound scars around the face, shoulders or rump. Wounded individuals were fewer amongst rhesus groups in rural habitats and forest areas, where spacing and protective covering greatly reduced the likelihood of intergroup contacts. Baboons have not been studied in a comparable natural situation, but it is reasonable to suppose, by interpolating from captivity situations to the natural ones, that similar manifestations of intergroup aggression would occur.

We have already noted how important a part social facilitation seems to play in the cumulative effect of aggressive encounters. Southwick *et al.*[25] noted that most of the inter-group fights were initiated by young adult (subordinate) males who would normally be the first to contact each other, because of their peripheral position *vis-a-vis* their own group. The sounds of fighting, particularly the vocalizations, would bring more and more animals on to the scene.

From the many years of study of the Japanese macaque groups, group interactions, characterized by tolerance or avoidance, appear to be very similar to those of baboons and of rhesus in habitat areas other than the urban and Temple. Changes in relative dominance as between adult males of a group usually proceed without fighting, and removal of an α male is likely to be followed by a take-over of status by the No. 2 male of the group. The idea that these males, or those in baboon and rhesus groups, achieve their dominance by fighting for it seems mainly to have arisen from inaccurate observations. Threat displays amongst baboon males, for example, may be exceedingly noisy and vigorous, and give the casual observer the impression that a kind of dog fight is going on.

For the only other macaque species studied (*M. radiata,* studied by Simonds,[24]) aggression within and between groups appears to be of much lower intensity and frequency than in rhesus. Males approach each other for grooming and play, and young adult males are not forced out to the periphery of the group, as in *fuscata, mulatta,* and baboon groups. The only threat behaviour recorded between these groups occurred when a young male dropped out of a tree into the wrong group, and was chased away. Contacts between groups were observed on five occasions. When they met, the young males and the adult males would move towards the other group, and then sit and look at each other, with distances sometimes of only about 20 feet separating them. Then the males of one group would begin to drift back in the opposite direction, and the groups would separate. No inter-group fighting was observed. Home range overlaps between groups was of the order of 20 per cent only, compared with the 80–90 per cent of the Temple rhesus. Probably this spacing difference is a critical factor. A baboon group in the Murchison Falls Park was observed to chase another, much larger, group when the latter had encroached almost to the middle of the former's home range. This is the only occasion on which a short chase by a baboon group has been observed. Other contacts between these two groups, near the respective home range limits, were of the sort already described as typical of the baboons.

While allowing for the probability that the aggressive potential may differ in degree from species to species within the macaque genus, and perhaps also regionally in the baboon genus, such differences cannot be comparatively assessed without a thorough knowledge of the ecological circumstances of the group that are being studied and compared. Under the most widely prevailing natural conditions, none of these species show aggressive interactions between groups. Where sampling has not yet been very extensive as in the bonnet macaque study, it remains possible that other environmental variants may be found to produce a more aggressively characterized social organization. In all studies so far available, however, the effectiveness of the natural controlling mechanisms are in evidence, so that reduction of numbers through actual fighting is rarely seen, and the necessary degree of group cohesion can usually be maintained by occasional threat or by chastisement short of physical injury. While it seems highly likely that there are genetic differences in aggressive potential as between monkey species, the pattern of conformity achieved by members of a group that live together all their lives is such as normally to ensure that fighting is extremely rare.

(2) Other Monkeys

Perhaps the most striking comparison with baboons and rhesus at present available comes from study of the terrestrial patas monkey, *Erythrocebus patas*.[8e] Overlapping extensively with baboons and vervets in the Murchison Falls Park woodland-savannah habitat, the species may be expected to have to deal with the same kind of survival problems. Physically, the full-grown patas male is less than half the weight of the full-grown baboon male, but stands almost as high off the ground, and has well-developed canine teeth. These animals are probably the fastest of all primates in running along the ground, being built on the greyhound pattern, rather than for fighting. The adult females are only half the size of the adult males. In each group so far observed, there has been only one large male with several adult females and young animals. Numerical sizes only went up to 23 animals, with an average size for 7 groups of 15 animals. Baboon groups in the same area had a far greater proportion of adult males. In a baboon group totalling 24 animals, there were six large males and nine adult females.

These considerations make it clear that the patas group could not survive predation by leopards or hyenas except by the habits observed in the field, namely dispersion, silence, watchfulness and concealment. Whereas a baboon group tended to cluster together high up in trees by the Nile bank at night, the patas remained out in the savannah, an individual going up into a tree as much as 400 yards distance from the next individual of the group. The group would reassemble about one hour after sunrise, and set off after the adult male on the day range through the long grass and into the erosion valleys. Isolated adult males are occasionally seen near a group or far away from any group.

Within the groups not a single threat-attack by an adult male was observed in over 500 hours of observation. In contrast to the noisy barking and squealing baboons, the patas group is, to the human observer at about 100 yards distance, almost completely silent throughout the day range. As we know from study of a laboratory group of the species,[10] the patas have several distinctive vocalizations in their repertoire, but these are audible only at very short ranges. On not a single occasion, again in striking contrast to baboons, has there been an audible vocalization from the large male or any other animal in the group when the observer has first encountered them or walked too close to them. No animal within these groups had any visible scar or injury. Again in marked contrast to baboons, females or young animals do not show any submissive postures or expressions if the large male passes near to them, nor do they tend to move out of his way. Our laboratory data suggest that adult females may play an important part in regulating the social relationships within the group, and the field data suggest that this large male's main function is watchfulness for predators rather than exerting any aggressive dominance within the group.

On the other hand, the large male patas was immediately aggressive and uttered a higher-pitched baboon-like bark when viewing an isolated male patas or another patas group. No fights were ever seen, nor would ever be likely to occur in such terrain, the isolate or the other group retreating very fast indeed. The patas groups range over a large area of savannah up to about 12 square miles in extent, and, the country being so open, close-range contact between groups is extremely unlikely, especially as the large male tended regularly to go high up into any tree that was available, from which he watched the surrounding countryside.

It would be premature to suggest that this is the "typical" pattern in patas groups, because sampling of other areas, particularly in West Africa, is necessary. Nevertheless, the physical and behavioural adaptations of the patas are clearly understandable in the kind of environment in which they have been observed. In such country, spacing between groups is easily maintained by long-range watchfulness, and there is little or no opportunity for between-group tolerance to be achieved, as in baboons, by a process of habituation. The social order is such as fits the particular environmental needs, and does not require overt aggression to maintain it. Evidently at some stage maturing males must be eliminated from the group, either through aggressive action by the large male, or, conceivably, by concerted action by the adult females. Probably the answer to this important problem can only be provided in the captive group setting.

In keeping with the general picture so far outlined, other monkey species, such as the common langur of India whose physical characteristics and routine behaviour would likewise dispose it to escape or avoid predators, also show far less overt aggression within groups than do baboons and rhesus. "Social relations in a North Indian langur group are not oriented primarily to protection of the individual by group action. Unlike macaques or baboons, a langur protects himself as an individual most effectively by dashing up the nearest tree, instead of depending for protection on large adult males with well-developed fighting powers. Relations among adult male langurs are relaxed. Dominance is relatively unimportant in langur daily life and most of the activities which occupy an individual's time are unrelated to dominance status. Aggressive threats and fights are exceedingly uncommon" (Jay,[13] p. 53). Jay was able to compare langur group behaviour directly with that of rhesus groups in the same area, noting that in the latter aggressive reactions in the group were frequent, and fighting was often severe. In this area, the langurs might spend as much as 80 per cent of the day on the ground, but, as noted, and in contrast to baboons and patas, tended to remain close to trees into which they could easily find refuge. Tolerance between langur groups was likewise the prevailing behaviour.

It will be realized that, so far, only species which spend much of their day time on the ground have been considered, but these samples are sufficient to indicate that it is not terrestrial habit as such which links with aggressive potential but the complex array of physical and behavioural adaptations.

Of the primarily arboreal species, only the South American howlers have been sufficiently studied to afford direct comparison with these Old World species. From Carpenter's[3] study, it is apparent that dominance relations amongst adult male howlers are far less clearly defined than they are in baboons and rhesus, actual fighting or any form of overt aggression being very rare indeed. Spacing between groups seems to be maintained chiefly by the vocal demonstrations of howler males, and this fits in with the forest habitat which does not allow of visually-derived spacing to be effective. It is an interesting fact that adult male baboons in groups studied in the fairly close woodland areas bordering the Zambesi River[8c] likewise tended to bark persistently in the early morning, these vocalizations being taken up by males of other groups in the vicinity which were completely out of sight of each other. Such vocal demonstrations very rarely occurred in the open terrain of other parts of Southern Africa.

(3) Anthropoid Apes

The study by Schaller[22] of gorilla groups in a mountain habitat and by Goodall[6] of a chimpanzee population in a savannah habitat provide important information as to the role of aggression in these primates.

From Goodall's data, it seems that the chimpanzees, in contrast to all the monkey species we have discussed, are loosely organized in temporary parties. Aggressive and submissive interactions between individuals were infrequent, and the concept of a dominance hierarchy amongst the males cannot be substantiated even within the temporary groupings. In the whole of the very long study period, only 72 clear-cut dominance interactions were observed in which one male gave way before another with respect to food or to place. Threat gestures, including vocalizations, were occasionally recorded. Nothing comparable to the between-group tensions sometimes observed in monkeys were recorded, adult males going peacefully from one grouping to another. Even during mating, tolerance between males was in evidence, as when several of them copulated in turn with the same oestrous female. As described by Hall and DeVore,[9] such a situation amongst baboons would almost certainly lead to great tension amongst the males, and, in most groups, the dominant male would have a temporary but exclusive consort relationship with an oestrous female, tending to keep away from the rest of the group, and thus avoiding interference.

The social organization in gorilla groups is similar to that of the monkeys, groups tending to retain their entity. However, although a dominance order is in evidence as between the silver-backed males and younger black-backed males, it is rarely exerted aggressively and interactions between groups were usually entirely peaceable, and sometimes occurred at very close range. The ranging habits of these gorilla groups differed markedly from those of the monkeys, because a group might in successive days, wander over a wide area, its course taking it criss-crossing amongst the paths taken by other groups. Thus, gorilla group home ranges not merely overlap with each other, but seem to be communally shared amongst the gorilla population. No monkey species so far studied has shown a comparable home range pattern, each monkey group, though overlapping with its neighbors, tending to remain most of the time in an area exclusive to its own use.

SUMMARY

Although the sample of data we still have available from which to draw comparisons is very limited, and includes only one arboreal species, it is probably sufficient for certain general points to be raised. In common with the comparative treatment of social organization as a whole, it is now obvious that the characteristic expressions and frequencies of aggression within and between groups cannot be meaningfully considered without detailed reference to their ecological context. The large size, the food needs, and the ranging habits of baboons require them frequently to go far away from shelter areas of trees or rocks. Controlled aggressiveness in this context is a valuable survival characteristic in that it ensures protection of the group and group cohesion. Indeed, in a situation where threat to the group arises, the adult males are immediately prominent and the remainder tend to cluster close together. The slim build and speed of the patas who range about as far in a day as a baboon group is correlated with quite a different set of behavioural adaptations, and the physique and habits of langurs and howler likewise are adapted to a relatively unaggressive way of life which is reflected in their social organization. In all the species, however, inter-group spacing is achieved, with the peculiar exception of the Temple rhesus, without fighting, and dominance, in some cases, as between groups ensures the withdrawal of one, just as it ensures the withdrawal of the subordinate individual.

The apes are difficult to place in comparison with the monkeys. Their physical adaptations of great size and strength are far superior to any monkey's, but they are in many respects perhaps less adaptable to survival in the contemporary environment. The relative placidity of the gorilla, coupled with great bulk, slow movement, and apparently restricted diet, put it at considerable disadvantage with the baboons or indeed with the rhesus, patas, or langur. The chimpanzee, with its high rating on the human comparative scale of intelligence, is apparently able to use tools for food-getting and even for defence, and yet lacks other characteristics of social organization and adaptability which must rate it as less successful than the baboons.

The question, of course, arises as to what our knowledge of the different forms that aggression takes in these wild primates has to tell us about the evolutionary role of aggression in the prehominids or early hominids. The closest parallel seems to be discernible in the baboons whose social organization is such as to allow of large groups (up to 200) maintaining their coherence without the aggressiveness of the adult males being in any way dangerous to the survival of the group. The same is true of the relationships between baboon groups, and it is, indeed, a remarkable fact that aggressive interactions between them are so rare, even when ecological needs require frequent and close contact. Probably the most important point to emphasize is that the inhibitory control system of baboon social organization is so effective that their lethal fighting potential is rarely released. One of the most significant tasks for future research will be to work out, under experimental conditions in captive groups, exactly what are the factors of spacing and social learning which determine the natural equilibrium. This equilibrium can, as is already known, be very easily disturbed, and it is necessary that group experiments be conducted to elucidate the tolerance limits in these animals and in other species. If the accounts cited by Dart[4] and Oakley[18] for the predatory behaviour of baboons in South Africa can be systematically reinforced in longterm field studies, we have one more line of evidence to support the view, long ago put forward by Carveth Read,[19] that the prehominids may have had many of the characteristics of a wolf-like primate, the nearest contemporary parallel to which is the baboon. The chimpanzee, whom one might assess as academically superior to the baboon, seems to lack other adaptations of a physical and social kind which have resulted in its being biologically less successful.

REFERENCES

1. Altmann, S. A. 1962. A field study of the sociobiology of rhesus monkeys, *Macaca mulatta*. *Ann. N.Y. Acad. Sci.*, **102**: 296–315.
2. Bolwig, N. 1959. A Study of the Behaviour of the Chacma Baboon, *Papio ursinus*. *Behaviour*, **14**: 136–63.
3. Carpenter, C. R. 1934. A field study of the behaviour and social relations of howling monkeys. *Comp. Psychol. Monogr.*, **10**(2): Serial No. 48.
4. Dart, R. A. 1963. Carnivorous propensity of baboons. *Symp. Zool. Soc. London,* No. **10**: 49–56.
5. DeVore, I. 1962. *The Social Behaviour and Organization of Baboon Troops.* Ph.D. thesis, University of Chicago.

5a. ———. 1963. Comparative ecology and behaviour of monkeys and apes. In *Classification and Human Evolution.* Edited by S. L. Washburn. New York: Viking Fund Publications.

6. Goodall, J. M. 1968. *The Behaviour of Free-Living Chimpanzees in the Gombe Stream Reserve.* Anim. Behav. Monographs, **1**(3): 161–311.
7. Haddow, A. J. 1952. Field and laboratory studies on an African monkey, *Cercopithecus ascanius.* Schmidti. *Proc. Zool. Soc., London,* **122**: 297–394.
8. Hall, K. R. L. 1962. Sexual, derived social, and agonistic behaviour patterns in the wild Chacma baboon, *Papio ursinus. Proc. Zool. Soc., London,* **139**: 284–327.
8a. ———. 1962. Behaviour of monkeys towards mirror-images. *Nature, London,* **196**: 1258–61.
8b. ———. 1963. Tool-using performances as indicators of behavioural adaptability. *Curr. Anthrop.,* **4**: 479–94.
8c. ———. 1963. Variations in the ecology of the Chacma baboon, *Papio ursinus. Symp. Zool. Soc., London,* No. 10: 1–28.
8d. ———. 1965. Ecology and Behaviour of Baboons, Patas and Vervet Monkeys. *Proc. 1st Int. Conf. on the Baboon as an Experimental Animal.* San Antonio, Texas.
8e. ———. 1965. Ecology and behaviour of patas monkeys, *Erythrocebus patas,* in Uganda. *Jour. Zool.,* **148**: 15–87.
9. Hall, K. R. L., and DeVore, I. 1965. Baboon social behaviour. Chap. 3 in *Primate Behavior.* Edited by I. DeVore. New York: Holt, Rinehart and Winston. pp. 53–110.
10. Hall, K. R. L., Boelkins, C., and Goswell, M. J. *Behaviour of the Patas Monkey, Erythrocebus patas.* In press.
11. Hinde, R. A., and Rowell, T. E. 1962. Communication by postures and facial expressions in the Rhesus monkey, *Macaca mulatta. Proc. Zool. Soc., London,* **138**: 1–21.
12. Miyadi, D. 1963. Studies on the social life of Japanese monkeys. *Proc. Amer. Assoc. Advance Sci.,* December 27.
13. Jay, P. 1965. The common Langur of North India. Chap. 7 in *Primate Behavior.* Edited by I. DeVore. New York: Holt, Rinehart and Winston. pp. 197–249.
14. Kling, A., and Orbach, J. 1963. The stump-tailed macaque: a promising laboratory primate. *Science,* **139**: 45–6.
15. Kummer, H. 1957. Soziales Verhalten Einer Mantelpavian Gruppe. *Schweiz. Zeitschr. Psychol.,* No. 33, 91 pp.
16. Kummer, H., and Kurt, F. 1963. Social units of a free-living population of Hamadryas baboons. *Folia Primat.,* **1**: 4–19.
17. Loveridge, A. 1923. Notes on East African mammals. *Proc. Zool. Soc., London.* 1923: 685–739.
18. Oakley, K. P. 1951. A definition of man. *Science News,* **20**: 69–81.
19. Read, C. 1917. On the differentiation of the human from the anthropoid mind. *Brit. J. Psychol.,* **8**: 395–422.
20. Reynolds, V. 1963. An outline of the behaviour and social organization of forest-living chimpanzees. *Folia Primat.,* **1**: 95–102.
21. Rowell, T. E., and Hinde, R. A. 1962. Vocal communications by the Rhesus monkey, *Macaca mulatta. Proc. Zool. Soc., London,* **138**: 279–94.
22. Schaller, G. B. 1963. *The Mountain Gorilla.* Chicago: University of Chicago Press.

23. Scott, J. P. 1958. *Aggression.* Chicago: University of Chicago Press.
24. Simonds, P. E. 1965. *The bonnet macaque in South India.* Chap 6 in *Primate Behavior.* Edited by I. DeVore. New York: Holt, Rinehart and Winston. pp. 175–96.
25. Southwick, C. H., Beg, M. A., and Siddiqi, M. R. 1965. Rhesus monkeys in North India. Chap. 4 in *Primate Behavior.* Edited by I. DeVore. New York: Holt, Rinehart and Winston. pp. 111–59.
26. Stevenson-Hamilton, J. 1947. *Wild Life in South Africa.* London: Cassell.
27. Washburn, S. L., and DeVore, I. 1961. Social behaviour of baboons and early man. In *Social Life of Early Man.* Edited by S. L. Washburn. New York: Viking Fund Publications.
27a. ———. 1962. Film entitled *Baboon Behaviour.* University of California, Berkeley.
28. Yerkes, R. M. 1943. *Chimpanzees: A Laboratory Colony.* New Haven: Yale University Press.
29. Zuckerman, S. 1932. *The Social Life of Monkeys and Apes.* London: Kegan Paul.

9

PHYSIOLOGIC FACTORS IN AGGRESSIVE BEHAVIOR

DAVID E. DAVIS
North Carolina State University

This selection is excerpted from Chapter 3, "The Physiological Analysis of Aggressive Behavior," in the book, Social Behavior and Organization among Vertebrates, *edited by William Etkin.*

A major purpose of this chapter is to place in perspective the physiologic factors in social behavior. To understand the causation of behavior, it is necessary to consider the hormones as "agents" that carry a message concerning a state or condition. Hormones are a means of communication supplementing the nervous system but sometimes acting in different ways. Hormone action is slow because the chemical must travel in adequate quantities from the gland to the site of action. When the hormone is present at the proper structure, however, action may be almost instantaneous. The well-known rapid action of adrenalin is an example. Even testosterone, when placed at a suitable place in the hypothalamus, promptly elicits sexual behavior.[6]

In many vertebrates the glands change in size seasonally so that many weeks are necessary in the spring to produce the hormones. The behavior may develop gradually and increase in frequency. As an example, cardinals begin to sing in early January, but their song is haphazard and weak, and their defense is mild. As the season progresses, their song becomes vigorous and their defense of territory becomes active. The appropriate hormones are now present in adequate quantities.

In addition to the hormones, an appropriate stimulus situation must always be present. Thus, a bird may defend its territory vigorously but feed peacefully with other birds in some common area away from the territory.

The "agent" cannot deliver its message unless suitable conditions are present. Thus, testosterone, when injected into a capon, can cause no behavioral expression unless another bird is present and reacts in certain stereotypic ways. Furthermore, the environment must be suitable (familiar; contain certain items). For example, some birds will not demonstrate aggressiveness unless a particular type of perch is available. Naturally, animals in nature are usually found in areas suitable simply because the animals chose them. Work in laboratories, however, often fails to mimic natural conditions, and hence the "agents" cannot deliver the messages.

The role of hormones in aggressive behavior has been recognized for a century. The frequent observation that roosters when castrated soon cease fighting is amply confirmed by detailed studies. Many species have been experimentally tested, either by injection of an androgen such as testosterone or by castration. Some of the species are swordtail fish, anolis lizard, painted turtle, domestic fowl, night herons, doves, rats, mice and, last but not least, boys. Other cases are mentioned by Scott and Fredericson.[12] In many cases female or sexually immature individuals respond to androgens as characteristically as do males. In addition to the aggressive behavior, several other masculine features, such as crowing by a rooster, appear. This almost universal reaction of animals to androgens unfortunately has permitted the assumption that aggressive behavior always depends upon androgens. An exception will be mentioned below.

An important problem that confuses the interpretation of results of injections with hormones is the production of anesthesia by high doses of steroids. Testosterone given in doses of 2.0 mg. per chick per day will cause many individuals to become so sleepy they may neither feed properly nor show any aggressive behavior. This unexpected action of testosterone may explain some of the apparently negative results obtained, for example, by Bevan *et al.*[1] To determine the influence of hormones on aggressive behavior, one must conduct enough experiments to determine dose-responses for several different doses of the hormone. Chicks given testosterone daily in the following doses: 0, 0.25, 0.50, 1.00 and 2.00 mg. showed the following weights of the comb after twenty-five days (average of four chicks): 380, 581, 704, and 643 mg., respectively. Obviously the high dose was detrimental. Those birds also had smaller testes, weighed less, and were very inactive. These data are cited as an example of some of the pitfalls in behavioral work using hormones. The current status of the work on androgens indicates that aggressive behavior is greatly accentuated in many species when the hormone is injected or is naturally present.

Females fight much less vigorously than do males but nevertheless show aggressive behavior that can often be accentuated by injection of testosterone. Presumably the endocrine glands in females produce enough androgens to stimulate aggressive actions. In mammals some special androgens apparently arise in the adrenal glands, and in birds androgens come from the ovary as well.

The hormones (estrogens) normally associated with female characters apparently stimulate aggressive behavior under some circumstances. For example, Birch and Clark[2] and Kislak and Beach[8] found evidence that estrogens accentuated aggressiveness in chimpanzees and hamsters. The female hamster, however, is remarkable in its inconsistent behavior.

Since the production of male and female hormones depends upon the activities of several organs, it is now necessary to consider these individually in order to explain the source of aggressive behavior. It is clear that the gonads as well as both parts of the adrenal are controlled by an area in the brain called the hypothalamus through its control of the pituitary. The hypothalamus influences aggressive behavior through many channels. Through its control of the pituitary it acts upon the gonads and the adrenal cortex. The gonads, in turn, produce testosterone which act upon the organs involved in such behavior. Acting through the sympathetic nerves to the adrenal medulla, the hypothalamus also controls the release of adrenalin, which is concerned in the physiologic processes active during aggressive behavior.

Until recently the hormones of the pituitary were not known to affect aggressive behavior directly. However numerous observations of social behavior in nature suggested that testosterone could not be responsible for the level of aggressiveness. Davis[4] showed, however, that testosterone did not affect the rank of starlings in the group hierarchy. Subsequently, Mathewson[10] showed that luteinizing hormones (LH) increased aggressiveness and caused birds to reverse rank (Figure 1).

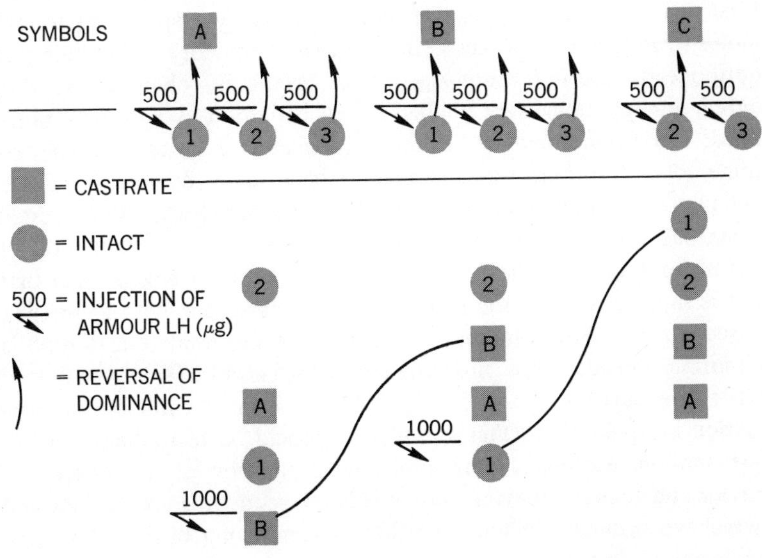

Figure 1 Reversal of dominance in male starlings injected with 1000μg. of luteinizing hormone is illustrated in this figure. Starlings are unusual in that castration increases dominance. Testosterone injections do not influence it. In this experiment pituitary hormone (LH) was shown to increase dominance. The bird which controlled the only perch available was the dominant. In the upper figure, A, which originally dominated 1, 2, and 3, was displaced after the subordinate bird was given an injection of 500 μg LH. B was similarly displaced. Only with C did one injected bird (3) fail to achieve dominance. Dominance shift of the lowest bird in A's hierarchy of four after injection of 1000 μg LH is shown in the lower figure.[10]

Some details of this work illustrate how research in aggressive behavior may be conducted. Several types of experiments were done, but one type demonstrates the relationships particularly well. Two birds which had been kept in different cages were put together in a large cage till one clearly showed dominance. Then the subordinate bird was given 0.5 mg. of LH. In six out of eight pairs studied, the subordinate bird assumed a dominant rank. Birds injected with saline did not change rank.

This recent discovery opens a new area in the study of social behavior and illustrates several points of general biological interest. First, it reveals another case of the utilization by a species of a hormone to influence a process (in this case, behavior). Animals put hormones to use in a variety of ways. Seemingly, chemicals serving only a few functions were applied during evolution to additional functions. At the moment we cannot say whether LH, testosterone, or some other hormone was the first to be associated with aggressive behavior. A speculation may be made, and perhaps it will be tested some day. Since one function of LH is to stimuate production of testosterone through the Leydig cells of the testis, it would seem that LH is more basic and the connection of testosterone with aggression is secondary. From another viewpoint, the fact that testosterone is important in specialized birds (domestic fowl) and LH, in generalized birds (starlings) suggests that LH is more basic. Until more information is available, further speculation should be restrained.

From the ecological viewpoint, the separation of aggressive behavior and sexual behavior may be advantageous to some species and may have occurred in the evolution of some song birds. Although evidence is not yet abundant, it is clear that in some species, at least, the male selects and defends a territory and also settles social rank problems in the fall. Androgens cannot be responsible because the as yet undeveloped gonads are tiny. When the breeding season arrives, these males have an advantage over others that have not settled. In spring perhaps another set of hormones (androgens) is responsible for the sexual behavior. A separation of function of the two kinds of hormones allows greater efficiency, since each type of hormone has a separate job. The induction of song by testosterone occurs in several species, however. Song usually has at least two functions: defense of territory and advertisement to the female. Perhaps in some species the latter is the major function, or, possibly, defense is an acquired function.

Several hitherto unexplained behaviors may be now clarified by experimental or field study. For example, many birds (e.g., blackbirds) defend a territory in the fall and winter when the gonads are very small.[13] The usual explanations have been that minimal amounts of androgens are derived either from the tiny gonads or from the adrenals. It may be that the LH produced by the pituitary is responsible. It has long been known[7] that gonadotropins (LH and FSH) are produced in large amounts in the fall. Another example of unexplained behavior is the aggressive behavior of female mammals immediately after copulation. It is well known[11] that LH appears in large amounts at ovulation in mammals and that it stimulates ovulation in birds. Aggressive behavior occurring at this time might result from LH. A further example may be the often-reported reversal of dominance for pairs of birds at the time of laying.

The preceding paragraphs are admittedly speculative but are included for two reasons. First, it is noteworthy that the observation of wild animals (starlings) in the field of social behavior led to a discovery in endocrinology. Second, the problem suggests many studies (either observational or experimental) feasible in modest laboratories because they can be done with a minimum of space and equipment.

The hormones mentioned thus far are produced in the gonads or pituitaries and are concerned with reproductive activities. Several additional hormones (progesterone, relaxin, etc.) are associated directly with reproduction, but investigations have thus far not demonstrated that they have any influence on aggressive behavior. Because there are no suggestions that such hormones influence aggression, only a few studies have been made. Other organs, such as the adrenal, thyroid, and pancreas, produce various hormones. But [of these] only certain hormones from the adrenal are [known to be] important in the study of aggressiveness.

The adrenal gland is a complicated structure composed of two very different parts, the cortex and the medulla. The cortex encompasses the medulla and consists of several zones. Some areas produce various hormones called glucocorticoids, which affect carbohydrate metabolism, certain reproductive processes, and inflammation. Other areas produce mineralocorticoids and affect the mineral balance. Also, some androgens appear. The direct measurement of corticoids and androgens is very difficult. Usually the best procedure is to determine the amounts of breakdown products in the urine. Since this measure requires careful interpretation, the results are often dubious.

The medulla may be considered part of the autonomic nervous system, since it develops from the same embryonic source and is homologous with a sympathetic ganglion. In keeping with this origin the medulla produces hormones—adrenalin (epinephrine) and noradrenalin (norepinephrine)—that are collectively called catechol amines. Since a number of detailed reviews[3, 5] are available, only a summary of pertinent functions will be given here. In general the effects of these two medullary hormones mimic those of the sympathetic nervous system. Both hormones act on the circulatory system to constrict the visceral vessels, but noradrenalin constricts the vessels in muscles while adrenalin dilates skeletal muscles. Adrenalin causes a greater rise in blood sugar than does noradrenalin. Both hormones have various effects on smooth muscle, the spleen, and the bladder, but an effect considered important for current purposes is the mobilization of sugar from the liver. Adrenalin is more effective than is noradrenalin, but the end result is to move carbohydrate from the liver to the muscles.

The sympathetic nervous system responds promptly in a difficult situation, whether it be environmental (cold, poison, etc.) or behavioral (sexual, aggressive). The various effects of the hormones prepare the animal for action in the classic "fight or flight" picture. Recent studies[5] suggest that aggressive or active situations tend to stimulate production of noradrenalin whereas tension produces more adrenalin. Thus, professional hockey players had a sevenfold rise in noradrenalin and a threefold rise in adrenalin during a game. Two men who sat on the bench had a trivial change in noradrenalin and a doubling of adrenalin. Several other studies with prize fighters confirmed these results, as did studies on psychotic patients, although the data here are meager at this time.

The pathways in the brain that conduct stimuli to secrete adrenalin are not known. Experimental work shows that the hypothalamus is involved, but the mechanism remains to be convincingly demonstrated. Certainly hormones (vasopressin) from the posterior pituitary can release adrenalin, but many details need clarification. Innumerable studies show that an increase in catechol amines follows psychologic stresses, presumably acting through the limbic region.[9]

While the action of the hormones from the medulla produces this vast array of physiologic responses, it is clear that these are merely symptoms of a situation leading to aggressive behavior rather than causes of it. Adrenalin permits an animal to carry out aggression rather than causes it to be aggressive. For example, persons receiving adrenalin demonstrate the physiologic reactions but do not feel mad or become aggressive. The physiologic responses of the adrenal medulla are merely concomitants of the phenomenon called emotion, which will be discussed later.

REFERENCES

1. Bevan, W., *et al.* 1957. Spontaneous aggressiveness in two strains of mice castrated and treated with one of three androgens. *Physiol. Zool.*, **30**(4): 341–49.
2. Birch, H. G., and Clark, G. 1946. Hormonal modification of social be-

havior, II: The effects of sex-hormone administration on the social dominance status of the female-castrate chimpanzee. *Psychosom. Med.,* **8**(5): 320–31.

3. Christian, J. J. 1963. Endocrine adaptive mechanisms and the physiologic regulation of population growth. In *Physiological Mammalogy.* Edited by Mayer and Van Gelder. New York: Academic Press. Pp. 189–353.
4. Davis, D. E. 1957. Aggressive behavior in castrated starlings. *Science,* **126**(3267): 253.
5. Elmadjian, F., Hope, J. M., and Lamson, E. J. 1958. Excretion of epinephrine and norepinephrine under stress. *Recent Progr. Hormone Res.,* **14**: 513–54.
6. Fisher, A. 1956. Maternal and sexual behavior induced by intracranial chemical stimulation. *Science,* **124**: 228.
7. Greeley, F., and Meyer, R. K. 1953. Seasonal variation in testis-stimulating activity of male pheasant pituitary glands. *Auk,* **70**(3): 350–58.
8. Kislak, J. W., and Beach, F. A. 1955. Inhibition of aggressiveness by ovarian hormones. *Endocrinology,* **56**: 684–92.
9. MacLean, P. D., Ploog, D. V., and Robinson, B. W. 1960. Circulatory effects of limbic stimulation, with special reference to the male genital organ. *Physiol. Rev. Suppl.,* **4**: 105–12.
10. Mathewson, S. F. 1961. Gonadotropic control of aggressive behavior in starlings. *Science,* **134**: 1522–23.
11. Sawyer, C. H. 1959. Nervous control of ovulation. In *Endocrinology of Reproduction.* Edited by C. W. Lloyd. New York: Academic Press. Pp. 1–20.
12. Scott, J. P. and Fredericson, E. 1951. The causes of fighting in mice and rats. *Physiol. Zool.,* **24**(4): 273–308.
13. Snow, D. W. 1961. *A Study of Blackbirds.* London: George Allen and Unwin. 192 pp.

10

CHRONIC PHYSIOLOGICAL EFFECTS OF FIGHTING IN MICE*

F. H. BRONSON
University of Texas
B. E. ELEFTHERIOU
The Jackson Laboratory, Bar Harbor, Maine

This article is reprinted from General and Comparative Endocrinology, **4***(1): 9–14, with the permission of Academic Press, Inc.*

The impact of variations in population density on adrenal physiology of rodents has been reviewed by Christian.[3b] The direct cause of the adrenal changes observed under crowded conditions is probably in the nature of a psychological stressor associated with the social environment.[3] Several workers have concluded that aggressive behavior may play a role as great or greater than crowding per se in stimulating adrenal response.[1, 2, 4] However, none of these laboratory studies, dealing either with cage density or aggression as the primary variable, has examined adrenal responses when animals are allowed to contact members of the same sex only for short periods each day, a situation known to be normal for many rodents under field conditions. The

* Supported by PHS grant M-4481 from the National Institutes of Health, Public Health Service. Special thanks are due Dr. M. X. Zarrow of Purdue University for partial financial assistance and laboratory facilities.

present experiment evaluates adrenal and some other physiological responses when mice are exposed to trained fighting mice for a varying number of 1-minute periods each day.

MATERIALS AND METHODS

Adult male mice of the C57BL/10J strain were isolated following weaning at 21–28 days of age. At 75–85 days of age, 120 mice were exposed a varying number of times each day to either (1) trained fighters of the same strain in the fighters' home cages, or (2) handling similar to that received by fighter-exposed animals, including exposure to an empty (clean) cage. Animals were exposed to these two types of treatments at the rate of 0, 1, 2, 4, or 8 times per day for 7 days. The experimental design, therefore, consisted of 10 treatments with 12 mice per treatment; however, since two treatments—no exposures to fighters and no exposures to empty cages—are identical, the 24 animals involved actually constituted a double control. Within these 24 mice, odd-numbered animals served as the controls for fighting and even-numbered animals as controls for empty cage exposures. Each exposure to a fighter or an empty cage lasted 1 minute and, when more than one exposure per day was required, a minimum of 5 minutes between exposures was maintained. All animals remained isolated in their home cages when not being exposed. A battery of 25 trained fighters (trained as suggested by Scott,[14]) was used in this investigation. Where possible, each animal scheduled for the fighter-exposure treatments was exposed to as many of the 25 fighters as its schedule would allow.

Body weights were obtained on days 1 and 6 of the experiment by using a shadowgraph balance, and body lengths were obtained on day 6 from unanesthetized animals. Four to six hours after the last exposure each animal was killed by decapitation, blood was collected, and the adrenals and seminal vesicles were weighed. Samples of blood and adrenals were pooled separately from 6 animals of each treatment and frozen for later biochemical analysis. It has been found in our laboratory that keeping plasma frozen up to 6 months does not alter corticosterone activity. Adrenal and plasma corticosterone levels were determined according to the method of Peron and Dorfman[10] and Moncloa *et al.*[8] Essentially, the procedure involved the following: adrenals were homogenized with 2.0 ml of 33% ethanol and made up to a volume of 5.0 ml with double-distilled water (original volume). Aliquots of 0.5, 0.7, 1.0, and 1.2 ml were taken and made up to 2 ml with 13% ethanol in a 12-ml ground glass-stoppered centrifuge tube. For plasma determinations, aliquots taken were: 0.2, 0.4, 0.6, and 0.8 ml. These were made up to a volume of 2.0 ml with 13% ethanol. Each aliquot was washed with 5 ml of ligroin, centrifuged, and the ligroin removed by aspiration. Samples were extracted with 5 ml of dichloromethane and centrifuged. The aqueous phase was removed by aspiration, and the dichloromethane phase was washed with 1.0 ml of ice-cold 0.1 N NaOH and centrifuged. The NaOH phase was removed and 2.0 ml of 30 N H_2SO_4 were added by transferring 4.0 ml of extract to 2.0 ml of H_2SO_4. The tubes were shaken vigorously and centrifuged. The H_2SO_4 phase was removed and the samples read in a Turner fluorimeter after 45 minutes. All extraction and washing steps were carried out by shaking vigorously by hand for exactly 1 minute. Centrifugation in all cases was for 5 minutes at 2000 rpm. Emulsions formed with NaOH could only be broken partially so that care was taken to remove 2.0-ml aliquots of the clear dichloromethane extract and to transfer these to clean tubes prior to the addition of sulfuric acid. A standard curve was run with corticosterone values of 0.02-0.1 μg per milliliter. A blank containing only 13% ethanol was also run. Fluorescence values for tissue and plasma were extrapolated to zero-tissue and plasma values, i.e., where the line intercepted the ordinate. These values were considered as true tissue blanks.

Since the mice used in this study were 80–90 days old at the time of autopsy, the fluorescence method was presumably measuring only corticosterone. No interference was detected from other adrenal steroids such as cortisol.

RESULTS

The treatments resulted in definite alterations of weight gain (Fig. 1). While control animals showed an average weight gain of about 2% of their body weight between days 1 and 6 of the experiment, weight gain decreased as the number of exposures to an empty cage or fighters increased. Mice exposed to 2, 4, or 8 fighters per day or exposed to empty cages 8 times per day lost weight during the experiment. Analysis of variance showed significance for empty cage vs. fighter-exposure treatments ($p < 0.05$), and for the number of exposures per day ($p < 0.01$), but revealed a nonsignificant interaction, thus supporting the obvious trends in Fig. 1.

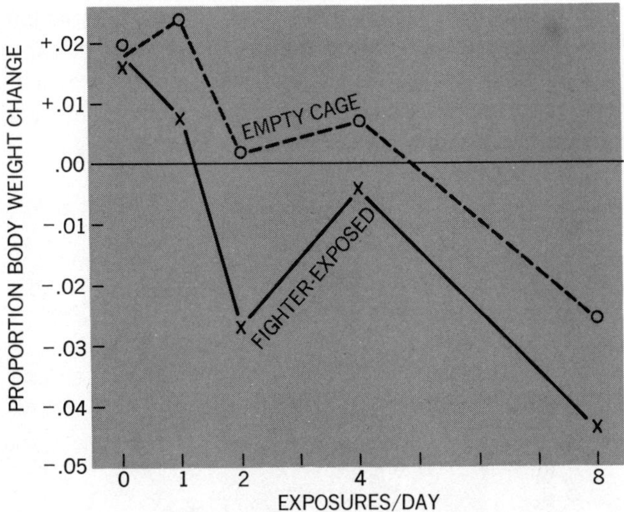

Figure 1 Relationship between mean proportion change of body weight (weight on day 6 minus weight on day 1 divided by weight on day 1) and various numbers of exposures per day to fighters or empty cages for one week. Twelve mice per average.

Adrenal weights also changed drastically due to the various treatments (Table 1). Because of the significant effects of the treatments on body weight, adrenal weights were adjusted to body length. Adrenal weight (mg)/body length (mm) × 100 is a conservative type of adjustment since 91% of the 120 mice used in this experiment had body lengths between 91 and 96 mm (range: 89–100 mm). Analysis of variance of the adrenal weights showed significance for (1) fighter vs. empty cage treatments ($p < 0.001$); (2) number of ex-

Table 1. *Mean Paired Adrenal Weights*[a] *of Mice Exposed to Trained Fighters or Empty Cages for 1 Week*

Exposed to	Number of exposures per day				
	0	1	2	4	8
Fighters	2.8	3.1	3.2	3.8	4.0
Empty Cages	2.6	2.8	2.8	3.0	3.1

[a] Paired adrenal weight (mg)/body length (mm) × 100; 12 mice per mean.

posures per day ($p < 0.001$); and (3) the interaction ($p < 0.01$). It is obvious from Table 1 that as the number of exposures per day to fighting or empty cages increased, adrenal weight increased also. It is also obvious that, of the two types of treatments, exposure to fighters had a much greater effect on adrenal weight.

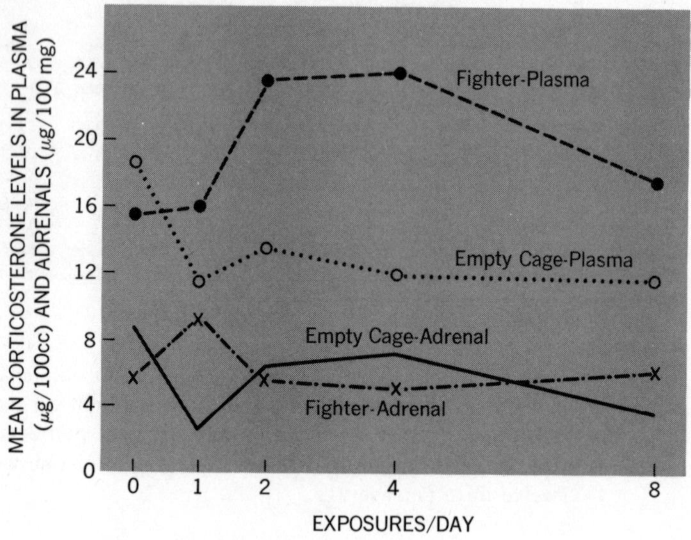

Figure 2 Corticosterone levels in the plasma (μg/100 ml plasma) and adrenals (μg/100 mg adrenal tissue after 0,1,2,4, or 8 exposures per day for 1 week to fighters or empty cages. Two samples of plasma or adrenals (each sample pooled from 6 mice) per average.

Plasma corticosterone levels, as measured 4–6 hours after the final exposure to a fighter or an empty cage, showed a distinct trend for higher levels in those mice that had been exposed to fighters (Fig. 2). This trend was tested by variance analysis and was significant ($p < 0.01$); however, there was no significance due to the number of exposures per day or to the interaction of these two variables. Adrenal corticosterone levels (Fig. 2), if adjusted for the increased adrenal weight caused by the treatments, showed no significant differences in any respect.

In addition to the effects on body weight and the adrenal, definite effects of the treatments on seminal vesicle weights were found

Table 2. *Mean Seminal Vesicle Weights[a] of Mice Exposed to Trained Fighters or Empty Cages for 1 Week*

Exposed to	Number of exposures per day				
	0	1	2	4	8
Fighters	2.4	2.3	2.2	2.1	2.0
Empty Cage	2.6	2.6	2.4	2.3	2.2

[a] Seminal vesicle weight (mg)/body length (mm) × 100; 12 mice per mean.

(Table 2). Analysis of variance revealed significant terms for fighting vs. empty cage ($p < 0.01$) and for number of exposures per day ($p = 0.01$), but a nonsignificant interaction. Because of the variation among the control samples, it would appear that only many repeated exposures to empty cages had any effect, while any amount of exposure to fighters caused some degree of decrease in seminal vesicle weight.

DISCUSSION

The objectives of this study were two-fold: (1) to investigate some possible physiological effects of exposure to very small amounts of aggression; and (2) to do so by utilizing a design that the authors feel has considerable merit for the laboratory study of the interrelationships between rodent population density and physiology.

With respect to the first objective of the study, the data reveal that exposure to small amounts of aggression was consistently followed by relatively large physiological changes. Effects of a chronic nature were found in adrenal, body, and seminal vesicle weights. As little as 2 1-minute exposures to trained fighters per day for 7 days resulted in a 19% increase in adrenal weight over untreated controls and a 14% increase over empty cage controls. Eight exposures per day resulted in a 48% increase in adrenal weight over untreated controls and a 29% increase over empty cage controls. Body weight was affected as the number of exposures to fighters increased. Mice exposed to 2, 4, or 8 fighters per day averaged weight losses for the period as did mice exposed 8 times per day to an empty cage. Analyses of seminal vesicle weights showed a significant decline in weight as number of exposures to fighters increased, but probably only excessive exposure to a strange cage (8 times per day) had any real effect on the weight of these glands.

Plasma corticosterone levels, as measured 4–6 hours after the final exposures to fighters or empty cages, averaged 20.2 μg/100 ml plasma in fighter-exposed mice and 12.1 μg in mice exposed to empty cages. The unexposed control mice averaged 17.0 μg of corticosterone/100 ml plasma. Since mice exposed several times per day to empty cages showed effects on body and adrenal weight, the reason that plasma corticosterone levels in these mice averaged below those of unexposed controls is not readily apparent unless this is a reflection of the time relationships involved in length of treatments and time of autopsy. The failure of increased numbers of exposure to fighters to be reflected in plasma levels might be attributable to the same reasons. Plasma corticosterone levels were measured between 2 and 4 P.M. and are similar in magnitude to those described for mice by Halberg *et al.*[6]

Adrenal corticosterone levels, when adjusted to micrograms/100 mg of adrenal tissue, were not affected by the treatments. Both adrenal weight and amount of corticosterone in the adrenals increased following fighter exposure, but, as expected, the relative ratio between the two remained essentially the same.[11]

Barnett[1] reported lipid depletion in the adrenal cortex after fighting in rats, and Bronson and Eleftheriou[2] reported depletion of adrenal ascorbic acid in two species of rodents exposed to trained fighters. Despite the problems associated with correlations of adrenal weight, ascorbic acid content, and secretory rates,[5, 12, 13, 17] it would seem that there could be little doubt that social domination by fighting has large effects on adrenal morphology and secretion. As shown by the present study, fighting can produce large adrenal changes even when occurring for only very short periods.

An important point here is that exposure to a trained fighter did not exclusively involve attacks on the subject mice, nor were the subjects wounded to any great degree. A random sample of 20 cumulative attack times obtained during the experiment revealed an average of 20 seconds and a range of 0–43 seconds of fighting during 1-minute exposures. Wounds were rare in mice exposed to one fight per day and common in those exposed to 8 fights per day. However, wounds were almost exclusively restricted to the tail and no severe wounds were found which parallel those that are often found when mice of this strain are isolated at weaning and then grouped as adults. Southwick[15] attributed increases in adrenal weight among crowded groups primarily to the wounded mice in those groups, but Christian[3a] found no correlation between wounding and adrenal weight in his caged populations. Barnett[1] observed that actual fighting was not always necessary to cause adrenal hypertrophy in crowded rats. In addition, Mason[7] reported an increase in circulating corticoid in a monkey that was watching two other monkeys fight. The physiological effects found in the present study were, therefore, probably more a result of psychological factors than wounding per se.

The large changes in adrenal and body weight, as well as the fact that the altered corticosterone levels were found 4–6 hours after exposure to fighters, would tend to argue that the psychological responses were sustained over a much longer span of time than just during the short exposures. However, the degree to which short-term "alarm" responses contributed to the altered plasma corticosterone levels cannot be evaluated by the present experiment.

With respect to the second objective of the study, i.e., examination of the general design for possible use in laboratory studies of the relationships between population density and rodent physiology, the authors feel that this design has considerable value for such investigations. The traditional models used in such studies are: (1) varying the number of animals per cage; and (2) sampling freely growing caged populations. The advantage of the present model is that all animals are always socially isolated except for a variable number of very short periods each day, a situation that comes much closer to duplicating field conditions for the majority of rodents (at least with respect to members of the same sex). The effect of increasing density can therefore be examined under conditions approximating field conditions by increasing the number of social contacts per day. An interesting conclusion of the present study is that effects were found on adrenal and seminal vesicle weights which parallel those found in studies where the number of mice per cage was varied;[3b] however, in the present study a design was used which avoids criticisms of unnaturally high densities.[9]

The applicability of the results from the present study is probably restricted to populations of highly aggressive rodents since all social contacts were made aggressive in nature by training some animals. The same design, however, could be used to study the relationships between density and physiology for less aggressive species of rodents[16] by using only naive animals or giving some mice a different type of training procedure (e.g., avoidance of other mice).

SUMMARY

Mice of the C57BL/10J strain were exposed to trained fighters or empty cages at the rate of 0, 1, 2, 4, or 8 times per day for 7 days. Each exposure lasted 1 minute. Mice exposed to fighters 2, 4, or 8 times per day or to an empty cage 8 times per day averaged losses in body weight during the experiment. Adrenal weight increased progressively as the number of exposures per day to fighters or empty cages increased, but the effects were much greater in mice exposed to fighters. Plasma corticosterone levels, as measured 4–6 hours after the last exposure, were significantly higher in mice exposed to fighters than in those exposed to empty cages. Adrenal corticosterone levels, if adjusted for the changes in adrenal weight, showed no effects of the treatments. Seminal vesicle weights decreased as the number of exposures to fighters increased.

REFERENCES

1. Barnett, S. A. 1958. Physiological effects of "social stress" in wild rats. I. The adrenal cortex. *Jour. Psychosom. Res.,* **3**: 1–11.
2. Bronson, F. H., and Eleftheriou, B. E. 1963. Adrenal responses to crowding in *Peromyscus* and C57BL/10J mice. *Physiol. Zool.,* **36**: 161–6.
3. Christian, J. J. 1957. A review of the endocrine responses in rats and mice to increasing population size including delayed effects on offspring. *Naval Med. Res. Inst. Lect. Rev. Series,* No. *57–2:* 443–62.

3a. ———. 1959. Lack of correlation between adrenal weight and injury from fighting in grouped male albino mice. *Proc. Soc. Exptl. Biol. Med.* **101**: 166–8.

3b. ———. 1960. Endocrine adaptive mechanisms and the physiologic regulation of population growth. *Naval Med. Res. Inst. Lect. Rev. Series,* No. 60–2: 49–150.

4. Clarke, J. R. 1953. The effect of fighting on the adrenals, thymus and spleen of the vole, *Microtus argestis. Jour. Endocrinol.,* **9**: 114–26.
5. Gray, C. H., Greenaway, J. M., and Holness, N. J. 1961. In *Hormones in Blood.* Edited by C. H. Gray and A. L. Bacharach. Pp. 440–514. New York: Academic Press.
6. Halberg, F., Peterson, R. E., and Silver, R. H. 1959. Phase relations of 24-hour periodicities in blood corticosterone, mitoses in cortical adrenal parenchyma, and total body activity. *Endocrinology,* **64**: 222–30.
7. Mason, J. W. 1959. Psychological influences on the pituitary-adrenal cortical system. *Recent Progr. Hormone Res.,* **15**, 343–89.
8. Moncloa, F., Peron, F. G., and Dorfman, R. I. 1959. The fluorimetic determination of corticosterone in rat adrenal tissue and plasma: Effect of administering ACTH subcutaneously. *Endocrinology,* **65**: 717–24.
9. Negus, N. C., Gould, E., and Chipman, R. K. 1961. Ecology of the rice rat, *Oryzomys palustris* (Harlan), on Breton Island, Gulf of Mexico, with a critique of the social stress theory. *Tulane Studies Zool.,* **8**: 95–123.
10. Peron, F. G., and Dorfman, R. I. 1959. A method for the evaluation of adrenocorticotropic hormone suppressing action of corticoids. *Endocrinology,* **64**: 431–6.

11. O'Donnell, V. J., and Preedy, J. R. K. 1961. In *Hormones in Blood.* Edited by C. H. Gray and A. L. Bacharach. Pp. 303–354. New York: Academic Press.
12. Sayers, G. 1961. In *Hormones in Blood.* Edited by C. H. Gray and A. L. Bacharach. Pp. 1–10. New York: Academic Press.
13. Schapiro, S., Geller, E., and Eiduson, S. 1962. Corticoid response to stress in the steroid-inhibited rat. *Proc. Soc. Exptl. Biol. Med.,* **109**: 935–7.
14. Scott, J. P. 1946. Incomplete adjustment caused by frustration of untrained fighting mice. *Jour. Comp. Psych.,* **39**: 379–90.
15. Southwick, C. H., and Bland, V. P. 1959. Effect of population density on adrenal glands and reproductive organs of CFW mice. *Am. Jour. Physiol.,* **197**: 111–4.
16. Terman, C. R. 1962. Spatial and homing consequences of the introduction of aliens into semi-natural populations of prairie deermice. *Ecology,* **43**: 216–23.
17. Vogt, M. 1957. In *Hormones in Blood.* Edited by G. E. W. Wolstenholme and E. C. P. Millar. Pp. 193–199. Ciba Foundation Colloquia on Endocrinology. Boston: Little, Brown.

11

THE NEURAL CONTROL OF AGGRESSION

JERRAM L. BROWN
University of Rochester

This paper was written while the author was in receipt of Research Grant MH 07700–06 from the U.S. Public Health Service. It is an original contribution written at the request of the editor.

Aggressive behavior in animals often occurs in the same contexts as escape and threat behavior. In many species, aggressive encounters are characterized mainly by various postures and actions known to ethologists as threat displays, and actual fights occur relatively infrequently. A species may have more than one type of threat display, and these often reflect the probabilities that the performing individual will act offensively or defensively or withdraw from the conflict altogether. The term, *agonistic behavior,*[46] has proven useful among ethologists for dealing with all of these functionally related behaviors and will be used here to refer to them collectively. This usage is particularly convenient for the discussion of brain mechanisms of aggression. Within the complex of agonistic behavior several rather different manifestations of aggressiveness can be recognized,[39] and the distinctions between some of them and their neural mechanisms will be brought out in the following discussions.

Agonistic behavior, although highly plastic in its ontogenetic development in some species, is clearly a product of evolution when viewed in comparative perspective, and so is necessarily under some degree of genetic guidance. This is manifested by conspicuous *species diversity* and *intraspecific constancy* in the types of agonistic behavior. These are often seen in various forms of threat display, including the well known defensive postures of domestic cats. Agonistic behavior provides another point of attack on one of the major problems in behavioral biology, the study of the neural basis of instinct.[12c] This article will discuss the neural mechanisms which mediate species-typical patterns of agonistic behavior in animals generally. More detailed reviews in which more emphasis is given to mammals, and particularly to cats, may be found in the reviews of Kaada[30] and Flynn.[20]

COMPARATIVE NEURO-ETHOLOGY OF AGONISTIC BEHAVIOR

By far the greatest amount of research on the neural bases of agonistic behavior has been done on the domestic cat, but there are important reasons for also examining other species. If findings for cats are to have wider biological significance, there should be some basis for generalization to other species, where this is possible. Furthermore, some behavioral phenomena are more easily studied and better illustrated in the lower vertebrates and invertebrates than in cats. The plan followed in this article will be to first establish a broad comparative base, while illustrating the basic principle of localization of function of aggressive behavior, and then to examine some of the complexities, details, and system properties as they have been revealed mainly in domestic cats.

Invertebrates. Among invertebrates the neural bases of agonistic behavior have received attention in crickets, cephalopods, and other groups. Male crickets of certain species may defend territories against each other, using a Calling Sound to announce their presence, and switching to an Aggressive Sound in encounters with rival males.[4] By stimulating various parts of the brain Huber[28] determined that the Calling Sound could be evoked by activation of the mushroom body in the protocerebrum, while the Aggressive Sound could be evoked by activation of a fiber tract leading to the mushroom body from the part of the brain receiving the antennal nerve. The evoked behavior in the latter case involved not only the calling, but also the general posture and other actions characteristic of aggressive behavior in crickets.

Squids and other members of the phylum Cephalopoda are famous for their giant axons—particularly in studies on conduction of action potentials. In this group, as well as in insects, crustacea, annelid worms, and other groups, certain rapid escape movements are coordinated by giant axons which may excite many different muscle groups over large areas of the body simultaneously and which are specialized for high speed of conduction.[13] These are clear cases of evolutionary specialization of the central and peripheral nervous systems for use in agonistic behavior—or, in other words, of the neural basis of instinct.

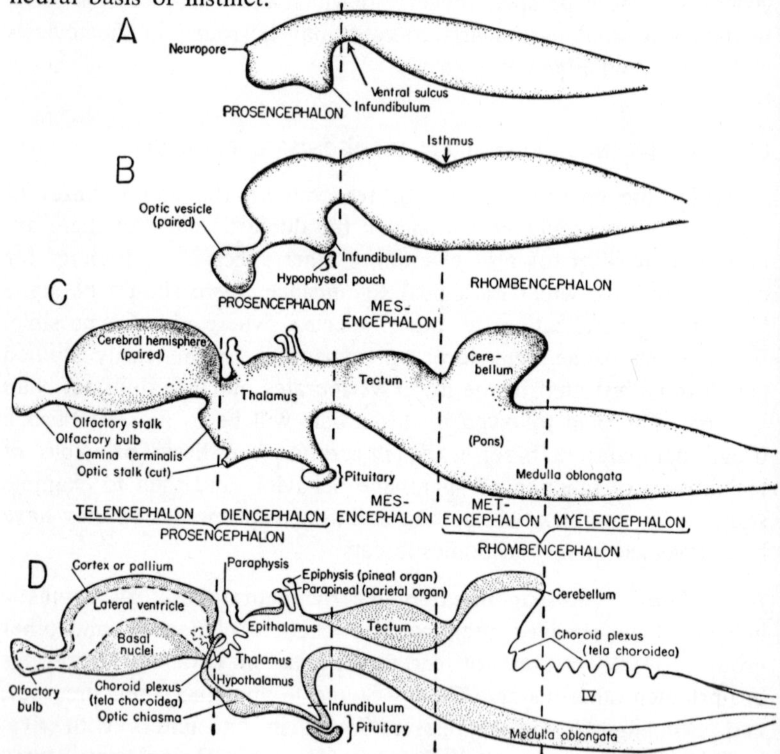

Figure 1 Diagrams to show the embryonic development of the principal divisions of the vertebrate brain and the structures derived from them. A, Only prosencephalon (embryonic forebrain) distinct from remainder of neural tube. B, Three main divisions established. C, More mature stage in lateral view. D, The same in median section to show ventricles. (From Romer, A.S. 1949. *The Vertebrate Body*. With permission of W. B. Saunders Co.)

Vertebrates. The brains of all vertebrates share certain basic similarities. These are best appreciated by examination of the embryological development of the brain. The developmental stages of a generalized vertebrate brain are shown in Fig. 1. Early in embryonic development three major divisions may be recognized, the prosencephalon (forebrain), the mesencephalon (midbrain), and the rhombencephalon (hindbrain). The forebrain becomes further differentiated into telencephalon (cerebral hemispheres, preoptic area) and diencephalon (mainly thalamus and hypothalamus); and the hindbrain differentiates into metencephalon (cerebellum, pons) and myelencephalon (medulla oblongata). Of the five major divisions, the telencephalon, diencephalon and mesencephalon are the most important in the control of agonistic behavior.

Lower Vertebrates. Among the lower vertebrates brain structures have been located which are directly involved with agonistic behavior. In fishes, lesions in the telencephalon interfere with the balance among 1) attacks on other males, 2) zig-zag sexual performances to females, and 3) the fanning movements used in care of the eggs.[47] Areas which are concerned with attacks, threat, and escape behaviors have been located in the anterior brain stem by stimulation experiments (Fiedler,[19] Demski,[15] and personal communications); for example, attack has been evoked by stimulation of the inferior lobe of the hypothalamus near the lateral recess of the third ventricle at the level of the nucleus rotundus pars glomerulosa in sunfish.

Birds. In the higher vertebrates the situation in birds is in some ways more easily understood than in mammals. The behavioral responses to electrical stimulation of the brain in feral pigeons have been studied by Åkerman.[3] Four basic categories of response were recognized, two related to *reproductive behavior,* 1) the bow-coo and 2) nest-coo sequences, and two related to *protective behavior,* 3) the defensive threat and 4) escape sequences. The nature of these behaviors is better appreciated from Figure 2 than from verbal descriptions. The reproductive behaviors were obtained at lowest threshold and in most complete and intense form by activation of the preoptic region of the brain. Similar responses were obtained by stimulation of nearby regions, but less complete and at higher thresholds. The responsive area for bow-cooing sequences was more extensive than that for nest-cooing and completely overlapped it. Reproductive behavior has been obtained by either electrical or chemical activation of the preoptic area in other vertebrates also.[15, 43c, 45]

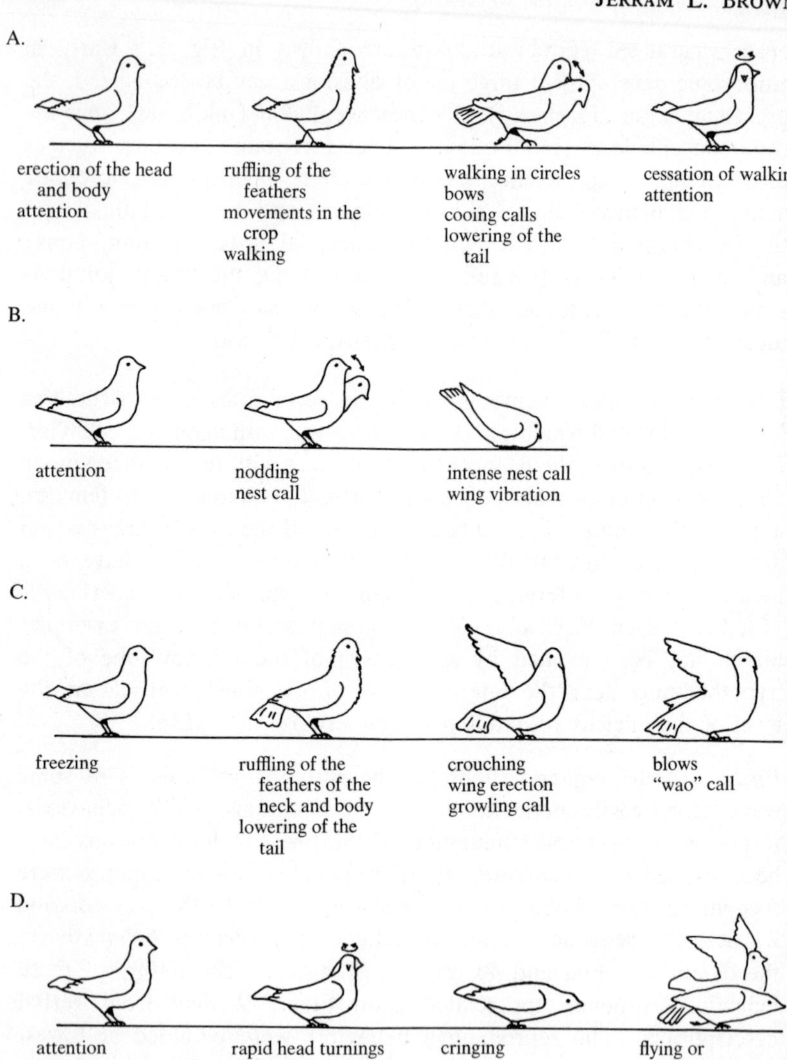

Figure 2 Different modes of agonistic and reproductive behavior as evoked by brain stimulation in the domestic pigeon A, The general pattern of the bowing and cooing behavior as a response to stimulation in the preoptic area. B, The general pattern of an intense nest demonstration as evoked by stimulation of the preoptic area. C, The defensive threat posture as the response to stimulation in the hypothalamus. D, Escape behavior as the response to stimulation in the lateral hypothalamus. (From Åkerman[3])

The bow-coo sequence in normal pigeons is a typical response of adult males toward rival males or toward females.[18, 24] It is aggressive in character; and when a rival male is present, he may be attacked. Females may also be attacked, but the male's behavior tends to change slowly toward nest-oriented and more strictly sexual activities. It is of especial interest that a solitary pigeon, which performs the bow-coo sequence in response to brain stimulation will attack any other pigeon who is with it during stimulation, even if the second pigeon is normally dominant to the experimental pigeon.[3,23] Here then is a fine example of aggressive behavior of an offensive character which is a normal component of a reproductive behavior pattern and is definitely not a part of a predatory or food catching response. This is an important point because the interpretation of aggressive attacks by cats on rats which have been studied by neurobiologists (see below) has been clouded by this ambiguity. In herbivores, such as pigeons, this ambiguity is absent.

The defensive threat sequence differs in its postural components from the bow-coo sequences and is accompanied by a different call, the "wao." It is used by normal pigeons while defending their nests from predators or in situations where they are cornered and cannot readily escape. Both the defensive and escape sequences are evoked from more posterior parts of the brain than are the reproductive behaviors; however, there is some overlap, and the responses intergrade somewhat behaviorally. The most intense and complete responses are obtained from hypothalamic stimulation.

A few similarities which exist between pigeons and cats in respect to protective behavior are worthy of note. In both species, defense and locomotor escape are behaviorally closely related; and in both, these behaviors are represented in adjacent and overlapping areas of the hypothalamus. Moreover, the spatial relationship between their responsive areas in the hypothalamus is similar; in both species defense areas tend to be located in the ventro-medial part of the hypothalamus and escape in the lateral hypothalamus. Since there is evidence of the same general relationship in other species too (e.g., opossum, see below), this may prove to be one of the more basic aspects of the neural mechanisms of agonistic behavior in the brains of vertebrates.

Another interesting similarity between pigeons and cats, and probably between other birds and mammals, is that aggression involving actual attacks may be associated with two quite different behavioral contexts (offensive and defensive, in this case) and that, judging by brain stimulation experiments, the neural mechanisms of these types of attacks are quite different. The two types are evoked by stimulation of different but partially overlapping regions in the brain and are associated with differnt behavior patterns. Although the offensive attacks are certainly different in cats and pigeons, the main point is that *more than one brain system may be involved in attack behavior*. This suggests that psychiatrists and other who must face the social consequences of aggression in man might be wise to allow for the possibility of more than one neural mechanism of aggression in man.[39]

Mammals. The first use of localized brain stimulation to locate brain structures relating to agonistic behavior was in mammals. One of the most thorough of such studies was done on the opossum *(Didelphis virginiana;* Roberts *et al.).*[43c] In this work a greater range of behaviors was investigated than usual in mammalian studies, and care was taken to provide apropriate sensory stimuli in order to bring out various responses to electrical stimulation which might not otherwise appear in the absence of the appropriate stimulus objects. Thus food, water, canned cat food, dog pellets, a rat, a stuffed long-haired toy dog, a slanting log, a wooden wedge, and plastic foliage were provided.

The behavioral responses which were obtained by electrical stimulation in the presence of appropriate goal objects were divided into major categories. These included 1) male mating behavior, 2) defensive threat, 3) attack, 4) eating, 5) grooming, and 6) escape-like activity. The anatomical locations of the electrode points together with synoptic indications of the evoked behavior patterns are shown in Figure 3. These data illustrate particularly well the anatomical relationships among the responsive regions for the different evoked responses. Those readers who are familiar with the anatomical representation of similar behavior patterns in the hypothalamus of the domestic cat will notice many similarities between opossums and cats. Similar data for cats are available but would have to be compiled from many different studies in which different methods of obtaining and plotting the data were used. The comprehensive and detailed nature of the opossum study is unique in the literature on brain mapping and agonistic behavior. Consequently, it is particularly worthy of study.

Consider first the location of points for biting attack. Surprisingly, these are found in two quite separate regions, one dorsal to the

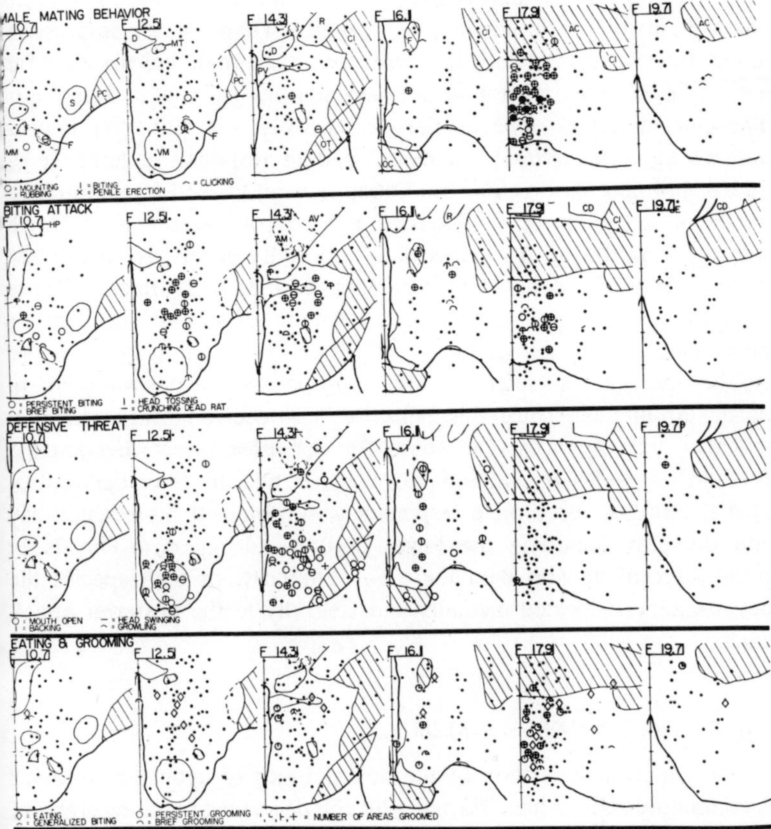

Figure 3 Locations of positive and negative points for motivational and species-typical behavioral responses plotted on transverse plane diagrams of the hypothalamus and preoptic area of the opossum. Negative points are indicated by small, black dots. Note that the clusters of positive points for a given behavior are partly separate and partly overlapping with those for other behaviors. AC, commissura anterior; AM; nucleus anterior medialis thalami; AV, nucleus anterior ventralis thalami; CD, nucleus caudatus; CI, capsula interna; D, nucleus dorsalis hypothalami; F. columna fornicis; HP, tractus habenulopeduncularis; MM, corpus mammillare; MT, tractus mammillothalamicus; OC, chiasma opticum; OT, tractus opticus; PC, pedunculus cerebri; PV, nucleus filiformis pars paraventricularis; R, nucleus reticularis; S, nucleus subthalamicus; VM, nucleus ventromedialis hypothalami. (From Roberts *et al.,* 1967. *Jour. Comp. and Physiol. Psychol.* **64**: p. 8. With permission of the American Psychological Association.)

ventromedial nucleus and slightly anterior to it, and the other more anterior in the central preoptic region. There is an impressive amount of overlap between the posterior attack zone and the zone for eating, as well as with that for locomotion, sniffing and looking. The anterior attack zone overlaps extensively with those for mating and eating. In addition, elements of both response patterns (e.g., attack and mating, or attack and eating) were evoked by stimulation at the same point in a moderate number of cases. It is worth remembering that in opossums biting normally occurs as an element of such different behaviors as mating, eating, and attack. These findings again emphasize the heterogeneity of neural mechanisms underlying attack behavior.

The location of defensive threat responses in opossums is of particular interest, since this behavior has received much attention in cats. The hypothalamic space for defensive threat in complete form in opossums is centered in the upper two-thirds of the ventromedial nucleus; incomplete responses were obtained more anteriorly and dorsally, including the lower perifornical region. This is in rough agreement with data for cats. Similarly, in both species the defense zone is located medially and ventrally to the posterior attack zone.

THE DEFENSE BEHAVIOR SYSTEM

The experimental study of the neural bases of agonistic behavior is commonly said to have started with the decorticate and decerebrate preparations of Goltz[22] on dogs and Dusser de Barenne[17] on cats. These and further experiments by others[9] showed that dogs and cats deprived of their forebrains reacted with defensive behavior (sometimes called sham rage in such preparations) to light touch and other normally inconsequential stimuli. These transection experiments suggested that a mechanism for the production of defensive behavior was located in the hypothalamus and that it was normally inhibited by the forebrain.

Mapping. Verification of an important hypothalamic role in defensive behavior was achieved through detailed mapping studies, which located the responsive zone more precisely in the ventromedial part of the hypothalamus (particularly the upper two-thirds of the ventromedial nucleus and the nearby "perifornical" area) with extensions forward into the bed nucleus of the stria terminalis and the preoptic region.[25, 29, 38] Further exploration with stimulation techniques led to the discovery that similar defensive responses could be evoked by activation of the amygdala in the forebrain[21] and of the central gray matter of the midbrain.[29] There are two major anatomical connections between the amygdala and hypothalamus, the ventral amygdalofugal pathway (VAF) and the stria terminalis. Both have been implicated in the defense reaction, but the role of the VAF suggested by Hilton and Zbroznya[26] has not yet been verified independently by other workers and has been questioned by Hunsperger and Bucher.[29a] Although anatomical connections between the defense zones of the hypothalamus and of the central gray matter of the midbrain are known, the route or routes by which these two important zones for defensive behavior influence each other have not been well delineated.

The descending pathway for facio-vocal components of defensive behavior from the central gray of the midbrain through the medulla in cats was shown to curve laterally and ventrally and to run posteriorly under the medial lemniscal tract.[13, 35]

In summary, the anatomical picture suggests that defensive behavior is organized in the brain as a system composed at the minimum of populations of neurons located at each of three important levels (midbrain, diencephalon, and forebrain) with connections between them and to lower brain-stem levels. The system is illustrated schematically in Figure 4. Consequently, it would be misleading to designate any one of these populations as a "center." A more heuristic concept would be that each of the three zones has its own integrative properties (mostly yet to be differentiated) and makes its own special contribution to the system as a whole. The relationships among these three levels will now be briefly considered.

System Properties. The defense reactions which can be evoked by stimulation at any one of the three levels vary greatly, depending on numerous factors including environmental conditions, electrode type and location, and stimulus parameters. The system is somewhat more difficult to excite from the forebrain level than posteriorly. Some general differences among the regions in the predominance of various response elements, such as growling or hissing, also seem to be present. Despite certain minor differences, the general nature of response is much the same for all three regions.

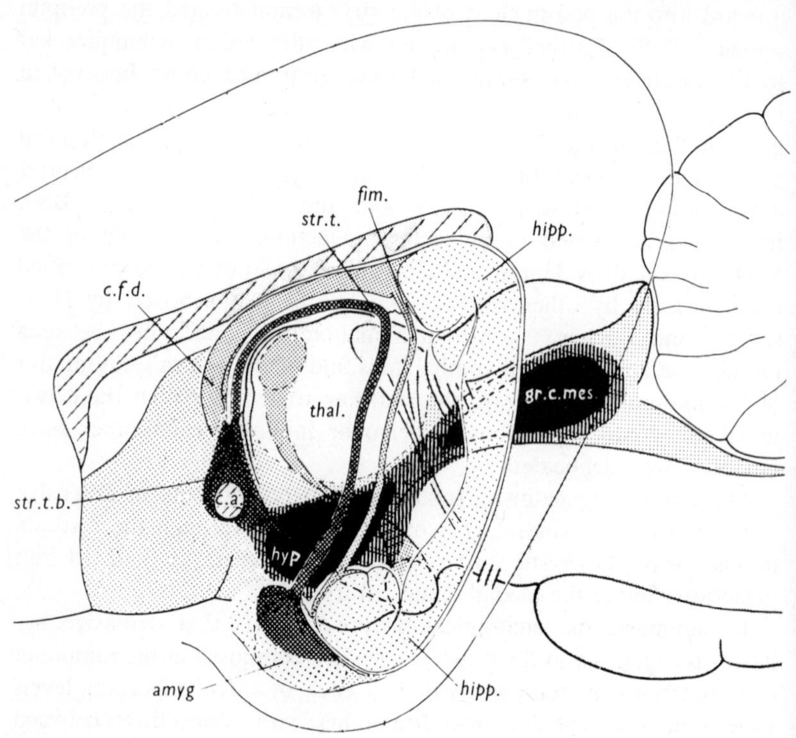

Figure 4 Schematic illustration representing the defensive threat and locomotor escape zones in the forebrain and brain stem. Sagittal section through the brain stem with amygdala and other more laterally situated structures superimposed. The ventral amygdalofugal pathway and the route through the medulla are not shown; see text. amyg., amygdala; c.a., anterior commissure; c.f.d., descending column of the fornix; fim, fimbria; gr. c. mes., central gray matter of the midbrain; hipp., hippocampus; hyp., hypothalamus; str. t., stria terminalis; str. t. b., bed nucleus of the stria terminalis; thal., thalamus. *White dots on a black background:* Responsive field of the amygdala, stria terminalis and stria bed at the level of the anterior commissure. *Solid black:* Responsive zones of the hypothalamus and central gray matter of the midbrain. *Vertical lines:* Responsive zones for locomotor escape behavior when cat is free to jump off the table. (After Hunsberger, R. W., and V. M. Bucher, 1967. *Progress in Brain Research,* Vol. 27. With permission of Elsevier Publishing Co., Amsterdam, Holland.)

Of the three neuronal populations, only that at the midbrain level would seem to be indispensable for normal defensive behavior. Experiments suggest a predominantly "downstream" pattern of activation in the defense system, in which upper levels act primarily by exciting lower levels. Bilateral lesions in the defense zones of the hypothalamus or amygdala do not eliminate defense behavior which is elicited either by sensory stimuli, such as from a dog, or by electrical stimulation of the midbrain. In contrast, lesioning of the defense zone of the midbrain produced an immediate and lasting loss of ability to respond appropriately to a dog or to other cats.[29, 32, 38a] There was, however, partial recovery of the response to electrical stimulation of the hypothalamus in some of the same cats. Certain lesions of the same region of the central gray matter of the midbrain abolished all vocalizations transiently or, in some cases, permanently.[48a] Destruction of midbrain vocalization regions has also caused mutism in dogs[48] and redwinged blackbirds.[12, 12a, 12b] These midbrain regions seem to be involved not only in defensive behavior, but in all sorts of vocal expression in these species.

In the medulla small lesions across the vocalization pathway (just under the medial lemniscus) block the vocal component of defensive responses which are evoked by electrical stimulation of the pons and hypothalamus in decorticate or decerebrate cats, but only if the lesion is on the same side as the stimulation.[31] At this level the different components of defensive behavior appear to follow separate pathways.

Afferent Connections. In cats the stimuli which evoke defensive behavior in nature are likely to involve primarily the visual sense, with lesser contributions from auditory and olfactory pathways. Only if the cat is actually bitten would excitation via pain pathways be expected. Consequently, pain-elicited aggression[7] and defensive reactions to trivial stimuli in decerebrate cats may depend upon different pathways, such as the collaterals from the spinothalamic tract which reach the defense zone in the midbrain, or certain patterns of activity in the ascending reticular formation.[1] Both excitatory and inhibitory effects of stimulation of the midbrain reticular formation on defensive responses in decorticate cats have been demonstrated.[11a] Recording electrical activity from the ventromedial nucleus and from the midbrain central gray in the defense zones has shown slow potentials and activity of single neurons to result from a variety of sensory stimuli, including visual and auditory ones.[1, 2, 2a] The main afferent routes are probably quite indirect and may possibly involve such limbic system structures as the septum, hippocampus, or cingulate gyrus.

A second class of afferents to the defense system may be recognized, which serves not so much to evoke defensive behavior directly, but probably to maintain the level of activity in the system within appropriate bounds by tonic and feedback excitation and inhibition. Since defensive behavior involves literally all parts of the animal, including both autonomic and somatic nervous systems, the potential sources of such feedback and tonic control are numerous. For example, in decorticate cats it has been shown that sham rage can be inhibited by increased blood pressure at the carotid sinus pressoceptors[10] and excited by chemoceptive afferents from the carotid bodies;[11] parallel effects were obtained from nerves from the aorta.[8, 8a] For the somatic nervous system it has long been known that light touch can set off sham rage in decerebrate cats; but more recently, discharges from Group I muscle afferents (primary muscle spindle endings and/or Golgi tendon organs) have also been shown to have an excitatory influence on sham rage in decorticate cats.[36]

ESCAPE BEHAVIOR

The close association in the normal behavior of cats between escape and other forms of agonistic behavior is reflected in the brain by the intimate anatomical and physiological relationship of these behavior patterns, particularly in the amygdala, hypothalamus and midbrain. From all of these regions what appears to be escape behavior, or at least compulsive locomótion, can be evoked from brain locations which are adjacent to or intermingled with those for defense. Moreover, at least from the hypothalamus a great variety of combinations of components of attack, threat, and escape can be elicited, depending on electrode locations, stimulus parameters, and environmental conditions, as partly shown in Table 1.

Table 1 shows schematically the relationship between the behavioral transition from evoked defense to evoked locomotor escape and the anatomical transition from ventromedial to lateral hypothalamus (at levels near the ventromedial nucleus). The same gradation in evoked behavior may also be found along other anatomical gradients. As suggested by the table, thresholds for locomotor escape by jumping off the table decrease toward the lateral hypothalamus and increase toward the ventromedial hypothalamus. Stimulation in the defense zone typically induces a "freezing" response and cessation of all other ongoing activity as the first effect of stimulation. With more lateral stimulation sites, movement becomes more prominent and defense, less prominent. Stimulation at sites in the medial forebrain bundle of the lateral hypothalamus may show essentially no components of agonistic behavior; the stimulated cat typically approaches and sniffs a dummy cat in the species-typical nose-to-nose manner, which if not necessarily friendly, is at least not defensive.[12d]

Table 1. *Simplified scheme showing behavioral and anatomical relationships among types of agonistic behavior evoked by electrical stimulation[a] of the hypothalamus of cats. A dummy, stuffed cat was used as the object of attack. (Partly from Brown* et al.[12d]*) G = Growl. H = Hiss. J = Jump off the table (locomotor escape). A_c = Attack with claws ("affective attack"). A_B = Biting attack ("stalking attack"). S = Sniff nose and face of dummy. VM = Ventromedial nucleus of hypothalamus. LHA = Lateral hypothalamic area.*

Stimulation Intensity	Behavioral Responses				
High	A_cJ	A_cJ	A_{cB}	A_B	J
	↑	↑	↑	↑	↑
Medium	GH	GH	HJ	A_B	S
	↑	↑	↑	↑	↑
Low	G —	H —	J —	J —	S
Stimulation Site	VM ———		transitional ———		LHA

[a] Stimulation was done with a Wyss stimulator and bipolar, concentric electrodes at 16 Hz, pulse duration 15 msec, and intensity from 1 to 5 volts.

The terms, escape and flight, as used in these types of experiment refer only to the locomotor aspects of behavior and not to the reinforcing effects of brain stimulation in a learning situation. The latter phenomenon is discussed separately below, but it should be mentioned here that stimulation at locomotor escape sites is not necessarily completely aversive, as might at first be anticipated.

ATTACK BEHAVIOR

An important advance in the study of the neural bases of aggression was the discovery by Wasman and Flynn[49] that two different types of attack could be evoked by hypothalamic stimulation and that they were represented in different parts of the hypothalamus. The first type had long been known; it was characterized by the presence of elements of defensive behavior preceding and accompanying the attack and by use of the claws rather than the teeth to hurt the opponent. It was designated "affective" atack, with reference to Freudian psychology, but ethologists have not found the concept of affect to be useful for animals generally. Consequently, I suggest that this type of attack be called defensive attack because of the objectively observable presence of hissing, growling and/or other elements of the defensive pattern.

In the second type, attacks typically involved biting and were not accompanied by defensive responses. The anatomical relationships between the two types are rather similar in cats and opossums and may be seen in Figure 3 (for opossums). Biting attack has also been evoked by stimulation of sites in the midline nuclei of the thalamus.[34]

In most of the work in Flynn's laboratory, rats were used as the object of attack, and these were often anesthetized; but live cats and various stuffed animals and inanimate objects have also been used. Stimulated cats will attack a wide variety of objects, including stuffed cats, dogs, foxes, and pigeons, but they are less likely to attack objects which do not resemble an animal.[12d, 33]

As shown in Table 1, attacks evoked from more lateral parts of the hypothalamus characteristically involve more locomotion, are more likely to involve biting, and are less likely to be accompanied by growling, hissing and other signs of defensive behavior than are attacks evoked by stimulation of more ventromedial parts. Cats stimulated in the ventromedial nucleus may lash out with their claws in the air even in the absence of a dummy. Cats stimulated in lateral regions of the hypothalamus show little if any sign of attack behavior in the absence of a dummy and may often perform typical locomotor escape. When experiments are done with the cat on an unenclosed table in the Hess manner, rather than confined in a small box, attack and locomotor escape may occur in the same evoked sequence. This may be an indication that the acts of attack and escape as evoked by brain stimulation, may not have all the qualities of their normal counterparts.

REINFORCING EFFECTS OF BRAIN STIMULATION IN RELATION TO EVOKED AGONISTIC BEHAVIOR

It has been shown in cats that stimulation of localized brain volumes can serve as negative reinforcement.[14, 51] The question then arises whether stimulation at the various sites from which attack, defense, and escape can be evoked is positively or negatively reinforcing.

For sites from which defense and defensive attack can be evoked, stimulation has generally been found to be negatively reinforcing,[41, 51] whereas some sites which evoke stalking attack have been found to be positively reinforcing. Roberts and Kiess,[43b] for example, found that stimulated cats would learn to run a Y-maze to obtain opportunity to attack a rat, while unstimulated cats would not. A comparison of sites for a stalking attack[43b, 49] with those for "strong reward"[51] also suggests an association between stalking and positive reinforcement (although precise comparisons are not possible because of numerous differences in experimental methods and electrode positions).

The reinforcing effects of brain stimulation at locomotor escape sites are confusing. Stimulation in the posterior hypothalamus in regions where Hunsperger[29] and others have obtained locomotor escape behavior revealed both rewarding and punishing effects from stimulation at the same site at the same stimulation parameters.[43, 43a] Cats would learn to escape from stimulation after a certain period but they would not learn to avoid it; some learned to turn on the stimulation and then to turn it off by entering the appropriate arms of a Y-maze. The regions from which locomotor escape have been evoked are so diverse that their reinforcing properties are probably also diverse. The more lateral hypothalamic escape sites are close to the medial forebrain bundle and in a region where positive reinforcement has been obtained, thus emphasizing the possible rewarding effects of stimulation at certain so-called "escape" sites.

Relatively little attention has been given to the reinforcing effects of brain stimulation at sites which were also tested for evoked behavior in cats. The relationship between the kinds of instinctive behavior patterns which are evoked by brain stimulation and their roles in reinforcement would seem to be an important one and worthy of more attention.

STUDIES ON SINGLE NEURONS

Although much remains to be learned about agonistic behavior using the now classical techniques of activation and inactivation of restricted brain regions (e.g., by stimulation or lesions), the relatively new methods of recording from single neurons (units) is beginning to provide an understanding of patterns of neural activity which would have been impossible to obtain with older methods. Only a start has been made on the investigation of agonistic behavior with single-unit techniques, but the promise of important discoveries to come in this area warrants at least brief consideration here.

The ventromedial nucleus (VM) of the hypothalamus has received considerable attention, not only because of its involvement in defensive behavior, but also as the site of glucose sensitive neurons[37] that appear to have an inhibitory effect upon neural mechanisms which activate feeding behavior in the lateral hypothalamic area (LHA). It has been shown that units in VM can be activated by a rise in blood glucose[5] and that some units in VM and LHA have a mutually inhibitory influence on each other.[42, 42a] The latter finding may well prove of considerable importance for the ethological analysis of conflict behavior, for the VM-LHA interaction might be hypothesized to participate in a variety of go-no go conflicts, including those in the motivation of threat displays and attack. Although glucostatic neurons have been investigated primarily with regard to feeding behavior, treatment of mice with gold-thio-glucose (GTG), which is thought to kill these cells, also has effects on male-male fighting and on sexual behavior.[50] Axons of GTG-sensitive neurons have been traced to the central gray matter[6a] in the defense zone, as well as to LHA.[6] Significant interactions between VM and LHA have also been found at the behavioral level in a variety of experiments.[12e, 27]

Since stimulation of the amygdala can evoke defensive behavior, and since this response can be blocked by lesions of VM, the stria terminalis (ST), or the ventral amygdalofugal pathway (VAF), a logical hypothesis is that the amygdala acts to produce defensive behavior by exciting VM units. The taming effects of amygdalar lesions[30] are also conducive to such an interpretation. It was, therefore, unexpected to find that amygdalar stimulation tends to inhibit many spontaneous VM units in anesthetized cats.[16, 44]

Further analysis by Murphy and Renaud[40] suggested that stimulation of the corticomedial nuclear group in the amygdala activates fibers which pass via ST and terminate on small, bipolar neurons mainly on the edge of VM; these in turn inhibit the spontaneous firing of larger, multipolar neurons in the central part of the nucleus. In contrast, stimulation of the basolateral nuclear group was thought to activate fibers passing via VAF which end on both the small bipolar and larger multipolar cells, thus causing an excitation-inhibition sequence. An unexpected finding of these studies was that the effects of fibers passing from the amygdala to VM by separate routes (ST, VAF) could converge on the same single neurons in VM. The behavioral significance of these details is not yet known.

The stimuli which affect unit activity in caged, awake cats under various conditions were investigated by Adams.[2, 2a] He found that two-thirds of the units found in VM, where defense could be evoked by electrical stimulation (with the same electrode), were inhibited during naturally elicited defensive behavior toward another cat and by other manipulations. This was in contrast to the midbrain, where no units were inhibited during defensive behavior. Neurons which fired only during defensive behavior and never or rarely in other contexts was found only in or close to the midbrain defense zone in the central gray matter and not at all in the hypothalamus.

The picture that emerges from these unit studies is not yet clear, but enough has been learned to suggest that inhibitory processes may be more important in the hypothalamic activation of defensive behavior than had previously been thought, and that single unit analysis will be profitable in studying the neural substrates of agonistic behavior.

AGGRESSION AND DEFENSE AS INSTINCTIVE BEHAVIOR

The dichotomy between genetic and environmental determination of behavior refers legitimately and in purest form only to the *source* of the influence (whether from inheritance or the environment), and *not to the end product* of development, the behavior itself—which is in all cases the result of cumulative interactions between these two sources. The two related phenomena of *uniformity* of agonistic behavior *within a species* and of *diversity* of agonistic behavior *between species* are both correlated with genetic factors and suggest an important role of evolution and inheritance in the ontogenetic development of behavior in the species involved. It is convenient to use the term "instinctive" to emphasize the role of evolution in determining patterns of species constancy and diversity in agonistic behavior (without excluding the role of environmental influences). Such usage is entirely consistent with modern knowledge of the diverse and subtle influences of environment on the nervous system and on behavior and does not exclude them from consideration.

In the nervous system one of the best types of evidence of an evolutionary influence on agonistic behavior is in the basic similarity of the brain mechanisms which mediate agonistic behavior in animals as diverse as fishes, birds, opossums and domestic cats, as discussed above. It is sometimes said that animals inherit only the capacity to behave aggressively and that it is their environment which shapes the final performance. This is true, but such statements are misleading in that they avoid mentioning the pervasive and subtle ways in which inheritance can affect behavior. Consider from a neurobiological viewpoint what is subsumed under "capacity." This includes not just the abilities to perceive stimuli, to perform elementary motor acts, and to learn to put them together according to the "law of effect." It also includes the various populations of neurons at different brain levels, the fiber tracts connecting them with each other and with other parts of the brain, and the physiological properties of the neurons comprising them.

The instinctive capacity to behave aggressively is based upon these neurons and their relations with the rest of the brain. To say that the capacity for agonistic behavior is instinctive and that it depends on certain demonstrable, species-typical patterns of neural organization in the brain is not a solution to the problem of understanding aggression. It serves mainly to raise questions about how these mechanisms work, how they are produced by the combined guidance of inheritance and environment on development, and how they can be modified by the manipulation of genetic and environmental variables.

REFERENCES

1. Abrahams, V. C., Hilton, S. M., and Malcolm, J. L. 1962. Sensory connexions to the hypothalamus and midbrain, and their role in the reflex activation of the defence reaction. *Jour. Physiol.,* **164**: 1–16.
2. Adams, D. B. 1968. Cells related to fighting behavior recorded from midbrain central gray neuropil of cat. *Science,* **159**: 894–6.

2a. ———. 1968. The activity of single cells in the midbrain and hypothalamus of the cat during affective defense behavior. *Arch. Ital. Biol.,* **106**: 243–69.

3. Åkerman, B. 1965. Behavioural effects of electrical stimulation in the forebrain of the pigeon. I. Reproductive behaviour. II. Protective behaviour. *Behaviour,* **26**: 323–50.
4. Alexander, R. D. 1962. Evolutionary change in cricket acoustical communication. *Evolution,* **16**: 443–67.
5. Anand, B. K., Chhina, G. S., and Singh, B. 1962. Effect of glucose on the activity of hypothalamic "feeding centers." *Science,* **138**: 597–8.
6. Arees, E. A., and Mayer, J. 1967. Anatomical connections between

medial and lateral regions of the hypothalamus concerned with food intake. *Science,* **157**: 1574–75.

6a. ———. 1968. The bundle of Schütz and its relation to the regulation of food intake. *Experientia,* **24**: 1220–21.

7. Azrin, N. H., Hutchinson, R. R., and Sallery, R. D. 1964. Pain-aggression toward inanimate objects. *Jour. Exp. Anal. Beh.,* **7**: 223–8.

8. Baccelli, G., Guazzi, M., Libretti, A. and Zanchetti, A. 1963. Effects of presso- and chemoceptive components of the cat's aortic nerve on sham rage behavior. *Experientia,* **19**: 534.

8a. ———. 1965. Pressoceptive and chemoceptive aortic reflexes in decorticate and in decerebrate cats. *Am. Jour. Physiol.,* **208**: 708–14.

9. Bard, P. 1928. A diencephalic mechanism for the expression of rage with special reference to the sympathetic nervous system. *Am. Jour. Physiol.,* **84**: 490–515.

10. Bartorelli, C., Bizzi, E., Libretti, A. and Zanchetti, A. 1960. Inhibitory control of sinocarotid pressoceptive afferents in hypothalamic activity and sham rage behavior. *Arch. Ital. Biol.,* **98**: 308–26.

11. Bizzi, E., Libretti, A., Malliani, A. and Zanchetti, A. 1961. Reflex chemoceptive excitation of diencephalic sham rage behavior. *Am. J. Physiol.,* **200**: 923–6.

11a. ———, Malliani, A., Apelbaum, J. and Zanchetti, A. 1963. Excitation and inhibition of sham rage behavior by lower brain stem stimulation. *Arch. Ital. Biol.,* **101**: 614–31.

12. Brown, J. L. 1965. Vocalization evoked from the optic lobe of a songbird. *Science,* **149**: 1002–3.

12a. ———, 1965. Loss of vocalization caused by lesions in the *Nucleus mesencephalicus lateralis* of the redwinged black bird. *Am. Zool.,* **5**: 693.

12b. ———, 1969. The control of avian vocalization by the central nervous system. In *Bird Vocalizations. Their Relation to Current Problems in Biology and Psychology.* Edited by R. A. Hinde. Cambridge: Cambridge University Press.

12c. ———. 1969. Neuro-ethological approaches to the study of emotional behavior: stereotypy and variability. *Proc. N. Y. Acad. Sci.,* (in press).

12d. ———. Hunsperger, R. W., and Rosvold, H. E. 1969. Defence, attack, and flight elicited by electrical stimulation of the hypothalamus of the cat. *Exper. Brain Res.,* **8**: 113–29.

12e. ———. 1969. Interaction of defense and flight reactions produced by simultaneous stimulation at two points in the hypothalamus of the cat. *Exper. Brain Res.,* **8**: 130–49.

13. Bullock, T. H., and Horridge, G. A. 1965. *Structure and Function in the Nervous Systems of Invertebrates.* Vols. I, II. San Francisco: W. H. Freeman.

14. Delgado, J. M. R., Roberts, W. W., and Miller, N. E. 1954. Learning motivated by electrical stimulation of the brain. *Am. Jour. Physiol.,* **179**: 587–93.

15. Demski, L. S. 1969. Behavioral effects of electrical stimulation of the brain of the sunfish, *Lepomis macrochirus.* Abstract. *Anat. Rec.,* **163**: 177.

16. Dreifuss, J. J., Murphy, J. T., and Gloor, P. 1968. Contrasting effects of two identified amygdaloid efferent pathways on single hypothalamic neurons. *Jour. Neurophysiol.*, **31**: 237–48.
17. Dusser De Barenne, J. G. 1920. Récherche expérimentale sur les fonctions du système nerveux central, faites en particulier sur deux chats dont le néopallium avait été enleve. *Arch. Neerl. Physiol.*, **4**: 31–123.
18. Fabricius, E., and Jannson, A. 1963. Laboratory observations on the reproductive behaviour of the pigeon, *Columbia livia*, during the pre-incubation phase of the breeding cycle. *Animal Behaviour*, **11**: 534–47.
19. Fiedler, K. 1967. Verhaltenswirksame Strukturen im Fischgehirn. Verh. Dtsch. Zool. Ges. Heidelberg. *Zool. Anz. Suppl.*, **31**: 602–616.
20. Flynn, J. P. 1967. The neural basis of aggression in cats. *Neurophysiology and Emotion*. Edited by D. C. Glass. Pp. 40–60. New York: Rockefeller University Press and Russell Sage Foundation.
21. Gastaut, H., Vigouroux, R., Corriol, J., and Badier, M. 1951. Effets de la stimulation électrique (par électrodes à demeure) du complexe amygdalien chez le chat non narcotisé. *Jour. Physiol. Paris*, **43**: 740–746.
22. Goltz, F. 1892. Der Hund ohne Grosshirn. *Pflügers Arch.*, **51**: 570–614.
23. Goodman, I. J., and Brown, J. L. 1966. Stimulation of positively and negatively reinforcing sites in the avian brain. *Life Sciences*, **5**: 693–704.
24. Heinroth, O., and Heinroth, K. 1949. Verhaltensweise der Felsentaube (Haustaube). *Zeitschrift für Tierpsychologie*, **6**: 153–201.
25. Hess, W. R., and Brügger, M. 1943. Das subkortikale Zentrum der Affektiven Abwehrreaktion. *Helv. Physiol. Acta*, **1**: 33–52.
26. Hilton, S. M., and Zbrozyna, A. W. 1963. Amygdaloid region for defence reactions and its efferent pathway to the brainstem. *Jour. Physiol.*, **165**: 160–73.
27. Hoebel, B. G., and Teitelbaum, P. 1962. Hypothalamic control of feeding and self-stimulation. *Science*, **135**: 375–7.
28. Huber, F. 1962. Central nervous control of sound production in crickets and some speculations on its evolution. *Evolution*, **16**: 429–43.
29. Hunsperger, R. W. 1956. Affektreaktionen auf elektrische Reizung im Hirnstamm der Katze. *Helv. Physiol. et Pharmacol. Acta*, **14**: 70–92.
29a. ———, and Bucher, V. M. 1967. Affective behaviour produced by electrical stimulation in the forebrain and brain stem of the cat. *Progress in Brain Research*, **27**: 103–27.
30. Kaada, B. 1967. Brain mechanisms related to aggressive behavior. *Brain Function*, **5**: 95–116. Clemente, C. D. and Lindsley D. B. (Editors). *Aggression and Defense*. Berkeley and Los Angeles: University of California Press.
31. Kanai, T., and Wang, S. C. 1962. Localization of the central vocalization mechanism in the brain stem of the cat. *Exper. Neurol.*, **5**: 426–34.
32. Kelly, A. H., Beaton, L. E. and Magoun, H. W. 1946. A midbrain mechanism for facio-vocal activity. *Jour. Neurophysiol.*, **9**: 181–9.
33. Levison, P. K., and Flynn, J. P. 1965. The objects attacked by cats during stimulation of the hypothalamus. *Animal Behaviour*, **13**: 217–20.
34. MacDonnell, M. F., and Flynn, J. P. 1964. Attack elicited by stimulation of the thalamus of cats. *Science*, **144**: 1249–50.

35. Magoun, H. W., Atlas, D., Ingersoll, E. H. and Ranson, S. W., 1937. Associated facial, vocal and respiratory components of emotional expression: an experimental study. *Jour. Neurol., Neurosurg. Psychiatr.*, **17**: 241–55.
36. Malliani, A., Carli, G., Mancia, G., and Zanchetti, A. 1968. Behavioral effects of electrical stimulation of Group I muscle afferents in acute thalamic cats. *Jour. Neurophysiol.*, **31**: 210–20.
37. Mayer, J., and Thomas, D. W. 1967. Regulation of food intake and obesity. Science, **156**: 328–37.
38. Molina, A. F. De, and Hunsperger, R. W. 1959. Central representation of affective reactions in forebrain and brain stem: electrical stimulation of amygdala, stria terminalis, and adjacent structures. *J. Physiol.*, **145**: 251–65.
38a. ———, 1962. Organization of the subcortical system governing defence and flight reactions in the cat. *J. Physiol.*, **160**: 200–13.
39. Moyer, K. E., 1968. Kinds of aggression and their physiological basis. *Comm. Beh. Biol., A*, **2**: 65–87.
40. Murphy, J. T., and Renaud, L. P. 1969. Mechanisms of inhibition in the ventromedial nucleus of the hypothalamus. *J. Neurophysiol.*, **32**: 85–102.
41. Nakao, H. 1958. Emotional behavior produced by hypothalamic stimulation. *Am. J. Physiol.*, **194**: 411–8.
42. Oomura, Y., Kimura, K. Ooyama, H., Maeno, T., Iki, M. and Kuniyoshi, M. 1964. Reciprocal activities of the ventromedial and lateral hypothalamic areas of cats. *Science*, **143**: 484–5.
42a. ———, Ooyama, H., Yaamato, T. and Naka, F. 1967. Reciprocal relationship of the lateral and ventromedial hypothalamus in the regulation of food intake. *Physiology and Behavior*, **2**: 97–115.
43. Roberts, W. W. 1958. Rapid escape learning without avoidance learning motivated by hypothalamic stimulation in cats. *Jour. Comp. Physiol. Psychol.*, **51**: 391–9.
43a. ———. 1958. Both rewarding and punishing effects from the stimulation of posterior hypothalamus of cat with same electrode at same intensity. Jour. Comp. Physiol. Psychol., **51**: 400–7.
43b. ———, and Kiess, H. O. 1964. Motivational properties of hypothalamic aggression in cats. *Jour. Comp. Physiol. Psychol.*, **58**: 187–93.
43c. ———. Steinberg, M. L. and Means, L. W. 1967. Hypothalamic mechanisms for sexual, aggressive, and other motivational behaviors in the opossum, *Didelphis virginiana. Jour. Comp. Physiol. Psychol.*, **64**: 1–15.
44. Sawa, M., Maruyama, N., Hanai, T. and Kaji, S. 1959. Regulatory influence of amygdaloid nuclei upon the unitary activity in ventromedial nucleus of the hypothalamus. *Folia Psychiatrica et Neurologica Japonica*, **13**: 235–56.
45. Schmidt, R. S. 1968. Preoptic activation of frog mating behavior. *Behaviour*, **30**: 239–57.
46. Scott, J. P., and Fredericson, E. 1951. The causes of fighting in mice and rats. *Physiol. Zool.*, **24**: 273–309.
47. Segaar, J., and Nieuwenhuys, R. 1963. Etho-physiological experiments

with male *Gasterosteus aculeatus,* with anatomical comments. *Animal Behaviour,* **11**: 331–44.

48. Skultety, F. M. 1962. Experimental mutism in dogs. *Arch. Neurol.,* **6**: 235–41.

48a. ——— 1965. Mutism in cats with rostral midbrain lesions. Arch. Neurol., **12**: 211–25.

49. Wasman, M., and Flynn, J. P. 1962. Directed attack elicited from hypothalamus. *Arch. Neurol.,* **6**: 220–7.

50. Wiepkema, P. R. 1968. Behaviour changes in CBA mice as a result of one goldthioglucose injection. *Behaviour,* **32**: 179–210.

51. Wilkinson, H. A., and Peele, T. L. 1963. Intracranial self-stimulation in cats. *J. Comp. Neurol.,* **121**: 425–40.

12

SOME ASPECTS OF BRAIN BIOCHEMISTRY CORRELATED WITH GENERAL NERVOUS REACTIVITY AND AGGRESSIVENESS

BRUCE L. WELCH and ANNEMARIE S. WELCH
Maryland Psychiatric Research Center
Baltimore, Maryland

This is an original article written at the request of the editor.

Living in different social environments results in the maintenance of different basal levels of nervous activation and, consequently, in different degrees of central nervous excitability and reactivity. When the general level of central nervous excitability is changed, there is a resulting change in the responsivity of animals to other animals in their environment, and this may result in an altered threshold for response to stimuli that trigger aggression.[14d]

In addition to altering excitability, living in different environments causes animals to metabolize various brain neurochemicals at different rates. Among the neurochemicals that have been shown to occur in different concentrations or to turn over at different rates in the brains of animals that live in, or are placed into, different environmental situations are norepinephrine, dopamine, serotonin, 5-hydroxyindoleacetic acid, aspartic acid, N-acetyl aspartic acid, glutamic acid, glutamine, gamma-aminobutyric acid, and the enzymes acetycholinesterase and cholinesterase.[1, 3, 5, 7, 13, 14a, 14b, 14c, 14e]

For several years we have been studying the first three of these compounds, the catecholamines norepinephrine and dopamine and the indolealkylamine, serotonin, in relation to the changes that they undergo in response to different social environmental conditions. All three of these amines are believed to serve as neurotransmitters or modulators of neurotransmission in the brain: they are released from nerve terminals by nervous stimulation, they have been localized histologically within specific neurons, and major neuronal systems that contain them have been recently mapped by fluorescent histochemical techniques.[4] Their release from neurons seems to be important in determining the level of activation and reactivity of the central nervous system.[10, 14d] Since a number of studies suggest that deviations in the normal metabolism of these amines may be involved in the development or persistence of abnormal emotional and mental states,[9] it seems important to study changes in their metabolism that can be produced by environmental manipulation and correlated with changes in behavior.

SOCIAL ENVIRONMENT, REACTIVITY AND AGGRESSIVENESS

When male mice are made excitable by long-term isolation, they also become more aggressive.[13, 14d] Indeed, their level of aggressiveness can be graded such that, on the average, they become progressively more aggressive with increasing lengths of time in isolation

Table 1. *Time-Dependent Enhancement of Aggressiveness in Isolation**

Strain	Isolation Time	Fights per Individual per 5 min.	Latency of Attack (sec.)
DUB/ICR	0	2	155
	2 wks.	9	130
	5 wks.	21	87
	15 wks.	45	39
C57BL/6**	4 hrs.	1.2	1050
	21 hrs.	5.5	588
	312 hrs.	7.3	243
SC-I**	4 hrs.	2.2	410
	21 hrs.	5.5	216
	312 hrs.	9.1	257

* From B. L. Welch, p. 152 in *Aggression and Defense,* edited by C. D. Clemente and D. B. Lindsley. Proceedings of the Fifth Conference on Brain Function, U.C.L.A. University of California Press, 1967. Reprinted with the permission of the University of California Press.
** Adapated from Bourgault *et al.*[2]

(Table 1) and progressively less aggressive with increasing size of the group in which they live (Table 2). The development of aggressiveness in these animals is, in no sense, dependent upon learning through the experience of fighting. To the contrary, it is inversely related to the opportunity for fighting, and it develops even in mice that have been isolated from the time of weaning and that have never had the opportunity to fight or to observe fighting.

Table 2. *Reduction of Aggressiveness by Grouping: Fights Occurring Spontaneously Within Groups (Number of fights/mouse/hour).**

Experiment	Sample Size	Group Size 2	4	5	8	10	20
A	202	2.5		2.1		1.1	
B	255	4.4		3.9		2.0	
C	210	5.0	5.7		1.5		0.5

* From B. L. Welch, p. 153 in *Aggression and Defense,* edited by C. D. Clemente and D. B. Lindsley. Proceedings of the Fifth Conference on Brain Function, U.C.L.A. University of California Press, 1967. Reprinted with the permission of the University of California Press.

Both the development of aggressiveness during isolation and the amelioration of aggressiveness after isolated mice are returned to groups are time-dependent processes that take place gradually over a period of weeks We assume that these changes are the consequence of definable neurological changes.

These differences in CNS responsivity may result from changes that occur at at least two levels of organization: (1) progressive changes in the tonic level of cortical inhibition of the ascending activating system of the brain stem, and (2) the development of an altered sensitivity of neurochemical receptors within this system to activation by neurotransmitters.

Dr. Frank Bronson (University of Texas, Austin) cogently remarked of the grouped mice in our experiments, "These animals are 'neurologically numb.'" This is an apt description, for there certainly is no question that they are less excitable, less responsive and less aggressive than isolated mice, and that they have a higher basal level of central nervous activation.

SOCIAL ENVIRONMENT AND RESPONSE TO *d*-AMPHETAMINE

Both of these mechanisms may contribute to the results of experiments in which *d*-amphetamine has been employed as an indicator of differences in central nervous responsivity among mice that had lived under different levels of social stimulation. *d*-Amphetamine, a structural analog of norepinephrine, is for the most part an indirectly acting sympathomimetic amine, i.e., it exerts its effects primarily through the release of endogenous catecholamines; it may also mimic their actions. The reduction of aggressiveness in grouped mice suggests that a progressive reduction in central nervous responsivity is produced by graded increases in the level of prior social stimulation. This is also compatible with the fact that social grouping for a long period of time causes a graded reduction in response to *d*-amphetamine.

A possible relationship between these stimulus-induced changes in responsiveness to *d*-amphetamine and the level of activation of the reticular activating system of the brainstem[6] is suggested by the fact that, although *d*-amphetamine crosses the blood-brain barrier and penetrates easily into the brain, even very large doses have no effect on either behavior or the EEG after midbrain transection of reticular fibers *(cerveau insolé)*. When such lesions are made in animals that have already been activated by *d*-amphetamine, slow waves and spindles immediately reappear and activation cannot be reinstated by additional injections of *d*-amphetamine. The inhibition of catecholamine biosynthesis prevents the excitatory effects of *d*-amphetamine, but protection against this is provided by monoamine oxidase inhibitors.[11] The majority of the cell bodies of catecholamine and serotonin-containing neurons originate in the brain stem and have terminals in the midbrain and forebrain; *d*-amphetamine alters their histochemically-detectable fluorescence, causing a decrease in the number and intensity of the very fine norepinephrine-containing nerve terminals in the reticular formation of the brainstem, the neocortex and gyrus cinguli.[4] These observations suggest that the central nervous excitatory effects of *d*-amphetamine may be exerted in part *via* the reticular activating system of the brain stem, and that an important neurohumor that is released may be norepinephrine.

It has been known for nearly 30 years that *d*-amphetamine causes greater excitation in mice, and is much more toxic to them, if they are aggregated rather than isolated subsequent to its administration.

This is an acute effect of grouping and isolation, however, in contrast to the chronic or long-term effect previously mentioned (long-term social grouping causes a reduction in response to *d*-amphetamine). Acute aggregation not only increases the sensitivity of mice to *d*-amphetamine but it also enhances the drug-induced lowering of brain norepinephrine; further, pharmacologic blockage of the action of norepinephrine by phenoxybenzamine, an adrenegic blocking agent, reduces both of these aggregation-induced effects.[8] This suggests that aggregation *per se* may release brain norepinephrine from neurons in the brain.

SOCIAL ENVIRONMENT AND BRAIN CATECHOLAMINES AND SEROTONIN

Indeed, it has been found that brain norepinephrine, and also brain dopamine and serotonin, are produced and utilized at higher basal rates in the brains of mice that live in groups than in those that live in isolation. Appropriately, brain catecholaminergic and serotoninergic neurons of mice living in groups seem to be adapted to relatively high basal levels of synthesis of these amines. Table 3 and Table 4 show the higher turnover rate of norepinephrine and serotonin in grouped than in isolated mice.

Table 3. *Influences of Grouping and Isolation upon Brian Norepinephrine* (NE) Metabolism****

Measurement	Size Sample	Group	Isolate	$p <$
NE drop after inhibiting biosynthesis with alpha-methyl-tyrosine	64	239 ± 9	164 ± 7	0.001
NE rise after inhibiting catabolism with pargyline (MO-911)	64	228 ± 4	145 ± 11	0.01
NE endogenous in pons + medulla**	30	197 ± 1	169 ± 1	0.05
NE endogenous in mesencephalon-** diecephalon	30	262 ± 1	208 ± 1	0.025
NE endogenous in neocortex**	30	94 ± 1	91 ± 1	n.s.

* ng (nannograms) brain tissue; all values reported are means ± s.e.
** Endogenous NE values from rabbits; others from mice.
*** From B. Welch,[13] page 156 in *Aggression and Defense,* edited by C. D. Clemente and D. B. Lindsley. Proceedings of the Fifth Conference on Brain Function, U.C.L.A. University of California Press, 1967. Reprinted with the permission of the University of California Press.

Table 4. *Influence of Grouping and Isolation upon the Rate of Turnover of Brain Serotonin in Male Mice**

No. of mice per cage	Rate of Turnover (ng/g/hr)**	
	20 days	30 days
1	387 ± 12	361 ± 10
5	466 ± 36	459 ± 30
10		466 ± 13
20	513 ± 35	515 ± 37
$p<$	0.001	0.001

* Adapted from Table 1 of Garattini *et al.*[3]
** ng/g/hr = m μg/g/hr.

The neuronal release of catecholamines and/or serotonin is thought to be necessary for the normal maintenance of central activation and alertness. Inferences that neurotransmission occurs at a higher basal rate in grouped than isolated mice are based upon the results of experiments in which drugs that either accelerate or slow the release, synthesis, or oxidative inactivation of these amines were administered to mice that were accustomed to living under various social environmental conditions.

Although the activating effect of these amine neurotransmitters may be temporarily enhanced by increasing their rate of release from nerve endings, it is also true that the response of neurochemical receptors is likely to be greater if the immediately preceding volley of released neurotransmitter has been small rather than large, and if the extant level of nervous activation at the time that the volley arrives is low rather than high. Hence, grouped mice may be less responsive than isolates partly because the basal level of neurotransmitter release is already high and the postsynaptic receptors are, accordingly, relatively unresponsive to an added increment of neurotransmitter bombardment.

An elegant example of the ability of brain norepinephrine to non-specifically modulate (either facilitate or impair) behavior is given by Wise and Stein.[12]

While the changes in general central nervous reactivity that occur in mice under different social environmental conditions may be functionally related to the changes that concomitantly occur in the metabolism of brain catecholamines and serotonin, there is little reason to suggest that these amines have a direct and specific relation to any particular behavior.

ALTERATION OF AGGRESSIVE BEHAVIOR WITH DRUGS THAT AFFECT BIOGENIC AMINES

If the increased aggressiveness that develops during isolation occurs secondary to a reduced rate of release of brain catecholamines and/or serotonin, it should be possible to increase aggressiveness by the chronic administration of drugs that block the biosynthesis of these amines. Although no such studies have yet been reported for mice, the mouse-killing tendencies of rats have been increased by the chronic administration of drugs that inhibit the biosynthesis of catecholamines and serotonin. On the other hand, the *acute* impairment of neurotransmitter availability by the administration of amine biosynthesis inhibitors reduces the tendency for mice to fight.

When drugs that accelerate the neuronal release of brain amines are administered, there is a dramatic increase in the general level of excitation and arousal in all species of animals that have been tested, and electroencephalographic measurements show fast low-amplitude activity and asyncrony, as is usual during behavioral arousal. The concomitant effects of these drugs upon fighting behavior in mice, however, are biophasic. Thus, low doses of either *d*-amphetamine or a quick-acting monoamine oxidase inhibitor may have a short-lived facilitating effect upon fighting behavior in mice that have previously been made aggressive by long-term isolation, whereas larger doses, the same low dose combined with physical stimulation, or the same low dose after longer periods of time actually reduce fighting or abolish it entirely.

The literature is replete with examples of biphasic effects of physical stimulation, biphasic effects of various drugs that modify biogenic amine metabolism, and of interactions between them. Thus electroshock-induced convulsions are slightly facilitated a short time after administration of the monoamine oxidase inhibitor JB-516, although the more general effect is to elevate the threshold for electroshock convulsion. Although electroshock can activate animals, when it is sufficiently strong they may become over-activated and "freeze." Likewise, a brief bout of prior fighting may cause arousal and intensify fighting in mice that have been made aggressive by prior isolation. If they are very intensely activated, however (as when under attack), they may "freeze" in a typical catatonic defense posture.

Apparently an appropriate degree of stimulation (physical, drug-induced or a combination thereof) contributes to attainment of the optimal level of activation that is necessary for enactment of a pattern of behavior that exists in the repertoire of the animals, but when the same stimulus is stronger it may impair the same behavior or prevent its enactment by causing disorganizing overactivation.

It appears that both the readiness with which fighting (an inherited pattern of aggressive behavior) can be triggered by appropriate stimuli and also the intensity of the fighting may be increased by either (1) lowering the threshold of the central nervous system for general stimulus response or (2) optimizing the level of general nervous activation that is necessary for the enactment of this particular integrated behavior.[14d]

SOCIAL ENVIRONMENT AND ENDOCRINE AND CARDIOVASCULAR FUNCTION

Since isolated mice are characterized by a relatively low level of stimulus-engendered central nervous activity, one might predict that there should also be a reduction of the peripheral endocrine and cardiovascular activities that are controlled by the brain. In fact, when compared with grouped mice, long-term isolated mice normally have slightly larger body weights, lower blood pressures, smaller adrenals, smaller stores of adrenal medullary catecholamines (undoubtedly representing an adaptation to a low basal level of catecholamine secretion), and larger kidneys. At an advanced age, the kidneys of grouped mice have a higher incidence of hyalinization of the glomerular tuft. Hearts of grouped mice are normally enlarged if the mice are grouped after attaining sexual maturity but not if they are grouped at weaning; blood pressure of the grouped mice is higher in either case.[13, 14b]

DIFFERENCES BETWEEN DOMINANT AND SUBORDINATE MICE

Thus far, we have discussed some neurochemical correlates of one pattern of the social distribution of aggressiveness, namely, that in which isolated mice become progressively more aggressive with time, and in which aggressiveness can be progressively reduced by increasing group size.

A more familiar pattern of the distribution of aggressiveness is that which exists between individuals that live together. In any group, some animals tend to become dominant and some subordinate.

Usually the dominants are few and distribute their attentions widely among many subordinates. In our mice, the dominance hierarchy is relatively stable. Once an animal is confirmed in a subordinate role it seldom fights back; it spends its life running from the attacks of the dominants and it seldom or never attacks another mouse. However, even when conditions are not crowded and food is abundant, dominant mice persist in making periodic unprovoked attacks on the subordinates. This may continue for a period of weeks or months until the dominant mouse kills the subordinate with which he is confined. It is almost as though the aggressive tendencies of the dominant are repeatedly, but only temporarily, reduced by the stimulus of attacking.

Obviously subordinate animals exist under a very high level of stimulation. In view of this, it is not too surprising that the subordinate and dominant mice are very different physiologically. It is particularly interesting to note that the dominant mice differ from the subordinate mice in many of the same general ways that isolated mice differ from grouped mice. Thus, the dominants (aggressors) are much more sensitive to *d*-amphetamine than the subordinates; they also have a lower basal rate of release and resynthesis of brain catecholamines, smaller adrenals, smaller hearts and smaller stores of catecholamines in the adrenal medulla (Table 5). They are also much more responsive to stimuli of all kinds, including handling, than the subordinates. It seems reasonable, therefore, to suggest that the neurophysiological factors underlying the differences in aggressiveness between dominant and subordinate mice may be quite similar to those that underlie the difference in aggressiveness between isolation-adapted and group-adapted mice. Of all our mice, badly scarred subordinates best qualify for the description "neurologically numb."

Severe scarring, however, occurs only under extreme conditions such as those that occur when mice that previously have been isolated for a long period of time are forced to live in groups. The majority of our subordinates are not scarred, for scarring seldom occurs if groups are constituted at weaning or within a few days thereafter, and this is our normal practice.

It seems certain that the dominant and subordinate mice differ as they do physiologically because of the social situation in which they live, and not primarily because of their genetic predisposition. While the fighting pattern is obviously inherited, the tendency to use it appears to be determined largely by the environment. Mr. Robert

Eskay in our laboratory has produced evidence that the tendency to become dominant or subordinate can largely be determined by the prior environmental housing conditions and, further, that positions of dominance and subordinance can be reversed by long-term isolation of subordinates and concomitant long-term grouping of dominants.

Table 5. *Representative Differences Between Aggressors and Subordinates Within Groups***

Four aggressors and four subordinate male mice which had been together for 22 weeks

	Aggressor	*Subordinate*	*p*
Body wt. (g)	38.3 ± 1.2	36.4 ± 0.8	n.s.
Adrenal wt. (mg)	2.23 ± 0.16	3.18 ± 0.24	0.025
Epinephrine (μg)*	13.14 ± 0.9	17.92 ± 1.3	0.001
Norepinephrine (μg)*	1.19 ± 0.2	2.64 ± 0.7	0.01

Aggressors and their subordinates in 30 newly constituted pairs (n = 60) were identified by systematic quantitative behavioral observations over a period of 10 days. Half of the aggressors and half of the subordinates were administered the monoamine oxidase inhibitor, MO-911, 25 mg/kg, i.p.; and half were given saline. All mice were then placed in isolation for exactly one hour until sacrifice.

	Aggressor	*Subordinate*	*p*
Body wt. (g)	39.2 ± 0.7	38.8 ± 1.0	n.s.
Brain NE, saline controls (ng/g)	514.0 ± 17	493 ± 14	n.s.
Brain NE, rise with MO-911 (ng/g)	22.0 ± 3	98 ± 4	0.001
Heart wt. (mg)	155.3 ± 6.0	162.7 ± 3.6	0.08

* Catecholamines assay on paired adrenals.
All values reported are means ± S.E.M.
** From B. L. Welch, p. 160 in *Aggression and Defense,* edited by C. D. Clemente and D. B. Lindsley. Proceedings of the Fifth Conference on Brain Function, U.C.L.A. University of California Press, 1967. Reprinted with the permission of the University of California Press.

EFFECTS OF FIGHTING

The effects of fighting upon the brain biogenic amines—norepinephrine, dopamine and serotonin—are complex. The intense nervous activity of engaging in fighting accelerates the release and utilization of these amines in neurotransmission, and compensatory mechanisms, probably of several kinds, are immediately called into play. Hence, although prolonged or intense stress may cause brain levels of amines to be lowered, the immediate effect of fighting is simultaneously to *elevate* all three brain amines. These rapid amine elevations may be caused by a natural stimulus-induced inhibition of mitochondrial monoamine oxidase, an enzyme that continually degrades the amines that are synthesized in excess of the amounts needed for maintaining normal neurotransmission. The lowering of brain amines occurs first in subcortical areas of the brain where the cell bodies of the amine-containing neurons are located; this relative depletion of amines in subcortex is frequently paralleled by elevations of amines in the telecephalon.

Fighting briefly only once each day for only five minutes may result in small but predictable sustained elevations of both brain norepinephrine and dopamine (as measured 24 hours after the last episode of fighting). The mechanisms of these apparently adaptive changes, which are paralleled by reductions in nervous reactivity, are not yet fully understood.[14f]

Brief daily fights also have dramatic concomitant effects upon peripheral organs and endocrines, effects that are much greater than those produced by the mere social stimulation of group living. As shown in Table 6, epinephrine and norepinephrine levels are markedly

Table 6. *Effect of Fighting 5 Minutes Once Each Day for 14 days vs. Group Living Upon Adrenals, Spleen, Heart and Kidneys in Male Mice*[a]

	Caged in Groups	Caged Individually	
		Undisturbed	Fight
Number mice	34	34	34
Body wt. (gm)	36 ± 0.6	36 ± 0.5	36 ± 0.5
Left adrenal (mg)	2.4 ± 0.07*	2.0 ± 0.05	2.8 ± 0.07*†
Epinephrine (ng)	4.9 ± 0.26*	3.6 ± 0.15	5.6 ± 0.30*†
Norepinephrine (ng)	1.6 ± 0.24	1.5 ± 0.13	2.5 ± 0.21*†
Heart, wet (mg)	155 ± 2.8	158 ± 2.3	172 ± 3.5*†
Heart, dry (mg)	33 ± 0.6	34 ± 0.5	37 ± 0.7*†
Left Kidney, wet (mg)	254 ± 6.2*	276 ± 6.5	287 ± 6.3†
Left Kidney, dry (mg)	54 ± 1.1*	59 ± 1.4	61 ± 1.5†
Spleen, wet (mg)	176 ± 14.8*	105 ± 4.5	215 ± 7.0*†
Spleen, dry (mg)	38 ± 3.3*	22 ± 1.0	45 ± 1.5*†

[a] Each value is a mean ± s.e. Mice were housed post-weaning for 3 months either individually or in groups of 8-10 mice. Some of the individually housed mice were placed together in pairs and allowed to fight for 5 min. each day for 14 days. Adapted from Table 2 of Welch and Welch.[14]

* Significantly different from undisturbed individually caged mice.

† Significantly different from grouped mice.

elevated in the adrenal medulla, and there is a distinct enlargement of the adrenal cortex and hypertrophy of the heart and spleen. Since the brain controls these peripheral responses to stress, it will be important in future research to study the possible functional relationship between the effects upon these brain amines and upon the endocrines and cardiovascular system.

Short, intermittent periods of stress undoubtedly approximate the conditions experienced in the real world of nature more nearly than do prolonged periods. Hence, it seems reasonable to suggest that the physiological effects of isolation, of group living, and of fighting that have been discussed here for mice under controlled laboratory conditions may also obtain under natural conditions.

This suggestion is supported by the fact that merely witnessing fighting may produce changes in brain norepinephrine and in adrenal activity that are similar to the changes produced by actually engaging in fighting (Table 7).

Table 7. *Reduction of Norepinephrine in the Lower Brainstem of Male Mice by Witnessing Fighting Among Other Male Mice*[a]

	Norepinephrine (ng/gm)		
	Undisturbed Controls	Strange Cage	Witness Fighting
Number of Mice	20	20	20
Telencephalon	568 ± 17	557 ± 11	531 ± 17
Diencephalon and mesencephalon	524 ± 25	583 ± 21	522 ± 27
Pons and medulla oblongata	472 ± 25	421 ± 22	319 ± 23*

[a] Values are means ± s.e. Mice which had been made hyperexcitable by long-term isolation were placed into a feed basket above an empty strange cage or above a strange cage that contained fighting mice for 75 min. Adapted from Table 1 of Welch and Welch.[14]

* Differs $p < 0.001$ from undisturbed controls and $p < 0.002$ from strange cage.

PSYCHOPHYSIOLOGICAL FACTORS IN POPULATION CONTROL

In view of the relative decrease in behavioral responsivity and the associated reduction in aggressiveness that occurs with what is effectively an increased population density in our model laboratory situation, it becomes apparent that the physiological effects of increased social stimulation cannot be attributed to an increase in the frequency of physical conflict *per se*. While it is obvious that the adverse physiological effects of overpopulation *may be* enhanced by fighting, they appear normally to be due to tonic stimulus-dependent influences of a much more generalized kind. It is thus important to recognize that aggressiveness is not necessarily increased by increasing population density, and that the behavioral and physiological effects of overpopulation are not necessarily the result of increased rates of physical conflict. The dynamics of natural population control appear to operate through much more subtle psychophysiological means.

It is our present opinion that the brain catecholamines and serotonin, as neurotransmitters, play central but not all-important roles in the complex behavioral and neuroendocrine changes that occur in individual animals within groups and populations in response to changing social conditions.

REFERENCES

1. Agrawal, H. C., Fox, M. W. and Hinwich, W. A. 1967. Neurochemical and behavioral effects of isolation rearing in the dog. *Life Sci.*, **6**: 71–8.
2. Bourgault, P. C., Karczmar, A. G., and Scudder, C. L. 1963. Contrasting behavioral, pharmacological, neurophysiological and biochemical profiles of C57BL/6 and SC-I strains of mice. *Life Sci.*, **2**: 533–53.
3. Garattini, S., Giacalone E. and Valzelli, L. 1969. Biochemical changes during isolation-induced aggressiveness in mice. In *Aggressive Behavior*, edited by S. Garattini and E. B. Sigg. Amsterdam: Excerpta Medica. pp. 179–187.
4. Hillarp, N. A., Fuxe, K. and Dahlstrom, A. 1966. Demonstration and mapping of central neurons containing dopamine, noradrenaline, and 5-hydroxy-tryptamine and their reactions to psychopharmaca. *Pharmacol. Rev.* **18**: 727–42.
5. Krech, D., Rosenweig, M. R. and Bennett, E. L. 1966. Environmental impoverishment, social isolation and changes in brain chemistry and anatomy. *Physiology and Behavior,* **1**: 99–104.
6. Magoun, H. W., 1963. *The Waking Brain.* Springfield: Charles C. Thomas.
7. Marcucci, F., Mussini, E., Valzelli, L. and Garattini, S. 1968. Decrease in N-acetyl-L-aspartic acid of aggressive mice. *Jour. Neuro. Chem.,* **15**: 53–4.
8. Moore, K. E., 1964. The role of endogenous norepinephrine in the toxicity of d-amphetamine in aggregated mice. *Jour. Pharm. Exptl. Therap.,* **144**: 45–51.
9. Schildkraut, J. J. and Kety, S. S. 1967. Biogenic Amines and Emotion. *Science,* **156**: 21–30.
10. Sheard, M. H., Appel, J. P. and Freedman, D. X. 1967. The effect of central nervous system lesions on brain monoamines and behavior. *Jour. Psychiat. Res.,* **5**: 237–42.

11. Weissman, A., Koe, B. K. and Tenen, S. C., 1966. Antiamphetamine effects following inhibition of tyrosine hydroxylase. *Jour. Pharm. Exptl. Therap.*, **151**: 339–52.

12. Wise, C. D. and Stein, L. 1969. Facilitation of brain self-stimulation by central administration of norepinephrine. Science 163: 299–301.

13. Welch, B. L., 1967. Discussion of a paper by A. Rothballer. In Aggression and Defense: Neural Mechanisms and Social Patterns, Brain Function, vol. 5, edited by C. D. Clements and D. B. Lindsley, Los Angeles: Univ. Calif. Press. pp. 150–70.

14. Welch, A. S. and B. L. Welch, 1968*a*. Reduction of norepinephrine in the lower brainstem by psychological stimulus. *Proc. Natl. Acad. Sci.* **60**: 478–81.

14a. Welch, B. L. and Welch, A. S., 1968*b*. Differential activation by restraint stress of a mechanism to conserve brain catecholamines and serotonin in mice differing in excitability. *Nature* 218: 575–577.

14b. Welch, B. L. and Welch, A. S. 1968*c*. Greater lowering of brain and adrenal catecholamines in group-housed than in individually-housed mice administered dl-alpha-methyltyrosine. *Jour. Pharm. Pharmacol.*, **20**: 244–6.

14c. Welch, A. S. and Welch, B. L., 1968*d*. Effect of stress and parachlorolalanine upon brain serotonin, 5-hydroxyindoleacetic acid and catecholamines in grouped and isolated mice. *Biochem. Pharmacol.*, **17**: 699–708.

14d. Welsh, B. L. and Welch, A. S., 1969*a*. Aggression and the biogenic amine neurohumors. In Aggressive Behavior, edited by S. Garattini and E. B. Sigg. Amsterdam: Excerpta Medica. pp. 188–202.

14e. Welch, B. L. and Welch, A. S., 1969*b*. Fighting: Preferential lowering of norepinephrine and dopamine in the brainstem, concomitant with a depletion of epinephrine from the adrenal medulla. *Comm. Behav. Biol.*, **3**: 125–130.

14f. Welch, B. L. and Welch, A. S., 1969*c*. Sustained effects of brief daily fights upon brain and adrenal catecholamines and adrenal, spleen and heart weights of mice. *Proc. Natl. Acad. Sci.*, **64**: 100–107.

14g. Welch, A. S. and Welch, B. L. 1970. Isolation, reactivity and aggression: Evidence for an involvement of brain catecholamines and serotonin. In Physiology of Fighting and Defeat, edited by B. E. Eleftheriou and J. P. Scott. Chicago: Univ. of Chicago Press. (In press).

13

EFFECTS OF ISOLATION ON MATERNAL AGGRESSIVENESS AND BODY GROWTH RATES OF OFFSPRING

A. S. WELTMAN, A. M. SACKLER, R. SCHWARTZ and S. STROMAN
Long Island University, New York

This article originally appeared in Experientia, **23**: *pp. 782–784, 1967. It is reprinted with permission.*

The present study was designed to determine the effects of prior periods of prolonged isolation on maternal fertility and fecundity and maternal-fetal and offspring interrelationships. Various investigators have reported that isolation stress caused behavioral abnormalities such as head-shaking,[1-4] heightened locomotor activity,[4-5] nervousness and aggressiveness,[1, 3, 6, 7] in mice. Physiologically, evidence of hyperadrenocorticalism has been noted in isolated mice[4, 7] and rats[8] accompanied by indications of thyroidal imbalances[4, 7, 8] and reductions in gonadal weights.[4, 7] Recent reports[9] claim that isolation caused pituitary-gonadal stimulation and that isolation-induced aggressiveness is dependent on an intact pituitary-gonadal axis with the adrenals exerting a modulating influence. Although other hormonal factors and balances, in addition to sex steroids, are involved in oogenesis as well as fertility and fecundity relationships, if pituitary-gonadal function is stimulated by isolation one might reasonably anticipate, in addition to organ and secondary sex characteristic changes, higher levels of fertility and fecundity in the isolated females.

A total of 60 albino females averaging 19 g were divided into test and control groups. All test or isolated mice were housed singly in stainless steel cages (6.5 x 10 x 7 inches) as opposed to control mice which were maintained in groups of 2/cage. The laboratory recognizes the sensitivity of animal growth and development to such environmental and physical stimuli as temperature,[10] noise[11] and handling.[12] Parameters measured were changes in litter size, pup mortality and the developmental growth rates of the young. Body weights and necktwitch responses were recorded weekly; locomotor activity[13] and aggressiveness at various intervals during the 6½ month isolation period. After observation of consistent significant increases in locomotor activity and aggressiveness, all test and control females were subjected to mating-behavior interaction studies with proven albino males on 4 consecutive days for ½ h intervals. Each female was then mated individually for 6 days. All males were then removed, control females regrouped into the original pairs and then separated shortly before parturition. By this procedure, each test and control female could thus raise and nurse her own litter, and isolated females were only in contact with another animal for the relatively short mating period. All females were checked daily for date of birth and size of litters. En masse weighings and counts were made weekly at the end of the 1st, 2nd and 3rd weeks. All offspring were weighed, weaned and sexed at 4 weeks of age.

In agreement with previous findings, isolation produced increased restlessness, hyperactivity, viciousness and the abnormal head-twitch response in the test female mice. Analyses[14] of aggressive tendencies during the mating-behavior studies revealed a statistically significant increase in the number of test females attacking males at the first trial. A significant increase was also noted in the total number of attacks made by the test versus control females during the 4 day mating-behavior study. Examination of fertility and fecundity findings (Table I) indicated no significant differences between the pregnancy frequencies and the respective litter sizes of the test versus control females at parturition and weaning. The depression noted in the average litter size of the control group at weaning could be attributed to chance. One control mother cannibalized all pups during the first week, and the second control mother's progeny died as she developed a severe hip infection. Chi-square analyses of mortality in the offspring from birth to weaning revealed no statistically significant effects on offspring viability between the 2 groups. It is apparent that the

Table I. *Effects of maternal isolation on pregnancy frequencies and litter sizes of isolated mice*

Group	No.	Adult Females		Total No. of Offspring				Average Litter Size	
		No. of pregnant females	% preg-nancy	Total No. at birth	Total No. at weaning	No. dead by weaning	% Mor-tality	At birth	At weaning
Isolated mice	27	19	70.4	143	119	24	16.8	7.5	6.3
S.E.								± 0.4	± 0.4
Control mice	27	20	74.1	150	115	35[c]	23.3	7.5	5.8[d]
S.E.								± 0.3	± 0.6
P value		> 0.90[a]				0.15[a]		> 0.90[b]	0.47[b]

[a] Chi-squate. [b] Student t-test. [c] Corrected by removal of 2 control mothers (21 offspring dead, 15.4% mortality). [d] Corrected by removal of 2 control mothers, average litter size, 6.4 weanlings/litter.

Table II. *Effects of maternal isolation on average pup and weanling weights of isolated mice*

Group	At end of 1st week		At end of 2nd week		At end of 3rd week		At end of 4th week			
							Males		Females	
	Total No. young	Average body wt (g)	Total No. young	Average body wt (g)	Total No. young	Average body wt (g)	No. wean-lings	Average wt (g)	No. wean-lings	Average wt (g)
Isolated mice	132	3.3	124	5.2	122	7.2	57	9.9	62	9.6
S.E.		± 0.2		± 0.2		± 0.4		± 0.3		± 0.2
Control mice	120	3.7	116	5.7	115	8.5	67	11.0	48	11.3
S.E.		± 0.1		± 0.2		± 0.4		± 0.4		± 0.4
% difference		− 10.8		− 8.8		− 15.3		− 10.0		− 15.0
P value[a]		0.09		0.12		< 0.01		0.02		< 0.001

[a] Student's *t*-test.

data failed to demonstrate any influence of prior periods of maternal isolation on birth frequency, litter size and offspring viability during the 4 week nursing and pre-weaning period.

Table II demonstrates that the body weights of the pups obtained from the isolated mothers at the completion of the 1st and 2nd weeks were markedly lower but not statistically significant. After the 3rd week, the 15% decrease in the individual body weights of the offspring of the isolated mothers was significant. When weaned at 4 weeks of age, significant decreases were similarly noted in the body weights of the male and female progeny obtained from the isolated mothers with the greater effects shown by the female offspring. The findings thus indicated inhibited developmental growth rates in these offspring.

It is of interest that study of aliquot populations of male and female offspring from the isolated mothers at 4½ weeks of age showed heightened evasiveness and significantly increased locomotor activity in open-field tests. Significant decreases were also noted in total leucocyte and eosinophil counts and thymus and splenic organ weights of such offspring, suggesting increased adrenocortical activity (to be published).

Questions to be resolved and defined, therefore, are the respective dominance and contributions of maternal endocrine imbalances and/or maternal abnormal behavior on prenatal embryological and postnatal developmental growth patterns of the offspring. Differences in maternal behavior, nursing care and degree of lactation may likewise produce postnatal modifications in the offspring. Sackler et al.[15, 16] present evidence indicative of a prenatal relationship between maternal thyroidal imbalances and subsequent childhood schizophrenics. Psychologically, Thompson[17] has reported that prenatal anxiety in laboratory animals increases the emotionality of progeny. Keeley,[18] similarly, noted that aberrant endocrine activity in pregnant females could possibly impair fetal response systems and influence postnatal behavior. Split-litter techniques may help to further define prenatal, maternal-fetal and postnatal, maternal-progeny relationships. In conclusion, the study demonstrated effects of maternal isolation prior to and during pregnancy on developmental growth rates and body weights of the offspring. These changes may have been in part precipitated by catabolic effects of maternal hyperadrenocorticalism in fetal metabolism. No change was noted in the fertility and fecundity of isolated mothers.

REFERENCES

1. Scott, J. P. and Marston, M. 1953. *Jour. of abnormal soc. Psychol.* **48**:417.
2. Keller, D. L. and Umbreit, W. W. 1956. *Science* **124**(723).
3. Yen, C. Y., Stranger, R. L. and Millman, N. 1959. *Archs. int. Pharmacodyn. Ther.* **123**(179).
4. Weltman, A. S., Sackler, A. M. and Sparber, S. B. 1966. *Aerospace Med.,* **37**(804).
5. Retzlaff, E. G. 1939. *Jour. exp. Zool.* **81**(343).
6. Christian, J. J. 1959. *Amer. Jour. Physiol.* **187**(353).
7. Weltman, A. S., Sackler, A. M., Sparber, S. B. and Opert, S. 1962. *Fedn. Proc. Am. Socs. exp. Biol.* **21**(184).
8. Hatch, A., Balazs, T., Wiberg, G. S. and Grice, H. C. 1963. *Science* **142**(507).
9. Sigg, E. B., Day, C. and Colombo, C. 1966. *Endocrinology* **78**(679).
10. Farris, E. J. 1957. *The Care and Breeding of Laboratory Animals.* New York: Wiley.
11. Sackler, A. M., Weltman, A. S. and Jurtshuk, Jr. P. 1960. *Aerospace Med.* **31**(749).
12. Weltman, A. S., Sackler, A. M. and Gennis, J. 1961. *Jour. appl. Physiol.* **16**(587).
13. Hall, C. S. 1936. *Jour. Comp. Psychol.* **22**(345).
14. Snedecor, G. W. 1946. *Statistical Methods.* Ames Iowa: Iowa State College Press.
15. Sackler, A. M., Sackler, R. R., Sackler, M. D., and Co Tui. 1951. *Jour. clin. exp. Psychopath.* **12**(224).
16. Sackler, M. D. Sackler, R. R., LaBurt, H. A., Co Tui and Sackler, A. M. 1952. The nervous child. 10, 43
17. Thompson, W. R. 1957. *Science.* **125**(698).
18. Keeley, K. 1962. *Science.* **135**(44).

14

GENOTYPIC FACTORS IN THE ONTOGENY OF BEHAVIOR*

BENSON E. GINSBURG
University of Connecticut

This article was originally published in the book, Animal and Human, *Volume XII*: Science and Psychoanalysis, *edited by Jules H. Masserman, pp. 12–17.*

Many studies of behavior, especially those dealing with animals, are typologic in orientation and deal primarily with patterns that are characteristic of a species or a group. Population geneticists and other students of the dynamics of the evolutionary process have long since abandoned such typologic concepts and sought instead to characterize a population in terms of the degrees of freedom inherent in its genetic potential.[6] The goal of this latter approach is to understand the range of possibilities open to a genetically variable population over the normative spectrum of environmental variability. While a central tendency will emerge for any population on any given measure, such a tendency is viewed by the behavior gencticist as representing a variety of genotype-environment interactions. Such an approach also gives full weight to those individuals who are not at the mean of the population behaviorally, some of whom may be at the extreme, primarily because they are genetic deviates, as in the case of

* This work was supported by Grant MH-03361 from the National Institutes of Mental Health.

Down's syndrome or phenylketonuria, while others, representing deviant phenotypes, are genetically within the more typical genotypic portion of the scale but deviate behaviorally because of external influences which may include traumatic experiences, disease, or accident.

The objective of many researches in behavioral genetics and of one of the major programs in my own laboratory is to understand this network of nature-nurture interactions that give rise to both the central tendencies and behavioral deviations in a population, so that individual behavior may be better understood, predicted, and controlled. This is hardly a novel objective to the clinician, whose typical population consists of deviates from the behavioral norms, and who encounters in each new case an example of individual differences in both biologic and experiential backgrounds.

In using experimental animals as biologic models, it is now possible to control to a large degree both the biologic and the environmental variables. In the simplest instance, one seeks repeatable genotypes that differ from each other only in one or a few known genes, where these genetic differences predispose to differences in behavioral outcome under similar conditions of rearing. Interactions with a variety of conditions of rearing can also be investigated, and physiologic, neurochemical, and neuro-endocrinologic variables can be studied in relation to these controlled situations. One can, utilizing such materials, begin with identical genotypes and seek to make them behaviorally different, or, conversely, one can begin with individuals whose differences in genetic predisposition would, under similar conditions, produce differences in behavior. In these instances, one can, by a variety of manipulations, attempt to make the behavior convergent. Where individual gene differences are not available, the use of inbred strains provides a series of complex genetic differences, each of which is biologically repeatable.

Experiments using these approaches have been reported in detail from our laboratory.[2a, 2d] I would like to summarize a few of the major findings that have a special pertinence for this topic and to add a few that represent work currently in progress in our laboratory.

Hunt and Otis,[4] Denenberg,[1] Levine,[5] Schaefer,[8] and others have shown that early handling of mice and rats immediately postpartum produces profound differences between experimental and control mice and rats much later in life. These differences are measured by a variety of so-called emotionality tests, which generally include activity measures and defecation in an open field. The physiologic mechanisms through which these effects are mediated are now thought to involve the early organization of neural mechanisms by adrenal steroids acting sooner than they normally would, and in augmented quantities, because of the early stimulation resulting from the handling.

Most of the work on so-called early handling effects involve genetically mixed populations. In our laboratory we have been attempting to investigate genotype-environment interactions and have found that these are profound. In a study involving three highly inbred strains of mice (C3H, C57BL/10, and C/albino), the first was found to respond sensitively to pain stimulation during the preweaning period. The males that had been so stimulated during early infancy were much more aggressive after sexual maturity than were the nonstimulated controls, where the aggressiveness was measured by latency to fighting and initiation of attacks on another mouse in a controlled round-robin situation.[2d] The controls did not differ from the experimentals in replicate experiments made with the other two strains. When C57BL/10 mice are reared by rat mothers, they are almost completely nonaggressive as sexually mature adults by comparison with mouse-reared controls.[1] In these latter experiments, another strain of mouse was not comparably affected by the foster rearing.

Table 1 is taken from a study in which six different strains were

Table 1. *Effect of Seizures and Early Handling on Incidence and Latency of Fighting Behavior in Six Inbred Strains of Mice*[a]

	DBA/1	DBA/2	C57-BL/6	C57-BL/10	HS	AJAX
Control Latency*	148	160	150	130	63	132
PD. Greatest ΔL	2-27	15-27	15-27	2-14	2-14	2-14
Value of ΔL	30 (−)	40 (−)	187 (+)	175 (+)	31 (−)	215 (+)
% Control Fights	69	85	35	26	95	23
PD. Greatest ΔF	2-14	2-27	2-14 15-27	2-27		2-27
Value of ΔF	28	68	28 27	69		74
F: Single Seizure	37.5	56				
F: Exposed, not Seized	73					
Not Exposed		80				

[a] With the technical assistance of Joanne Ellsworth Jumonville. See Ginsberg.[2b]
* Latencies expressed in seconds; PD = periods in days postpartum; ΔL = greatest change in latency; Value of ΔL expressed in seconds; F = greatest change in fighting; Value of ΔF expressed in percentages fighting; Data for seizures, exposed and not exposed also expressed in percentages.

compared on the same parameters—namely, latency to and success in fighting. It should be noted that the sensitive period during which early handling produces its maximum effect is different for each strain. In one strain there is essentially no effect. In another the effect is cumulative, so that stimulation during the entire preweaning period is more effective than the massing of stimulation at a particular time. Still other strains are sensitive early in preweaning life, by contrast with those that are affected only after the second week. The data also compare the direction and magnitude of the effects, and demonstrate that exactly the same stimulation during the preweaning sensitive period that increases adult aggressiveness in males of one strain of mice will decrease aggressiveness in another. The central tendency of a genetically mixed population, therefore, represents an amalgam of styles, times and directions of responses. That a population should have such a variable response repertoire is very probably adaptive, since, depending on conditions of crowding and other aspects of ecology that may be expected to augment or decrease stressful stimulation during various periods in early infancy, members of a population will be able to react in a variety of ways, and the forces of natural selection will be able to favor those styles of response that are most adaptive to any long continued ecologic situation.[9] Our analyses of other mouse populations, as well as populations of other mammals, suggest that one major feature of adaptedness is a flexible genetic repertoire of the kind illustrated by the data just mentioned. In nature, a great deal of genetic variability appears to be assimilated to a normative phenotype because of dominance, epistasis, low penetrance and other buffering effects of the prevailing genotype, thus affording the population both maximum phenotypic conformity to the range of usual environmental demands and maximum genetic flexibility against an unknown future. It is in this sense that we may consider the normative phenotype as typologic or species-specific. Ethologists who emphasize species-specific behavior usually have no quarrel with the notion of genetic variability. Most of them have simply not come to this stage of genetic parsing of the behavioral capacities of a population in their particular studies.

The search for ontogenetic mechanisms by means of which these individual differences in later personality response to very early postnatal stress are possibly mediated, is largely centered, as mentioned, on neuro-endocrinologic mechanisms involving the adrenal steroids.[3] Our current work in this area is directed towards those CNS mechanisms that serve to mediate between outside stimulation and the activation of the hypothalamic-pituitary-adrenal axis. Thus far we have evidence for the involvement of discrete genes that affect the development of at least two identifiable neural mechanisms. One of these affects the rate of the development of glutamic acid decarboxylase activity, an enzyme that is unique to central nervous activity in mammals; and the other affects the rate of development of nucleoside triphosphatase activity in the dentate fascia of the hippocampus. Still another gene affects the ultimate level of enzymatic activity reached in this particular structure. Glutamic acid decarboxylase is involved in the synthesis of GABA, an inhibitory neural transmitter.[7] The hippocampal anomaly has been related to seizure activity and to other over-reactions to early stress. Work on these systems is currently being actively pursued in our laboratory by J. S. Cowen, S. C. Maxson, J. Jumonville, and P. Sze.* Correlations with timing of sensitive periods affecting particular aspects of later behavior make it appear that simple genetic variations in such enzymatic mechanisms may be the key factor in the establishing of sensitive periods and may constitute the filter and the activating mechanism between external stimulation and the subsequent adrenal steroid responses.

These data permit one to create biologic models by means of genetic manipulation in experimental animals, in which the hypotheses mentioned can be critically tested. If similar situations obtain for other mammals, including the human being, they would be expected to rest on homologies of mechanism. As a consequence, individual differences with comparable genetic bases to those suggested by the experimental models could be tested, for example, by monitoring steroid responses to mildly augmented stimulation in early infancy, especially among premature twins. Predictions of possible later effects on personality profiles could thus be made by analogy with experimental results in animals, and once these systems are more completely understood, such mechanisms are manipulable and could pro-

*Cowen J. S.:, A metabolic hippocampal anomaly associated with hereditary susceptibility to sound induced seizures. Master's dissertation, Department of Psychology, University of Chicago, September, 1966. Maxson, S.C.: The effect of genotype on brain mechanisms involved in audiogenic seizure susceptibility. Doctoral dissentation, Department of Psychology, University of Chicago, September, 1966.

Ginsburg, B.E.: Cowen, J.S.; Maxson, S.C.; and Sze, P.: Neurochemical effects of gene mutations associated with audiogenic seizures. Second International Congress of Neuro-Genetics and Neuro-Ophthalmology, September, 1967.

Jumonville, J.: Personal communication, Doctoral dissertation, Department of Psychology, December, 1967.

vide a basis, not only for understanding the biologic structuring of behavior, but also for preventative and therapeutic measures.

REFERENCES

1. Denenberg, V. H., Hudgens, G. A., and Zarrow, M. X. 1964. Mice reared with rats: modification of behavior by early experience with another species. *Science* **143**: 380–381.
2. Ginsburg, B. E. 1958. Genetics as a tool in the study of behavior. *Perspect. Biol. Med.* **1**: 397–424.

2a. ———, and Miller, D. S. 1963. Genetic factors in audiogenic seizures. In *Pyschophysiologie, Neuropharmacologie et Biochimie de la Crise Audiogene.* Paris: Colloques Internationaux du Centre National de la Recherche Scientifique, **112**: pp. 217–225.

2b. ———. 1963. Causal mechanisms in audiogenic seizures. In *Psychophysiologie, Neuropharmacologie et Biochimie de la Crise Audiogene.* Paris: Colloques Internationaux du Centre National de la Recherche Scientifique, **112**: pp. 227–240.

2c. ———. 1966. All mice are not created equal: recent findings on genes and behavior. *Social Serv. Review,* **40**: 121–134.

2d. ———. 1967. Genetic parameters in behavior research. In *Behavior-Genetic Analysis.* Edited by J. Hirsch. New York: McGraw-Hill.

3. Hamburg, D. A. 1967. Genetics of adrenocortical hormone metabolism in relation to psychological stress. In *Behavior-Genetic Analysis.* Edited by J. Hirsch. McGraw-Hill.
4. Hunt, H. F., and Otis, L. S. 1955. Restricted experience and "timidity" in the rat. *Amer. Psychol.,* **10**: 432. (abstract).
5. Levine, S., Albert, M., and Lewis, G. W. 1958. Differential maturation of an adrenal response to cold stress in rats manipulated in infancy. *Jour. Comp. Physiol. Psychol.,* **51**: 774–777.
6. Mayr, E. 1958. Behavior and systematics. In *Behavior and Evolution.* Edited by A. Roe and G. Simpson. Pp. 341–62. New Haven: Yale University Press.
7. Roberts, E. 1967. Synaptic neurochemistry: a projection. In *Behavior-Genetic Analysis.* Edited by J. Hirsch. New York: McGraw-Hill.
8. Schaefer, T. 1959. The effects of early experience: infant handling and later behavior in the white rat. Doctoral dissertation, Department of Psychology, University of Chicago.
9. Wynne-Edwards, V. C. 1963. Self-regulating systems in populations of animals. *Science,* **147**: 1543–48.

15

GENETIC AND ENVIRONMENTAL VARIABLES INFLUENCING ANIMAL AGGRESSION

CHARLES H. SOUTHWICK
The Johns Hopkins University

Several recent studies have demonstrated the complexity of genetic and environmental interactions in the expression of aggressive behavior in animals. Both kinds of factors obviously influence the development of behavior, and in experimental work it may be possible to obtain some assessments of this interaction.

Strain differences in aggressive behavior of animals have been known for many years. Perhaps the most famous examples are fighting game cocks and Siamese fighting fish which have been bred for maximum aggressive tendencies and fighting abilities. In other experimental animals there has been no purposeful selection for aggressive behavior, but in breeding for other traits, considerable differences in aggressive tendencies have resulted. In inbred mice, for example, conspicuous strain differences in aggressive behavior are found. Figure 1 shows the results of aggression studies on male mice of 14 strains. This graph shows the average number of aggressive chases, attacks, and fights (C-A-F score) per hour after 4 young adult males were grouped following a period of isolation. Some strains, such as the C57Br, AKR, CFW and Balb/c are notably aggressive with a C-A-F score of 50 to 80, whereas others such as the A/J, CBA and A/He are quite passive, with a C-A-F score under 20. These fights are often violent, and may result in injury or even death in the more aggressive strains. This type of aggressive behavior is sometimes called non-competitive fighting because the animals are not obviously fighting over the possession of food, water, mates, or

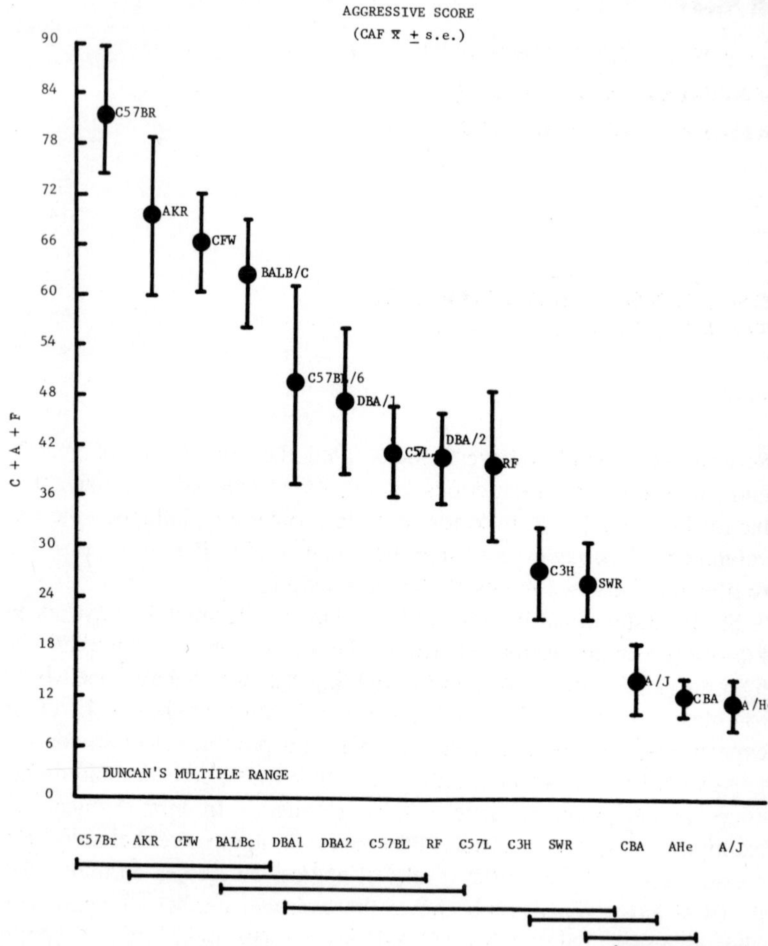

Figure 1 Aggressive scores (chase + attack + fight frequencies) for 14 different strains of inbred mice. Black circles represent means for groups of four mice per hour; vertical bars represent standard errors. Horizontal bars at bottom represent Duncan's multiple range analysis. All strains within each horizontal bar are statistically not distinct at the 5 percent level, but they are different from all strains outside the horizontal bar.

other material item—they are primarily reacting to the presence of social strangers, though perhaps it could be said they are competing for space or status.

It is quite significant that the way this behavior is most easily evoked is to rear young mice in social isolation during the juvenile period; i.e., the time from wearing (3 weeks of age) to sexual maturity (6 weeks of age). Thus this type of fighting is also called isolation-induced aggression,[26] and it can be demonstrated in all vertebrate classes from fish to mammals. Social isolation during the juvenile period apparently stimulates the full development and expression of noncompetitive aggressive behavior. Conversely, one might hypothesize that the lack of social experience during this time prevented or disrupted a normal socialization process in which the animal would have acquired the social ability and communicative skills to avoid aggressive conflict. In any case, the fact remains that if mice and many other animals are isolated during the juvenile period, they fight savagely when grouped as adults, whereas those which have always been in social groups usually do not. In many experiments we have re-mixed groups of male mice which grew up together but were then re-grouped at sexual maturity with a new set of social strangers to determine if their favorable socialization was limited to certain individuals or extended to others of the same species. This experimental procedure has always resulted in some fighting, but never as much as in males previously isolated. Even the highly aggressive strains such as C57Br and CFW do not show pronounced fighting if males grow up together in the same cage. In fact, CFW mice raised together during the juvenile period exhibit less aggression within their group than A/J mice reared in isolation and then grouped. This simple experiment demonstrates the forceful influence of the social environment in determining the aggressive behavior of an individual —an influence which can override the genetic background of the animal.

It should be pointed out that isolation-induced aggression also occurs in adults which have had normal developmental histories, and it can often appear after short isolation periods of only a few days. For example, adult male Siamese fighting fish *(Betta splendens)* or paradise fish (*Macropodus opercularis*) may fight vigorously after an isolation of only one or two days. The pattern and intensity of the fight is primarily a function of the nature of the social relationship which existed between the individuals prior to isolation. If they had an unsettled social relationship of very similar rank, the fight may be prolonged and vicious. If they had a definite pattern of dominance and subordination, and the "social memory" of this still exists within the animals, the subordinate individual will probably assume a subordinate posture immediately and no fight will occur. The consistency of isolation-induced aggression in many vertebrates including fish, lizards, birds, and mammals provides an experimental tool for measuring the stability of social relations between individuals and the memory span over which these relations may be maintained.

Vale and Vale[25] have analyzed the interaction of genotype and social environment in response to crowding in mice by systemmatically varying both strain and population density. They found that some strains of inbred mice responded to increased crowding with increased aggression (Balb/c and C57B1 strains), whereas other strains did not (A/J, DBA/2, and C3H). They also found significant differences in the physiologic responses of the strains to different densities. Some strains showed adrenal enlargement in response to high density (Balb/c), whereas others did not (A/J, DBA/2). Careful experiments of this type show the complexity of genotype-environment interactions, and also help to explain some of the contradictions which exist in the literature.

Mutual contributions of genetic and environmental backgrounds can also be seen in cross-breeding and cross fostering studies on inbred mice. Tables 1-3 show the results of cross-breeding tests on inbred mice. In the first cross between C57Br (aggressive) and CBA (passive), the F_1 offspring were at least as aggressive or more so than the aggressive parent, regardless of which strain was the male or female parent. This suggests, but does not prove, that the tendency toward aggressive behavior is genetically dominant in these mice (Table 1).

When two aggressive strains were crossed (CFW x C57BL) the F_1 offspring were extremely aggressive—much more aggressive than

Table 1. *Inheritance of Aggressive Behavior in Mice: Aggression Scores of F_1 from C57Br × CBA*

Generation	Aggression Score (Chase-Attack-Fight Frequency)
P – C57Br	82.2 ± 7.7
P – CBA	12.1 ± 2.0
F_1 – C57Br ♀ × CBA ♂	84.2 ± 9.9
F_1 – CBA ♀ × C57Br ♂	98.6 ± 11.4

either parent (Table 2). When two passive strains were crossed (CBA x A/J), the F_1 offspring were also more aggressive than either parent (Table 2). These two crosses demonstrate a heterotic influence in the inheritance of aggressive behavior; that is, the phenomenon of hybrid vigor in relation to a social trait. Although heterosis or hybrid vigor has been well documented in individual behavior patterns, such as activity,[3, 10] it has not been adequately studied in regard to social behaviors.

Table 2. *Inheritance of Aggressive Behavior in Mice: Aggression Scores of F_1 from CFW × C57BL/6 and CBA × A/J*

Generation	Aggression Score (Chase-Attack-Fight Frequency)
P – CFW	66.4 ± 5.9
P – C57BL/6	49.7 ± 12.0
F_1 – CFW ♀ × C57BL/6 ♂	249.7 ± 23.1
P – CBA	12.1 ± 2.0
P – A/J	14.1 ± 4.8
F_1 – CBA ♀ × A/J ♂	44.0 ± 4.9

When the aggressive CFW strain was crossed with the passive A/J strain, different results were obtained depending upon which strain was the maternal parent (Table 3). If the mother was the aggressive strain (CFW), the offspring were very aggressive, more so than either parent. If the mother was the passive strain (A/J), the offspring were intermediate between both parents.

This indicated either a sex-linked pattern of genetic inheritance, or the existence of a maternal influence. Cross-fostering studies suggested that the latter was possibly true.

Table 3. *Aggressive Behavior of F_1 Generation from A/J × CFW*

Generation	n	C-A-F Score ($x \pm$ s.e.)	Latency to Fight (min.)
P – CFW	28	67.6 ± 9.1	2.3
P – A/J	36	14.2 ± 4.8	33.4
F_1 – A/J ♀ × CFW ♂	40	41.3 ± 5.2	3.5
F_1 – CFW ♀ × A/J ♂	40	107.8 ± 9.4	1.5

Table 4 shows the results of fostering studies between CFW and A/J strains. Cross-fostering refers to the exchange of newborn young between mothers of the opposite strain. Thus the young of the passive A/J strain were reared by a mother of the aggressive CFW strain, and vice versa. In-fostering refers to the exchange of young between mothers of the same strain, and this served as a control on the effects of the fostering process *per se*. Two additional types of control were used: lab-reared controls were normally raised young which were born in our colony, and Bar Harbor or Carworth controls were normally raised young obtained from the laboratories of the suppliers.

Table 4. *Aggressive score (chase-attack-fight frequency), attack latency, and percent wounding in groups of four males*

Strain	Treatment	*n*	C-A-F Score	Attack Latency	Percent Wounded
A/J	lab control	36	14.2 ± 4.8	33.4	2.8
A/J	Bar Harbor control	72	14.5 ± 3.9	35.4	4.1
A/J	In-fostered	32	17.5 ± 4.9	35.3	0
A/J	Cross-fostered	40	26.6 ± 4.7*	13.4**	17.5**
CFW	lab control	28	67.6 ± 9.1	2.3	64.3
CFW	Carworth control	72	66.4 ± 5.9	4.4	72.1
CFW	In-fostered	16	68.0 ± 12.8	1.2	68.7
CFW	Cross-fostered	44	65.1 ± 7.4	1.7	68.7

* Significantly different from in-fostered and control groups, $P = 0.05$ by X^2.
** Significantly different from infostered and control groups, $P = 0.01$.

These experiments show a significant maternal influence on the amount of aggressive behavior expressed by the A/J strain. The C-A-F score of A/J young was increased about 80% by fostering to a female of the CFW strain. This was a significant increase in aggressive behavior above that of the in-fostered controls.

The aggressive behavior of the CFW young was not reduced by fostering them to a passive mother. These results are compatible with studies of J. P. Scott which showed that aggressive behavior can be a learned phenomenon which is more easily elevated than reduced; that is, fighting in mice may be an acquired response, and once acquired, it is extinguished very slowly or with difficulty.

We do not yet know the mechanism by which maternal care influences the development of aggressive behavior in young mice, but we think it may be related to the amount and patterning of time the mother spends on the litter. A pilot study indicated that the CFW females have shorter nursing bouts with the litter and are on and off the litter much more frequently than the A/J females. This influences both the ambient temperature in which the young developed and also the feeding pattern of the young. The young on a CFW mother experienced shorter and presumably more competitive feeding bouts than those young on an A/J mother. These variables could be expected to affect growth and behavioral development, though by what means are not yet clear. The experimental tests of whether or not maternal activity patterns are a major influence on the development of aggression in the young, through experimental modification of these activity patterns, have not yet been done. There are, of course, many mechanisms by which maternal behavior could influence the behavioral development of offspring, and there has been relatively little research on these possible mechanisms.

Different species of primates also exhibit widely different patterns of aggressive behavior, and these variations similarly illustrate the interaction of genetic and environmental influences. Patas monkeys are a species of primate with a striking lack of aggressive behavior. These animals live in a woodland-savannah habitat in Africa, and they typically have small social groups of about 15 animals per group. The groups are strictly territorial, and there is a virtual lack of overt aggressive behavior within groups. In a major field study by the late K. R. L. Hall,[9] aggressive threats were seen between males of different groups, but direct attacks or fights were never observed.

In most species of primates, the frequency of aggressive behavior is related to environmental and social conditions. For example, in a study of baboons *(Papio doguera* or *P. anubis)* of Nairobi Park, Kenya, by Irven DeVore and K. R. L. Hall,[7] where population density was low (10 baboons per square mile) and group sizes were small (41 baboons per group), overt aggression was rarely seen. In Amboseli Park, Kenya, where population density was high (25 baboons per square mile) and average group size was high (80 per group), integroup fighting was frequent. In the Hamadryas baboon *(Papio hamadyras),* Kummer[13] also observed a higher frequency of aggression in large groups than in small groups.

Rhesus monkeys are interesting for the analysis of aggressive behavior, because they show more aggression than most species of primates. In cities, towns, and temple grounds of north India, where rhesus live a free-ranging, but rather crowded existence, fighting is common and wounded animals are frequently seen. In forest areas, where rhesus are much less crowded, fighting still occurs, but much less often, and wounded animals are rarely seen.[17, 22, 24]

In 1964 and 1965, I undertook a series of experimental studies to investigate the effects of various environmental and social variables on the frequency and intensity of aggression in a captive group of rhesus monkeys. In Calcutta I established in a colony cage of 1000 square feet a captive group of 17 rhesus which had been wildtrapped in north central India. The group was given several months to develop a social unity, and then over a period of eight months, a series of experiments were conducted to study the effects of varying food, space, and social composition on aggressive behavior.[21]

When the group was first formed, there was a high frequency of aggressive interactions as dominance relations were established and social adjustments were made. Over a period of 5 weeks, the frequency of aggressive interactions declined from an average of 26.0 aggressive interactions per hour (including all threats, submissive responses, attacks and fights) to 10.3 (Figure 2). Subsequently, the level of 10 to 13 aggressive interactions per hour was stable, and this was considered the baseline norm for this captive group. It should be

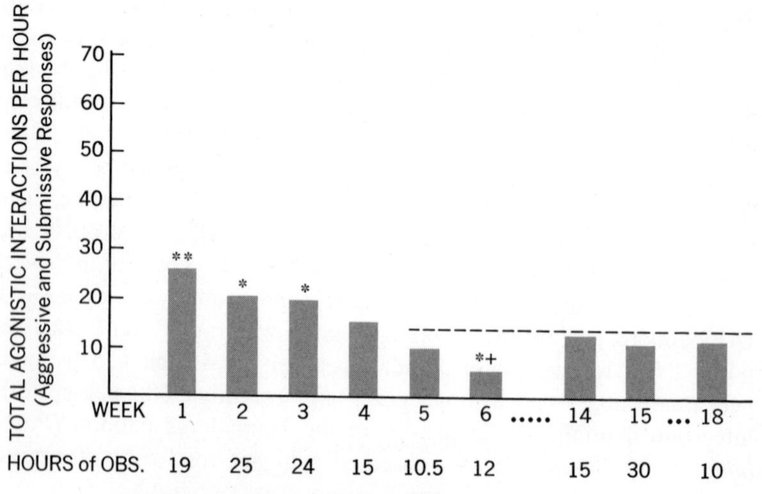

Figure 2 Agonistic behavior in formation of confined rhesus monkey group. Dashed line represents baseline average after group stabilization.

remembered that this is a much higher frequency of aggression than in natural groups: approximately 14 times more aggression than in a free-ranging temple group of rhesus monkeys, and 50 times more than in a free-ranging forest group of rhesus.[22] Nonetheless, this baseline was considered typical for this captive group, and various experiments were planned around this figure.

One of the first experiments was to test the effect of food surpluses and shortages on the aggressive behavior of the group. The monkeys were receiving a very ample supply of food, given 5 times daily, but when the amount was increased 25%, a slight but nonsignificant decline in aggressive interactions occurred (Figure 3). A 25% reduction in food, contrary to all expectations, also resulted in a decrease in aggression below baseline levels. Even a 50% food shortage, in which the monkeys were unquestionably without adequate food for 5 days, resulted in a significant decrease in aggression (Figure 3).

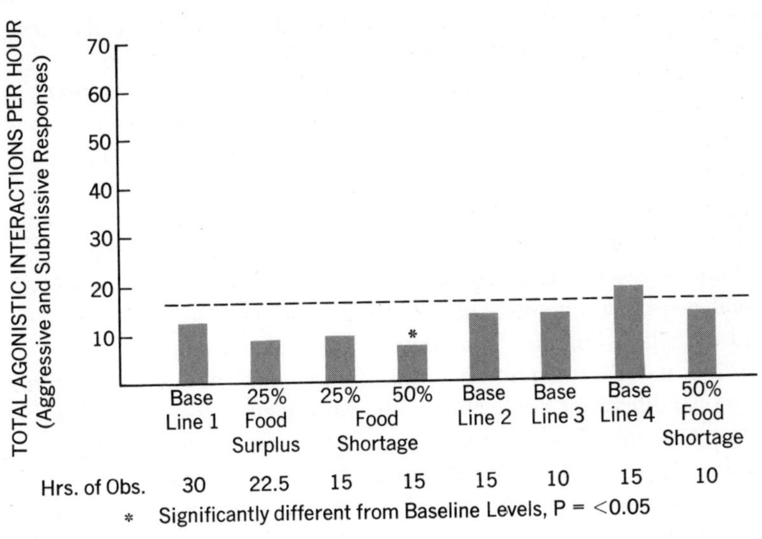

Figure 3 Effects of food shortages on agonistic behavior of confined rhesus group.

During this time, total aggressive interactions (including threats, submissive responses, attacks and fights) diminished from a normal level of 13.2 per hour to 5.9 per hour. When normal quantities of food were restored, the amount of aggression increased to normal levels.

Behavioral changes during the week of reduced food supplies involved not only a reduction of aggression, but also a reduction of grooming, resting, play behavior and sexual behavior, all accompanied by a great increase in lethargic investigation. The animals spent most of their time in slow lethargic investigation of all parts of their cage. They picked up and examined minute bits of leaves, twigs, bark and miscellaneous debris.

In contrast to this reduction of aggression during semi-starvation, the replacement of group members with strangers resulted in a tremendous increase in aggressive activity. When two of the resident juveniles were removed from the group and two other juveniles were replaced, the group erupted in violent attacks against the two newcomers. Total aggressive interactions per hour increased fourfold from 11.5 to 47.2 (Figure 4). Most of the attacks were initiated and led by the two member juveniles against the two new juveniles. The attacks were biting, slashing, and striking attacks which inflicted wounds, and would have probably caused the death of the newcomers if they had not been removed on the second day.

When two new females were added, an even greater increase in aggressive behavior occurred. Total aggressive interactions increased tenfold from 11.6 to 110.0 per hour. In this case the main attack initiative was led by the resident females. Their attacks were vicious and damaging, and would have resulted in severe wounds and even death if the new females had not been removed on the second day.

Similar results occurred when two new males were introduced. Total aggressive interactions increased from 11.5 to 84.3 per hour, and the attack initiative was taken by the resident male.

Thus it was apparent that this group could not tolerate, within these conditions of confinement, the introduction of social strangers into the group. It also appeared as if there were a "social template," so that the sex and age group whose status was threatened by the introduction was the one most likely to initiate and promote the attack.

As pointed out in several of the preceding chapters, animal societies have evolved two general means of reducing and controlling aggressive behavior: territorialism and dominance hierarchies. Both systems are mediated through communicative displays which regulate overt behavior. These displays are essentially messages which convey information between individuals and thus permit social integration of behavior.

In the case of threat displays, the display itself usually determines

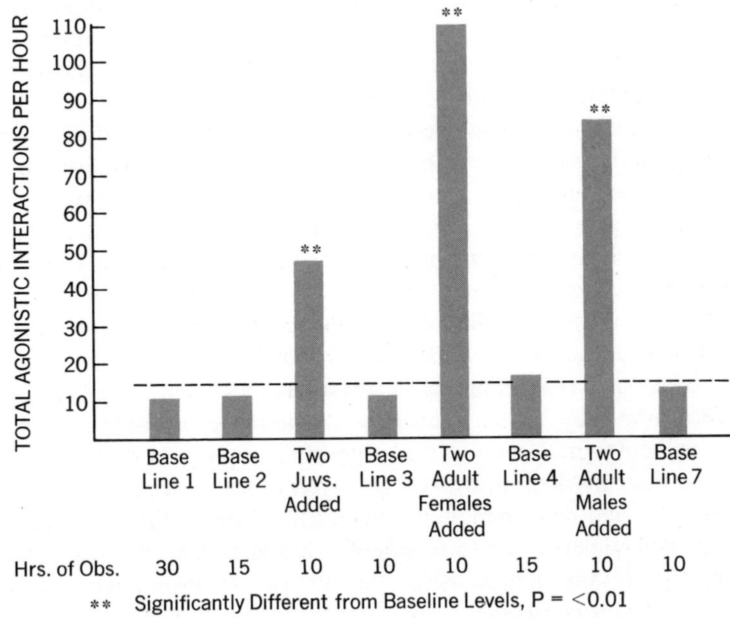

Figure 4 Effects of social changes on agonistic behavior of confined rhesus group.

the outcome of a dispute and thus substitutes for direct fighting. Under natural circumstances in most animals, the great majority of aggressive behavior consists of threat displays and submissive responses, and not direct injurious fighting. Only when communicative channels become impaired or confused, so that messages are mistakenly transmitted or perceived, does injurious fighting become prominent. This often occurs in overcrowded conditions, various types of social disorganization, or disturbed environmental settings. Then the phenomenon of injurious fighting, once begun, becomes self-stimulating, because it continues to produce disturbance and confusion. As Scott emphasized several years ago, fighting engenders more fighting.

Territorialism is essentially a pattern of social behavior which regulates the use of space. Territories may be held by individuals or groups and they have the usual characteristics of being exclusively held and defended against other members of the same species. This is, by no means, a universal social phenomenon among animals, but it is of wide occurrence. It is obviously a successful social system which has arisen by parallel or convergent evolution in animals as diverse as insects, fish, birds and mammals.

Among primates, some species are conspicuously territorial, such as the *Callicebus* monkey, lutong, gibbon, howler monkey, while others are not territorial, including most of the macaques, baboons, chimpanzee and gorilla. For this reason, I do not believe that there is a basic primate instinct for territorial behavior, but I do consider it a very successful form of social behavior which is widely represented in primate behavior at both the individual and group level. Descriptively, man is territorial in many of his activities, but not to the exclusion of other kinds of aggregational behavior as well.

Territories may be maintained by a wide range of display modalities, including vocal song in birds, postural displays in deer and antelopes, odor marking in wolves and tigers, vocal roaring in primates (Figure 5), and fence-building in man. In all cases, these communicative displays serve to inform potential intruders that this territory is occupied. In most natural cases, this prevents intrusion. One of the most important consequences of excessive population density in animals is increased territorial intrusion, which leads to increased fighting, and this creates behavioral pathologies such as nest desertion, improper parental care, cannabalism, violence, and a variety of stress-associated diseases. This damaging chain of events is normally prevented by stable populations and well regulated territorial behavior.

The analogies with human problems are obvious, and I agree with Robert Ardrey[2] when he states that many human problems arise from inadequate appreciation of man's territorial nature. I deny, however, that this is an instinctive trait of man. I prefer to consider it a highly evolved social and cultural trait, but I also believe, as does Ardrey, that territorialism is a significant part of man's behavior. We have failed to give it adequate recognition.

Dominance hierarchies are an equally conspicuous part of animal behavior and human behavior. In animals, individuals within a group are usually organized in a social rank system which gives certain individuals priority access to limited resources. The determinants of social rank vary considerably in different species. In lower vertebrates, high rank may be primarily determined by size and physical strength. In higher vertebrates, especially primates, a variety of social and psychological factors play significant roles.[23] In Japanese macaques and rhesus monkeys, for example, one of the primate deter-

Figure 5 Wanderoo or lion-tailed macaque (*Macaca silenus*) in an aggressive threat. Although this species appears ferocious, it is considerably less aggressive than most macaques, including the rhesus macaque. (Photograph by Ylla, with permission of La Guilde du Livre, Lausanne, Copyright © 1958.)

minants of the social rank of a young male is the status of his mother, according to the work of Imanishi[11] and Koford.[12] The sons of high ranking mothers achieved high rank with greater frequency than the sons of low ranking mothers. Detailed studies in primate behavior have shown that rank involves a complex set of behavioral traits and habits—traits which are acquired developmentally throughout a long infant and juvenile period.

Dominance hierarchies and territorialism must not be thought of as mutually exclusive forms of behavior. Many primate groups are territorial as groups, but within the group a clear social hierarchy of individuals exists. In rodents, and probably other vertebrates, there may be a continuum from territorialism to dominance hierarchies related to population density or other ecologic factors. Davis[5] pointed out that house mice are normally territorial at low population densities, but under crowded conditions territories break down and a large aggregation of animals live together under a hierarchial system in which all space is shared. Miyadi[15] has demonstrated the same phenomenon in salmon. Anderson and Hill[1] have shown experimentally some of the factors leading to territoriality in male house mice. These include, in addition to low population density, at least three factors in proper sequence: (1) familiarization with a home area, (2) successful combat and social dominance over another male who was then removed from the home area, (3) defeat on the home ground of another male coupled with victory over this male on the original familiar ground. Thus we can see that territorialism may involve a complex interaction of environmental and experiential factors.

There has been and will continue to be much uncertainty and debate about the applicability of research on animal behavior to human problems. No one can yet formulate all the criteria for valid comparisons, but we are beginning to recognize biological and social principles which are common determinants of behavior in man and animals. It is increasingly important to recognize the biological and ecological bases of human behavior as well as its cultural uniqueness.

The question of whether or not there is a basic aggressive instinct in man and animals is unanswerable in simple terms since the word "instinct" has a wide range of meanings. An instinct can be variously considered as anything from a behavioral tendency, capacity or aptitude to an inherited pattern of discrete behavior which is genetically coded into an animal at conception. By the first definition, there is no doubt that man and most animals have a behavioral tendency, aptitude and capacity toward aggressive behavior. Thus, with this definition, one would have to agree with Lorenz[14] than an aggressive instinct does exist. By the latter more rigorous definition, however, there is not good evidence that a pattern of aggressive behavior is coded into most animals in the same sense as are more basic behavioral patterns such as clinging, feeding, locomotion, escape and alarm behavior, etc. By this more rigorous definition, one would agree with Scott[20] and Moyer[16] that an aggressive instinct does not exist.

Related to this dilemma on the meaning of instinct, is the question of the intrinsic or extrinsic nature of stimuli required to evoke aggressive behavior in animals. Scott[20] believes, "There is no evidence for the existence of a physiological mechanism that could produce spontaneous internal stimulation to fight. Rather there is much evidence that neurophysiological mechanisms exist which magnify and prolong the results of external stimulation." Thus Scott finds no evidence for a "drive center" within the brain which stimulates aggressive behavior. On the other hand, Jose Delgado[6] has found that electrical stimulation of the midline thalamus, nucleus ventralis posterior lateralis of the thalamus, and Forel's field in rhesus monkeys has produced aggressive behavior. In subsequent work, Plotnik and Delgado[18] feel that this is a result of pain stimulation. Bryan Robinson[19] has shown complete aggressive behavior in rhesus monkeys, resulting from telestimulation of the pre-optic area. In these experiments, brain stimulation elicited complex and well organized sequences of aggressive behavior. It can still be argued, of course, that this required exogenous electrical input, but it is plausible that endogenous neural activity might trigger the same behavior. Delgado[6] further believes that the cerebral mechanism for the perception of pain and for aggressive behavior have different anatomical and physiological systems which are closely interrelated but are not always the same.

There is little doubt that man and most animals show a great capacity for aggressive behavior—a capacity which is easily evoked by developmental experiences and environmental stimuli. We can associate some of these stimuli with various ecologic and social conditions: crowding, social change, territorial intrusion, and so forth, but we still have much to learn about the interaction of these factors throughout behavioral development and group dynamics.

The problem of controlling aggressive behavior is essentially one of understanding these developmental and ecologic backgrounds.

Such understanding may eventually permit the management of these backgrounds so that we can reduce the damaging aspects of aggression to a minimum without impairing its worthwhile functions.

REFERENCES

1. Anderson, P. K. and Hill, J. L. 1965. *Mus musculus:* Experimental induction of territory formation. *Science,* **148**: 1753–5.
2. Ardrey, R. 1966. *The Territorial Imperative.* New York: Atheneum.
3. Bruell, J. H. 1964. Inheritance of behavioral and physiological characters of mice and the problem of heterosis. *Amer. Zool.,* **4**(2): 125–38.
4. Carthy, J. D. and Ebling, F. J. (Editors). 1964. *The Natural History of Aggression.* London and New York: Academic Press.
5. Davis, D. E. 1958. The role of density in aggressive behavior of house mice. *Anim. Behav., VI*: 207–10.
6. Delgado, Jose M. R. 1966. Aggressive behavior evoked by radio stimulation in monkey colonies. *Amer. Zool.,* **6**(4): 669–81.
7. DeVore, I. and Hall, K. R. L. 1965. Baboon ecology. In *Primate Behavior: Field Studies of Monkeys and Apes.* Edited by I. DeVore. Pp. 20–52. New York: Holt, Rinehart and Winston.
8. Garattini, S. and Sigg, E. B. (Editors). 1969. *Aggressive Behaviour.* Amsterdam: Excerpta Medica Foundation.
9. Hall, K. R. L. 1965. Behaviour and ecology of the wild Patas monkey, *Erythrocebus patas,* in Uganda. *Jour. Zool.,* **148**: 15–87.
10. Hirsch, J. (Editor). 1967. *Behavior-Genetic Analysis.* New York: McGraw Hill.
11. Imanishi, K. 1960. Social organization of subhuman primates in their natural habitat. *Current. Anthropol.,* **1**: 393–407.
12. Koford, C. B. 1963. Rank of mothers and sons in bands of rhesus monkeys. *Science,* **141**: 365–57.
13. Kummer, H. 1968. *Social Organization of Hamadryas Baboons.* Chicago: University of Chicago Press.
14. Lorenz, K. 1966. *On Aggression.* New York: Harcourt, Brace and World.
15. Miyadi, D. 1956. Perspectives of experimental research on social interference among fishes. In *Perspectives in Marine Biology.* Edited by A. A. Buzzati-Traverso. La Jolla, Cal.: Scripps Inst. of Oceanography.
16. Moyer, K. E. 1968. Kinds of aggression and their physiological basis. *Comm. in Behavioral Biology,* **A**, **2**: 65–87.
17. Neville, M. 1966. A study of the free-ranging behavior of rhesus monkeys. Ph.D. thesis, Harvard University, Cambridge, Massachusetts.
18. Plotnik, R. and J. M. R. Delgado. 1970. Aggression and pain in unrestricted rhesus monkeys. In *Physiology of Fighting and Defeat.* Edited by J. P. Scott. Chicago: University of Chicago Press.
19. Robinson, B. 1968. *Personal Communication.* Yerkes Regional Primate Research Center, Atlanta, Georgia.

20. Scott, J. P. 1958. *Aggression.* Chicago: The University of Chicago press.
21. Southwick, C. H. 1967. An experimental study of intragroup agonistic behavior in rhesus monkeys *Macaca mulatta. Behaviour,* **28**: 182–209.
22. ———. 1969. Aggressive behaviour of rhesus monkeys in natural and captive groups. In *Aggressive Behaviour.* Edited by S. Garattini and E. B. Sigg. Pp. 32–43. Amsterdam: Excerpta Medica Foundation.
23. Southwick, C. H. and Siddiqi, M. R. 1967. The role of social tradition in the maintenance of dominance in a wild rhesus group. *Primates,* **8**: 341–53.
24. Southwick, C. H., Beg, M. A., and Siddiqi, M. R. 1965. Rhesus monkeys in North India. In *Primate Behavior: Field Studies of Monkeys and Apes.* Edited by I. DeVore. Pp. 111–59. New York: Holt, Rinehart and Winston.
25. Vale, J. R. and Vale, C. 1970. Genotype and population density: a problem in organism-environment interaction. Unpublished ms.
26. Valzelli, L. 1969. Aggressive behaviour induced by isolation. In *Aggressive Behaviour*. Edited by S. Garattini, and E. B. Sigg. Pp. 70–6. Amsterdam: Excerpta Medica Foundation.